PEARSON

ALWAYS LEARNING

Financial Risk Manager (FRM®) Part I
Quantitative Analysis

Fourth Custom Edition for
Global Association of Risk Professionals
2014

GARP | Global Association of Risk Professionals

Excerpts taken from:

Introduction to Econometrics, Brief Edition, by James H. Stock and Mark W. Watson

Options, Futures, and Other Derivatives, Eighth Edition, by John C. Hull

Excerpts taken from:

Introduction to Econometrics, Brief Edition
by James H. Stock and Mark W. Watson
Copyright © 2008 by Pearson Education, Inc.
Published by Addison Wesley
Boston, Massachusetts 02116

Options, Futures, and Other Derivatives, Eighth Edition
by John C. Hull
Copyright © 2012, 2009, 2006, 2003, 2000 by Pearson Education, Inc.
Published by Prentice Hall
Upper Saddle River, New Jersey 07458

Pearson Learning Solutions, 501 Boylston Street, Suite 900, Boston, MA 02116
A Pearson Education Company
www.pearsoned.com

Printed in the United States of America

1 2 3 4 5 6 7 8 9 10 V011 17 16 15 14 13

000200010271841523

JH/LC

ISBN 10: 1-269-59104-5
ISBN 13: 978-1-269-59104-1

Contents

CHAPTER 4   HYPOTHESIS TESTING & CONFIDENCE INTERVALS   47

CHAPTER 5   LINEAR REGRESSION WITH ONE REGRESSOR   59

2014 FRM Committee Members

Probabilities

Learning Objectives

Candidates, after completing this reading, should be able to:

- Describe and distinguish between continuous and discrete random variables.
- Define and distinguish between the probability density function, the cumulative distribution function, and the inverse cumulative distribution function.
- Calculate the probability of an event given a discrete probability function.
- Distinguish between independent and mutually exclusive events.

- Define joint probability, describe a probability matrix and calculate joint probabilities using probability matrices.
- Define and calculate a conditional probability, and distinguish between conditional and unconditional probabilities.
- Describe Bayes' Theorem and apply this theorem in the calculation of conditional probabilities.

Excerpt is Chapter 2 of Mathematics and Statistics for Financial Risk Management, *by Michael Miller.*

In this chapter we will explore the application of probabilities to risk management. We will also introduce basic terminology and notations that will be used throughout the rest of this book.

DISCRETE RANDOM VARIABLES

The concept of probability is central to risk management. Many concepts associated with probability are deceptively simple. The basics are easy, but there are many potential pitfalls.

In this chapter, we will be working with both discrete and continuous random variables. Discrete random variables can take on only a countable number of values—for example, a coin, which can only be heads or tails, or a bond, which can only have one of several letter ratings (AAA, AA, A, BBB, etc.). Assume we have a discrete random variable X, which can take various values, x_i. Further assume that the probability of any given x_i occurring is p_i. We write:

$$P[X = x_i] = p_i \text{ s.t. } x_i \in \{x_1, x_2, \ldots, x_n\} \qquad \textbf{(1.1)}$$

where $P[\cdot]$ is our probability operator.*

An important property of a random variable is that the sum of all the probabilities must equal one. In other words, the probability of any event occurring must equal one. Something has to happen. Using our current notation, we have:

$$\sum_{i=i}^{n} p_i = 1 \qquad \textbf{(1.2)}$$

CONTINUOUS RANDOM VARIABLES

In contrast to a discrete random variable, a continuous random variable can take on any value within a given range. A good example of a continuous random variable is the return of a stock index. If the level of the index can be any real number between zero and infinity, then the return of the index can be any real number greater than −1.

---

* Note that "s.t." is shorthand for "such that," and $x_i \in \{x_1, x_2, \ldots, x_n\}$ indicates that x_i is a member of a set that includes n possible values, $x_1, x_2, \ldots, x_n$. You could read the full equation as: "The probability that X equals x_i is equal to p_i, such that x_i is a member of the set $x_1, x_2,$ to x_n."

Even if the range that the continuous variable occupies is finite, the number of values that it can take is infinite. For this reason, for a continuous variable, the probability of any *specific* value occurring is zero.

Even though we cannot talk about the probability of a specific value occurring, we can talk about the probability of a variable being within a certain range. Take, for example, the return on a stock market index over the next year. We can talk about the probability of the index return being between 6% and 7%, but talking about the probability of the return being exactly 6.001% or exactly 6.002% is meaningless. Even between 6.001% and 6.002% there are literally an infinite number of possible values. The probability of any one of those infinite values occurring is zero.

For a continuous random variable X, then, we can write:

$$P[r_1 < X < r_2] = p \qquad \textbf{(1.3)}$$

which states that the probability of our random variable, X, being between r_1 and r_2 is equal to p.

Probability Density Functions

For a continuous random variable, the probability of a specific event occurring is not well defined, but some events are still more likely to occur than others. Using annual stock market returns as an example, if we look at 50 years of data, we might notice that there are more data points between 0% and 10% than there are between 10% and 20%. That is, the density of points between 0% and 10% is higher than the density of points between 10% and 20%.

For a continuous random variable we can define a probability density function (PDF), which tells us the likelihood of outcomes occurring between any two points. Given our random variable, X, with a probability p of being between r_1 and r_2, we can define our density function, $f(x)$, such that:

$$\int_{r_1}^{r_2} f(x)dx = p \qquad \textbf{(1.4)}$$

The probability density function is often referred to as the probability distribution function. Both terms are correct, and, conveniently, both can be abbreviated PDF.

As with discrete random variables, the probability of any value occurring must be one:

Sample Problem

Question:

Define the probability density function for the price of a zero coupon bond with a notional value of $10 as:

$$f(x) = \frac{x}{50} \text{ s.t. } 0 \leq x \leq 10$$

where x is the price of the bond. What is the probability that the price of the bond is between $8 and $9?

Answer:

First, note that this is a legitimate probability function. By integrating the PDF from its minimum to its maximum, we can show that the probability of any value occurring is indeed one:

$$\int_0^{10} \frac{x}{50} dx = \frac{1}{50} \int_0^{10} x \, dx = \frac{1}{50}\left[\frac{1}{2}x^2\right]_0^{10} = \frac{1}{100}(10^2 - 0^2) = 1$$

If we graph the function, we can also see that the area under the curve is one. Using simple geometry:

$$\text{Area of triangle} = \frac{1}{2} \cdot \text{Base} \cdot \text{Height} = \frac{1}{2} \cdot 10 \cdot 0.2 = 1$$

To answer the question, we simply integrate the probability density function between 8 and 9:

$$\int_8^9 \frac{x}{50} dx = \left[\frac{1}{100}x^2\right]_8^9 = \frac{1}{100}(9^2 - 8^2) = \frac{17}{100} = 17\%$$

The probability of the price ending up between $8 and $9 is 17%.

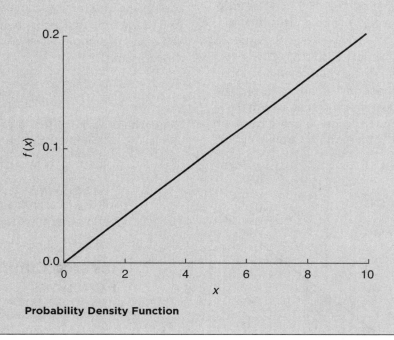

Probability Density Function

$$\int_{r_{min}}^{r_{max}} f(x)dx = 1 \qquad \text{(1.5)}$$

where r_{min} and r_{max} define the lower and upper bounds of $f(x)$.

Cumulative Distribution Functions

Closely related to the concept of a probability density function is the concept of a cumulative distribution function or cumulative density function (both abbreviated

CDF). A cumulative distribution function tells us the probability of a random variable being less than a certain value. The CDF can be found by integrating the probability density function from its lower bound. Traditionally, the cumulative distribution function is denoted by the capital letter of the corresponding density function. For a random variable X with a probability density function $f(x)$, then, the cumulative distribution function, $F(x)$, could be calculated as follows:

$$F(a) = \int_{-\infty}^{a} f(x)dx = P[X \leq a] \tag{1.6}$$

As illustrated in Figure 1-1, the cumulative distribution function corresponds to the area under the probability density function, to the left of a.

By definition, the cumulative distribution function varies from 0 to 1 and is nondecreasing. At the minimum value of the probability density function, the CDF must be zero. There is no probability of the variable being less than the minimum. At the other end, all values are less than the maximum of the PDF. The probability is 100% (CDF = 1) that the random variable will be less than or equal to the maximum. In between, the function is nondecreasing. The reason that the CDF is nondecreasing is that, at a minimum, the probability of a random variable being between two points is zero. If the CDF of a random variable at 5 is

50%, then the lowest it could be at 6 is 50%, which would imply 0% probability of finding the variable between 5 and 6. There is no way the CDF at 6 could be less than the CDF at 5.

Just as we can get the cumulative distribution from the probability density function by integrating, we can get the PDF from the CDF by taking the first derivative of the CDF:

$$f(x) = \frac{dF(x)}{dx} \tag{1.7}$$

That the CDF is nondecreasing is another way of saying that the PDF cannot be negative.

If instead of wanting to know the probability that a random variable is less than a certain value, what if we want to know the probability that it is greater than a certain value? Or between two values? We handle both cases by adding and subtracting cumulative distribution functions. To find the probability that a variable is between two values, a and b, assuming b is greater than a, we would simply subtract:

$$P[a < X \leq b] = \int_{a}^{b} f(x)dx = F(b) - F(a) \tag{1.8}$$

To get the probability that a variable is greater than a certain value, we simply subtract from 1:

$$P[X > a] = 1 - F(a) \tag{1.9}$$

This result can be obtained by substituting infinity for b in the previous equation, remembering that the CDF at infinity must be 1.

Inverse Cumulative Distribution Functions

The inverse of the cumulative distribution can also be useful. For example, we might want to know that there is a 5% probability that a given equity index will return less than −10.6%, or that there is a 1% probability of interest rates increasing by more than 2% over a month.

More formally, if $F(x)$ is a cumulative distribution function, then we define $F^{-1}(p)$, the inverse cumulative distribution, as follows:

$$F(x) = p \Leftrightarrow F^{-1}(p) = x \text{ s.t. } 0 \leq p \leq 1 \tag{1.10}$$

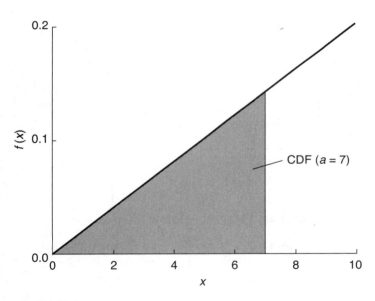

FIGURE 1-1 Cumulative distribution function.

Sample Problem

Question:

Calculate the cumulative distribution function for the probability density function from the previous problem:

$$f(x) = \frac{x}{50} \text{ s.t. } 0 \leq x \leq 10 \qquad \textbf{(1.11)}$$

Then answer the previous problem: What is the probability that the price of the bond is between $8 and $9?

Answer:

The CDF can be found by integrating the PDF:

$$F(x) = \int f(x)dx = \int \frac{x}{50}dx = \frac{1}{50}\int xdx = \frac{1}{50}\frac{1}{2}x^2 = \frac{x^2}{100}$$

To get the answer to the question, we simply evaluate the CDF at $8 and $9 and subtract:

$$P[\$8 < x \leq \$9] = F(9) - F(8) = \frac{9^2}{100} - \frac{8^2}{100}$$

$$= \frac{81}{100} - \frac{64}{100} = \frac{17}{100} = 17\%$$

As before, the probability of the price ending up between $8 and $9 is 17%.

Sample Problem

Question:

Given the cumulative distribution from the previous sample problem:

$$F(x) = \frac{x^2}{100} \text{ s.t. } 0 \leq x \leq 10$$

Calculate the inverse cumulative distribution function. Find the value of x such that 25% of the distribution is less than or equal to x.

Answer:

We have:

$$F(x) = p = \frac{x^2}{100}$$

Solving for p:

$$x = 10\sqrt{p}$$

Therefore, the inverse CDF is:

$$F^{-1}(p) = 10\sqrt{p}$$

We can quickly check that $p = 0$ and $p = 1$, return 0 and 10, the minimum and maximum of the distribution. For $p = 25\%$ we have:

$$F^{-1}(0.25) = 10\sqrt{0.25} = 10 \cdot 0.5 = 5$$

So 25% of the distribution is less than or equal to 5.

As we will see in Chapter 4, while some popular distributions have very simple inverse cumulative distribution functions, for other distributions no explicit inverse exists.

MUTUALLY EXCLUSIVE EVENTS

For a given random variable, the probability of any of two mutually exclusive events occurring is just the sum of their individual probabilities. In statistics notation, we can write:

$$P[A \cup B] = P[A] + P[B] \qquad \textbf{(1.12)}$$

where $A \cup B$ is the union of A and B. This is the probability of either A *or* B occurring. This is true only of mutually exclusive events.

This is a very simple rule, but, as mentioned at the beginning of the chapter, probability can be deceptively simple, and this property is easy to confuse. The confusion stems from the fact that *and* is synonymous with addition. If you say it this way, then the probability that A or B occurs is equal to the probability of A *and* the probability of B. It is not terribly difficult, but you can see where this could lead to a mistake.

This property of mutually exclusive events can be extended to any number of events. The probability that any of n mutually exclusive events occurs is simply the sum of the probabilities of those n events.

Sample Problem

Question:

Calculate the probability that a stock return is either below −10%, *or* above 10%, given:

$$P[R < -10\%] = 14\%$$
$$P[R > +10\%] = 17\%$$

Answer:

Note that the two events are mutually exclusive; the return cannot be below −10% and above 10% at the same time. The answer is: 14% + 17% = 31%.

INDEPENDENT EVENTS

In the preceding example, we were talking about one random variable and two mutually exclusive events, but what happens when we have more than one random variable? What is the probability that it rains tomorrow *and* the return on stock XYZ is greater than 5%? The answer depends crucially on whether the two random variables influence each other or not. If the outcome of one random variable is not influenced by the outcome of the other random variable, then we say those variables are independent. *If* stock market returns are independent of the weather, then the stock market should be just as likely to be up on rainy days as it is on sunny days.

Assuming that the stock market and the weather are independent random variables, then the probability of the market being up and rain is just the product of the probabilities of the two events occurring individually. We can write this as follows:

$$P[\text{rain and market up}] = P[\text{rain} \cap \text{market up}]$$

$$= P[\text{rain}] \cdot P[\text{market up}] \qquad \textbf{(1.13)}$$

We often refer to the probability of two events occurring together as their joint probability.

Sample Problem

Question:

According to the most recent weather forecast, there is a 20% chance of rain tomorrow. The probability that stock XYZ returns more than 5% on any given day is 40%. The two events are independent. What is the probability that it rains *and* stock XYZ returns more than 5% tomorrow?

Answer:

Since the two events are independent, the probability that it rains *and* stock XYZ returns more than 5% is just the product of the two probabilities. The answer is: 20% × 40% = 8%.

PROBABILITY MATRICES

When dealing with the joint probabilities of two variables, it is often convenient to summarize the various probabilities in a probability matrix or probability table. For example, pretend we are investigating a company that has issued both bonds and stock. The bonds can either be downgraded, be upgraded, or have no change in rating. The stock can either outperform the market or underperform the market.

		Equity		
		Outperform	Underperform	
Bonds	Upgrade	15%	5%	**20%**
	No Change	30%	25%	**55%**
	Downgrade	5%	20%	**25%**
		50%	**50%**	**100%**

In this table, the probability of both the company's stock outperforming the market *and* the bonds being upgraded is 15%. Similarly, the probability of the stock underperforming the market *and* the bonds having no change in rating is 25%. We can also see the unconditional probabilities, by adding across a row or down a column. The probability of the bonds being upgraded, irrespective of the stock's performance, is: 15% + 5% = 20%. Similarly, the probability of the equity outperforming the market is: 15% + 30% + 5% = 50%. Importantly, all of the joint probabilities add to 100%. Given all the possible events, one of them must happen.

Sample Problem

Question:

You are investigating a second company. As with our previous example, the company has issued both bonds and stock. The bonds can either be downgraded, be upgraded, or have no change in rating. The stock can either outperform the market or underperform the market. You are given the following probability matrix, which is missing three probabilities, *X, Y,* and *Z*. Calculate values for the missing probabilities.

		Equity		
		Outperform	Underperform	
Bonds	Upgrade	5%	0%	5%
	No Change	40%	*Y*	*Z*
	Downgrade	*X*	30%	35%
		50%	50%	100%

Answer:

All of the values in the first column must add to 50%, the probability of the equity outperforming the market; therefore, we have:

$$5\% + 40\% + X = 50\%$$

$$X = 5\%$$

We can check our answer for X by summing across the third row: 5% + 30% = 35%.

Looking down the second column, we see that Y is equal to 20%:

$$0\% + Y + 30\% = 50\%$$

$$Y = 20\%$$

Finally, knowing that $Y = 20\%$, we can sum across the second row to get Z:

$$40\% + Y = 40\% + 20\% = Z$$

$$Z = 60\%$$

CONDITIONAL PROBABILITY

The concept of independence is closely related to the concept of conditional probability. Rather than trying to determine the probability of the market being up *and* having rain, we can ask, "What is the probability that the stock market is up *given* that it is raining?" We can write this as a conditional probability:

$$P[\text{market up} \mid \text{rain}] = p \qquad \textbf{(1.14)}$$

The vertical bar signals that the probability of the first argument is conditional on the second. You would read this as "The probability of 'market up' given 'rain' is equal to p."

If the weather and the stock market are independent, then the probability of the market being up on a rainy day is the same as the probability of the market being up on a sunny day. If the weather somehow affects the stock market, however, then the conditional probabilities might not be equal. We could have a situation where:

$$P[\text{market up} \mid \text{rain}] \neq P[\text{market up} \mid \text{no rain}] \qquad \textbf{(1.15)}$$

In this case, the weather and the stock market are no longer independent. We can no longer multiply their probabilities together to get their joint probability.

BAYES' THEOREM

Assume we have two bonds, Bond A and Bond B, each with a 10% probability of defaulting over the next year. The probability that both bonds default is 6%. The probability that neither bond defaults is 86%. It follows that the probability that only Bond A defaults is 4%, and the probability that only Bond B defaults is also 4%. We can summarize all of this information in a probability matrix:

		Bond A		
		No Default	Default	
Bond B	No Default	86%	4%	**90%**
	Default	4%	6%	**10%**
		90%	**10%**	**100%**

As required, the rows and columns of the matrix add up, and the sum of all the probabilities is equal to 100%.

Notice however that the probability of both bonds defaulting is 6%. This is higher than the 1% probability we would expect if the default events were independent (10% × 10% = 1%). This might be because both bonds are issued by similar companies, because the issuers are located in the same geographic region, or because defaults are correlated in general. The probability that neither bond defaults, 86%, is also higher than what we would expect if the defaults were independent (90% × 90% = 81%).

We could also express features of the probability matrix in terms of conditional probabilities. What is the probability that Bond A defaults, given a default by Bond B? Bond B defaults in 10% of the scenarios, but the probability that Bond A and Bond B both default is 6%. In other words, Bond A defaults in 60% of the scenarios in which Bond B defaults. We write this as follows:

$$P[A \mid B] = \frac{P[A \cap B]}{P[B]} = \frac{6\%}{10\%} = 60\% \qquad \textbf{(1.16)}$$

Notice that the conditional probability is different from the unconditional probability. The unconditional probability of default is 10%.

$$P[A] = 10\% \neq 60\% = P[A \mid B] \qquad \textbf{(1.17)}$$

It turns out that Equation 1.16 is true in general. More often the equation is written as follows:

$$P[A \cap B] = P[A \mid B] \cdot P[B] \qquad \textbf{(1.18)}$$

In other words, the probability of both A and B occurring is just the probability that A occurs, given B, multiplied by the probability of B occurring. What's more, the ordering of A and B doesn't matter. We could just as easily write:

$$P[A \cap B] = P[B \mid A] \cdot P[A] \qquad \textbf{(1.19)}$$

Combining the right-hand side of both these equations and rearranging terms leads us to a very important result:

$$P[A \mid B] = \frac{P[B \mid A] \cdot P[A]}{P[B]} \qquad \textbf{(1.20)}$$

This result is known as Bayes' theorem, named after the eighteenth-century English mathematician Thomas Bayes, who first described this relationship. Bayes never actually publicized his eponymous theorem in his own lifetime. The result might have been confined to the dustheap of history had not a friend submitted it to the Royal Society two years after his death. As simple as it looks, the result has wide-ranging applications.

In the example, in which the default rate is the same for both bonds, the application of Bayes' theorem is trivial. The probability that Bond A defaults, given a default by Bond B, is 60%, which is equal to (60% × 10%)/10%. As we will see, in more complicated situations the results can be far less intuitive.

Sample Problem

Question:

Imagine there is a disease that afflicts just 1% of the population. A new test has been developed to detect the disease, which is 99% accurate. That is, for people with the disease, the test correctly indicates that they have the disease in 99% of cases. Similarly, for those who do not have the disease, the test correctly indicates that they do not have the disease in 99 out of 100 cases.

If a person takes the test and the result comes back positive, what is the probability that he or she actually has the disease?

Answer:

While not exactly financial risk, this is a classic example of how conditional probability can be far from intuitive. This type of problem is also far from being an academic curiosity. A number of studies have asked doctors similar questions; see, for example, Gigerenzer and Edwards (2003). The results are often discouraging. The physicians' answers vary widely and are often far from correct.

If the test is 99% accurate, it is tempting to guess that there is a 99% chance that the person who tests positive actually has the disease. Unfortunately, this turns out to be a very bad guess. According to Bayes' theorem, the correct answer is 50%:

$$P[\text{have disease} \mid \text{positive test}]$$
$$= \frac{P[\text{positive test} \mid \text{have disease}] \cdot P[\text{have disease}]}{P[\text{positive test}]}$$

In the denominator, the unconditional probability of a positive test is simply the sum of the probability of a positive test being produced by somebody with the disease and the probability of a positive test being produced by somebody without the disease:

$$P[\text{positive test}] = P[\text{have disease}]$$
$$\cdot P[\text{positive test} \mid \text{have disease}]$$
$$+ P[\overline{\text{have disease}}] \cdot P[\text{positive test} \mid \overline{\text{have disease}}]$$
$$P[\text{positive test}] = 1\% \cdot 99\% + 99\% \cdot 1\% = 2\% \cdot 99\%$$

where we use the line above "have disease" to represent logical negation. In other words, $P[\overline{\text{have disease}}]$ is the probability of not having the disease.

Substituting this result into our Bayes' theorem equation, we arrive at the final answer:

$$P[\text{have disease} \mid \text{positive test}] = \frac{99\% \cdot 1\%}{2\% \cdot 99\%} = 50\%$$

The reason the answer is 50% and not 99% is because the disease is so rare. Most people don't have the disease, so even a small number of false positives overwhelms the number of actual positives. It is easy to see this in a matrix. Assume 10,000 trials:

		Actual		
		+	−	
Test	+	99	99	198
	−	1	9,801	9,802
		100	9,900	10,000

If you check the numbers, you'll see that they work out exactly as described: 1% of the population with the disease, and 99% accuracy in each column. In the end though, the number of positive test results is identical for the two populations, 99 in each. This is why the probability of actually having the disease given a positive test is 50%. In order for a test for a rare disease to be meaningful, it has to be extremely accurate.

Bayes' theorem is often described as a procedure for updating beliefs about the world when presented with new information. For example, pretend you had a coin that you believed was fair, with a 50% chance of landing heads or tails when flipped. If you flip the coin 10 times and it lands heads each time, you might start to suspect that the coin is not fair. Ten heads in a row could happen, but the odds are only 1:1,024 for a fair coin. How do you update your beliefs? If you believed there was a 90% probability that the coin was fair before you started flipping, then your view of the coin after seeing 10 heads should probably be between 0% and 90%. You are less certain than you were before about the coin's fairness, but there is still some chance that the coin is fair. As the previous sample problem makes clear, Bayes' theorem provides a framework for deciding exactly what our new beliefs should be.

Sample Problem

Question:

You are an analyst at Astra Fund of Funds. Based on an examination of historical data, you determine that all fund managers fall into one of two groups. Stars are the best managers. The probability that a star will beat the market in any given year is 75%. Other managers are just as likely to beat the market as they are to underperform it. For both types of managers, the probability of beating the market is independent from one year to the next.

Stars are rare. Of a given pool of managers, only 16% turn out to be stars. A new manager was added to your portfolio of funds three years ago. Since then, the new manager has beaten the market every year. What was the probability that the manager was a star when the manager was first added to the portfolio? What is the probability that this manager is a star now?

Answer:

We start by summarizing the information from the problem, and introducing some notation. The probability that a manager beats the market given that the manager is a star is 75%:

$$P[B \mid S] = 75\% = \frac{3}{4}$$

The probability that a manager who is not a star beats the market is 50%:

$$P[B \mid \bar{S}] = 50\% = \frac{1}{2}$$

At the time the manager was added to the portfolio, the probability that the manager was a star was just the probability of any manager being a star, 16%, the unconditional probability:

$$P[S] = 16\% = \frac{4}{25}$$

To answer the final question, we need to find $P[S \mid 3B]$, the probability that the manager is a star, given that the manager has beaten the market for three years. We can find this using Bayes' Theorem:

$$P[S \mid 3B] = \frac{P[3B \mid S] \, P[S]}{P[3B]}$$

We know $P[S]$. Because outperformance is independent from one year to the next, the other part of the numerator, $P[3B \mid S]$, is just the probability that a star beats the market in any given year to the third power:

$$P[3B \mid S] = \left(\frac{3}{4}\right)^3 = \frac{27}{64}$$

The denominator is the unconditional probability of beating the market for three years. This is just the weighted average probability of three beats over both types of managers:

$$P[3B] = \frac{4}{25}\left(\frac{3}{4}\right)^3 + \frac{21}{25}\left(\frac{1}{2}\right)^3 = \frac{4}{25}\frac{27}{64} + \frac{21}{25}\frac{1}{8} = \frac{69}{400}$$

Putting it all together, we get our final result:

$$P[S \mid 3B] = \frac{\frac{27}{64}\frac{4}{25}}{\frac{69}{400}} = \frac{9}{23} \approx 39\%$$

Our updated belief about the manager, having seen the manager beat the market three times, is approximately 39%, a significant increase from our prior belief of 16%. A star is much more likely to beat the market three years in a row—almost four times as likely—so it makes sense that we believe our manager is more likely to be a star now.

Even though it is much more likely that a star will beat the market three years in a row, we are still far from certain that this manager is a star. At 39%, the odds are more likely that the manager is not a star. As before, the reason has to do with the overwhelming number of false positives. There are so many nonstar managers that some of them are bound to beat the market three years in a row. The real stars are simply outnumbered by these lucky nonstar managers.

Basic Statistics

2

■ Learning Objectives

Candidates, after completing this reading, should be able to:

- Define and interpret the mean, standard deviation, and variance of a random variable.
- Define, calculate, and interpret the covariance and correlation between two random variables.
- Calculate the mean and variance of sums of variables.
- Describe the four central moments of a statistical variable or distribution: mean, variance, skewness and kurtosis.

- Interpret the skewness and kurtosis of a statistical distribution, and interpret the concepts of coskewness and cokurtosis.
- Describe and interpret the best linear unbiased estimator.

Excerpt is Chapter 3 of Mathematics and Statistics for Financial Risk Management, *by Michael Miller.*

In this chapter we will learn how to describe a collection of data in precise statistical terms. Many of the concepts will be familiar, but the notation and terminology might be new. This notation and terminology will be used throughout the rest of the book.

AVERAGES

Everybody knows what an average is. We come across averages every day, whether they are earned run averages in baseball or grade point averages in school. In statistics there are actually three different types of averages: means, modes, and medians. By far the most commonly used average in risk management is the mean.

Population and Sample Data

If you wanted to know the mean age of people working in your firm, you would simply ask every person in the firm his or her age, add the ages together, and divide by the number of people in the firm. Assuming there are n employees and a_i is the age of the ith employee, then the mean, μ, is simply:

$$\mu = \frac{1}{n}\sum_{i=1}^{n} a_i = \frac{1}{n}(a_1 + a_2 + \cdots + a_{n-1} + a_n) \qquad (2.1)$$

It is important at this stage to differentiate between population statistics and sample statistics. In this example, μ is the population mean. Assuming nobody lied about his or her age, and forgetting about rounding errors and other trivial details, we know the mean age of people in your firm *exactly*. We have a complete data set of everybody in your firm; we've surveyed the entire population.

This state of absolute certainty is, unfortunately, quite rare in finance. More often, we are faced with a situation such as this: estimate the mean return of stock ABC, given the most recent year of daily returns. In a situation like this, we assume there is some underlying data generating process, whose statistical properties are constant over time. The underlying process still has a true mean, but we cannot observe it directly. We can only estimate that mean based on our limited data sample. In our example, assuming n returns, we estimate the mean using the same formula as before:

$$\hat{\mu} = \frac{1}{n}\sum_{i=1}^{n} r_i = \frac{1}{n}(r_1 + r_2 + \cdots + r_{n-1} + r_n) \qquad (2.2)$$

where $\hat{\mu}$ (pronounced "mu hat") is our *estimate* of the true mean based on our sample of n returns. We call this the sample mean.

The median and mode are also types of averages. They are used less frequently in finance, but both can be useful. The median represents the center of a group of data; within the group, half the data points will be less than the median, and half will be greater. The mode is the value that occurs most frequently.

Sample Problem

Question:

Calculate the mean, median, and mode of the following data set:

−20%, −10%, −5%, −5%, 0%, 10%, 10%, 10%, 19%

Answer:

$$\text{Mean} = \frac{1}{9}(-20\% - 10\% - 5\% - 5\% + 0\% + 10\% + 10\% + 10\% + 19\%) = 1\%$$

Mode = 10%

Median = 0%

If there is an even number of data points, the median is found by averaging the two center-most points. In the following series:

5%, 10%, 20%, 25%

the median is 15%. The median can be useful for summarizing data that is asymmetrical or contains significant outliers.

A data set can also have more than one mode. If the maximum frequency is shared by two or more values, all of those values are considered modes. In the following example, the modes are 10% and 20%:

5%, 10%, 10%, 10%, 14%, 16%, 20%, 20%, 20%, 24%

In calculating the mean in Equation 2.1 and Equation 2.2, each data point was counted exactly once. In certain situations, we might want to give more or less weight to certain data points. In calculating the average return of stocks in an equity index, we might want to give more weight to larger firms, perhaps weighting their returns in proportion to their market capitalization. Given n data points, $x_i = x_1, x_2, \ldots, x_n$, with corresponding weights, w_i, we can define the weighted mean, μ_w, as:

$$\mu_w = \frac{\sum_{i=1}^{n} w_i x_i}{\sum_{i=1}^{n} w_i} \qquad (2.3)$$

The standard mean from Equation 2.1 can be viewed as a special case of the weighted mean, where all the values have equal weight.

Discrete Random Variables

For a discrete random variable, we can also calculate the mean, median, and mode. For a random variable, X, with possible values, x_i, and corresponding probabilities, p_i, we define the mean, μ, as:

$$\mu = \sum_{i=1}^{n} p_i x_i \qquad (2.4)$$

The equation for the mean of a discrete random variable is a special case of the weighted mean, where the outcomes are weighted by their probabilities, and the sum of the weights is equal to one.

The median of a discrete random variable is the value such that the probability that a value is less than or equal to the median is equal to 50%. Working from the other end of the distribution, we can also define the median such that 50% of the values are greater than or equal to the median. For a random variable, X, if we denote the median as m, we have:

$$P[X \geq m] = P[X \leq m] = 0.50 \qquad (2.5)$$

For a discrete random variable, the mode is the value associated with the highest probability. As with population and sample data sets, the mode of a discrete random variable need not be unique.

Continuous Random Variables

We can also define the mean, median, and mode for a continuous random variable. To find the mean of a continuous random variable, we simply integrate the product of the variable and its probability density function (PDF). In the limit, this is equivalent to our approach to calculating the mean of a discrete random variable. For a continuous random variable, X, with a PDF, $f(x)$, the mean, μ, is then:

Sample Problem

Question:

At the start of the year, a bond portfolio consists of two bonds, each worth $100. At the end of the year, if a bond defaults, it will be worth $20. If it does not default, the bond will be worth $100. The probability that both bonds default is 20%. The probability that neither bond defaults is 45%. What are the mean, median, and mode of the year-end portfolio value?

Answer:

We are given the probability for two outcomes:

$$P[V = \$40] = 20\%$$
$$P[V = \$200] = 45\%$$

At year-end, the value of the portfolio, V, can only have one of three values, and the sum of all the probabilities must sum to 100%. This allows us to calculate the final probability:

$$P[V = \$120] = 100\% - 20\% - 45\% = 35\%$$

The mean of V is then $140:

$$\mu = 0.20 \cdot \$40 + 0.35 \cdot \$120 + 0.45 \cdot \$200 = \$140$$

The mode of the distribution is $200; this is the most likely single outcome. The median of the distribution is $120; half of the outcomes are less than or equal to $120.

$$\mu = \int_{x_{min}}^{x_{max}} x f(x) dx \qquad (2.6)$$

The median of a continuous random variable is defined exactly as it is for a discrete random variable, such that there is a 50% probability that values are less than or equal to, or greater than or equal to, the median. If we define the median as m, then:

$$\int_{x_{min}}^{m} f(x) dx = \int_{m}^{x_{max}} f(x) dx = 0.50 \qquad (2.7)$$

Alternatively, we can define the median in terms of the cumulative distribution function. Given the cumulative distribution function, $F(x)$, and the median, m, we have:

$$F(m) = 0.50 \qquad (2.8)$$

The mode of a continuous random variable corresponds to the maximum of the density function. As before, the mode need not be unique.

Sample Problem

Question:

Using the now-familiar probability density function from Chapter 1:

$$f(x) = \frac{x}{50} \text{ s.t. } 0 \leq x \leq 10$$

What are the mean, median, and mode of x?

Answer:

As we saw in a previous example, this probability density function is a triangle, between $x = 0$ and $x = 10$, and zero everywhere else.

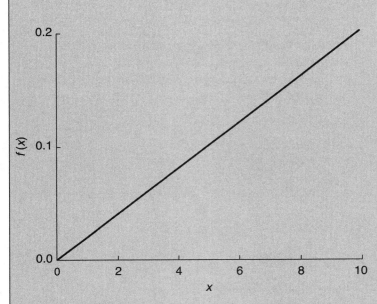

Probability Density Function

For a continuous distribution, the mode corresponds to the maximum of the PDF. By inspection of the graph, we can see that the mode of $f(x)$ is equal to 10.

To calculate the median, we need to find m, such that the integral of $f(x)$ from the lower bound of $f(x)$, zero, to m is equal to 0.50. That is, we need to find:

$$\int_0^m \frac{x}{50} dx = 0.50$$

First we solve the left-hand side of the equation:

$$\int_0^m \frac{x}{50} dx = \frac{1}{50} \int_0^m x \, dx = \frac{1}{50}\left[\frac{1}{2}x^2\right]_0^m = \frac{1}{100}(m^2 - 0) = \frac{m^2}{100}$$

Setting this result equal to 0.50 and solving for m, we obtain our final answer:

$$\frac{m^2}{100} = 0.50$$
$$m^2 = 50$$
$$m = \sqrt{50} = 7.07$$

In the last step we can ignore the negative root. If we hadn't calculated the median, looking at the graph it might be tempting to guess that the median is 5, the midpoint of the range of the distribution. This is a common mistake. Because lower values have less weight, the median ends up being greater than 5.

The mean is approximately 6.67:

$$\mu = \int_0^{10} x \frac{x}{50} dx = \frac{1}{50}\int_0^{10} x^2 dx = \frac{1}{50}\left[\frac{1}{3}x^3\right]_0^{10}$$
$$= \frac{1000}{150} = \frac{20}{3} = 6.67$$

As with the median, it is a common mistake, based on inspection of the PDF, to guess that the mean is 5. However, what the PDF is telling us is that outcomes between 5 and 10 are much more likely than values between 0 and 5 (the PDF is higher between 5 and 10 than between 0 and 5). This is why the mean is greater than 5.

EXPECTATIONS

On January 15, 2005, the Huygens space probe landed on the surface of Titan, the largest moon of Saturn. This was the culmination of a seven-year-long mission. During its descent and for over an hour after touching down on the surface, Huygens sent back detailed images, scientific readings, and even sounds from a strange world. There are liquid oceans on Titan, the landing site was littered with "rocks" composed of water ice, and weather on the moon includes methane rain. The Huygens probe was named after Christiaan Huygens, a Dutch polymath who first discovered Titan in 1655. In addition to astronomy and physics, Huygens had more prosaic interests, including probability theory. Originally published in Latin in 1657, *De Ratiociniis in Ludo Aleae*, or *The Value of All Chances in Games of Fortune*, was one of the first texts to formally explore one of the most important concepts in probability theory, namely expectations.

Like many of his contemporaries, Huygens was interested in games of chance. As he described it, if a game has a 50% probability of paying $3 and a 50% probability of paying $7, then this is, in a way, equivalent to having $5 with certainty. This is because we *expect*, on average, to win $5 in this game:

$$50\% \cdot \$3 + 50\% \cdot \$7 = \$5 \qquad \textbf{(2.9)}$$

As one can already see, the concepts of expectations and averages are very closely linked. In the current example, if we play the game only once, there is no chance of winning exactly $5; we can win only $3 or $7. Still, even if we play the game only once, we say that the expected value of the game is $5. That we are talking about the mean of all the potential payouts is understood.

We can express the concept of expectation more formally using the expectations operator. We could state that the random variable, X, has an expected value of $5 as follows:

$$E[X] = 0.50 \cdot \$3 + 0.50 \cdot \$7 = \$5 \qquad \textbf{(2.10)}$$

where $E[\cdot]$ is the expectation operator.*

In this example, the mean and the expected value have the same numeric value, $5. The same is true for discrete and continuous random variables. The expected value of a random variable is equal to the mean of the random variable.

While the value of the mean and the expected value may be the same in many situations, the two concepts are not exactly the same. In many situations in finance and risk management the terms can be used interchangeably. The difference is often subtle.

As the name suggests, expectations are often thought of as being forward-looking. Pretend we have a financial asset for which the mean annual return is equal to 15%. This is not an estimate; in this case, we *know* that the mean *is* 15%. We say that the expected value of the return

next year is 15%. We expect the return to be 15%, because the probability-weighted mean of all the possible outcomes is 15%.

Now pretend that we don't actually *know* what the mean return of the asset is, but we have 10 years' worth of historical data, for which the sample mean is 15%. In this case the expected value may or may not be 15%. In most cases if we say that the expected value is equal to 15%, we are making two assumptions: first, we are assuming that the returns in our sample were generated by the same random process over the entire sample period; second, we are assuming that the returns will continue to be generated by this same process in the future. These are very strong assumptions. In finance and risk management, we often assume that the data we are interested in are being generated by a consistent, unchanging process. Testing the validity of this assumption can be an important part of risk management in practice.

The concept of expectations is also a much more general concept than the concept of the mean. Using the expectations operator, we can derive the expected value of functions of random variables. As we will see in subsequent sections, the concept of expectations underpins the definitions of other population statistics (variance, skew, kurtosis), and is important in understanding regression analysis and time series analysis. In these cases, even when we could use the mean to describe a calculation, in practice we tend to talk exclusively in terms of expectations.

The expectations operator is linear. That is, for two random variables, X and Y, and a constant, c, the following two equations are true:

$$E[X + Y] = E[X] + E[Y] \qquad \textbf{(2.11)}$$
$$E[cX] + cE[X]$$

If the expected value of one option, A, is $10, and the expected value of option B is $20, then the expected value of a portfolio containing A and B is $30, and the expected value of a portfolio containing five contracts of option A is $50.

Be very careful, though; the expectations operator is not multiplicative. The expected value of the product of two random variables is not necessarily the same as the product of their expected values:

$$E[XY] \neq E[X]E[Y] \qquad \textbf{(2.12)}$$

---

* Those of you with a background in physics might be more familiar with the term *expectation value* and the notation $<X>$ rather than $E[X]$. This is a matter of convention. Throughout this book we use the term *expected value* and $E[\cdot]$, which is currently more popular in finance and econometrics. Risk managers should be familiar with both conventions.

Sample Problem

Question:

At the start of the year, you are asked to price a newly issued zero-coupon bond. The bond has a notional of $100. You believe there is a 20% chance that the bond will default, in which case it will be worth $40 at the end of the year. There is also a 30% chance that the bond will be downgraded, in which case it will be worth $90 in a year's time. If the bond does not default and is not downgraded; it will be worth $100. Use a continuous interest rate of 5% to determine the current price of the bond.

Answer:

We first need to determine the expected future value of the bond, that is the expected value of the bond in one year's time. We are given the following:

$$P[V_{t+1} = \$40] = 0.20$$

$$P[V_{t+1} = \$90] = 0.30$$

Because there are only three possible outcomes, the probability of no downgrades and no default must be 50%:

$$P[V_{t+1} = \$100] = 1 - 0.20 - 0.30 = 0.50$$

The expected value of the bond in one year is then:

$$E[V_{t+1}] = 0.20 \cdot \$40 + 0.30 \cdot \$90 + 0.50 \cdot \$100 = \$85$$

To get the current price of the bond we then discount this expected future value:

$$E[V_t] = e^{-0.05} E[V_{t+1}] = e^{-0.05} \$85 = \$80.85$$

The current price of the bond, in this case $80.85, is often referred to as the present value or fair value of the bond. The price is considered fair because the discounted expected value of the bond is the rational price to pay for the bond, given our knowledge of the world.

Imagine we have two binary options. Each pays either $100 or nothing, depending on the value of some underlying asset at expiration. The probability of receiving $100 is 50% for both options. Further, assume that it is always the case that if the first option pays $100, the second pays $0, and vice versa. The expected value of each option separately is clearly $50. If we denote the payout of the first option as X and the payout of the second as Y, we have:

$$E[X] = E[Y] = 0.50 \cdot \$100 + 0.50 \cdot \$0 = \$50 \quad (2.13)$$

It follows that $E[X]E[Y] = \$50 \times \$50 = \$2,500$. In each scenario, though, one option is valued at zero, so the product of the payouts is always zero: $\$100 \cdot \$0 = \$0 \cdot \$100 = \$0$. The expected value of the product of the two option payouts is:

$$E[XY] = 0.50 \cdot \$100 \cdot \$0 + 0.50 \cdot \$0 \cdot \$100 = \$0 \quad (2.14)$$

In this case, the product of the expected values and the expected value of the products are clearly not equal. In the special case where $E[XY] = E[X]E[Y]$, we say that X and Y are independent.

If the expected value of the product of two variables does not necessarily equal the product of the expectations of those variables, it follows that the expected value of the product of a variable with itself does not necessarily equal the product of the expectations of that variable with itself; that is:

$$E[X^2] \neq E[X]^2 \quad (2.15)$$

Imagine we have a fair coin. Assign heads a value of +1 and tails a value of −1. We can write the probabilities of the outcomes as follows:

$$P[X = +1] = P[X = -1] = 0.50 \quad (2.16)$$

The expected value of any coin flip is zero, but the expected value of X^2 is +1, not zero:

$$E[X] = 0.50 \cdot (+1) + 0.50 \cdot (-1) = 0 \quad (2.17)$$

$$E[X]^2 = 0^2 = 0$$

$$E[X^2] = 0.50 \cdot (+1^2) + 0.50 \cdot (-1^2) = 1$$

As simple as this example is, this distinction is very important. As we will see, the difference between $E[X^2]$ and $E[X]^2$ is central to our definition of variance and standard deviation.

VARIANCE AND STANDARD DEVIATION

The variance of a random variable measures how noisy or unpredictable that random variable is. Variance is defined as the expected value of the difference between the variable and its mean squared:

$$\sigma^2 = E[(X - \mu)^2] \quad (2.18)$$

where σ^2 is the variance of the random variable X with mean μ.

The square root of variance, typically denoted by σ, is called standard deviation. In finance we often refer to standard deviation as volatility. This is analogous to

Sample Problem

Question:

Given the following equation:

$$y = (x + 5)^3 + x^2 + 10x$$

What is the expected value of y? Assume the following:

$$E[x] = 4$$

$$E[x^2] = 9$$

$$E[x^3] = 12$$

Answer:

Note that $E[x^2]$ and $E[x^3]$ cannot be derived from knowledge of $E[x]$. In this problem, $E[x^2] \neq E[x]^2$. As forewarned, the expectations operator is not necessarily multiplicative. To find the expected value of y, then, we first expand the term $(x + 5)^3$ within the expectations operator:

$$E[y] = E[(x + 5)^3 + x^2 + 10x] = E[x^3 + 16x^2 + 85x + 125]$$

Because the expectations operator is linear, we can separate the terms in the summation and move the constants outside the expectations operator. We do this in two steps:

$$E[y] = E[x^3] + E[16x^2] + E[85x] + E[125]$$

$$= E[x^3] + 16E[x^2] + 85E[x] + 125$$

At this point, we can substitute in the values for $E[x]$, $E[x^2]$, and $E[x^3]$, which we were given at the start of the exercise:

$$E[y] = 12 + 16 \cdot 9 + 85 \cdot 4 + 125 = 621$$

This gives us the final answer, 621.

Sample Problem

Question:

A derivative has a 50/50 chance of being worth either +10 or −10 at expiry. What is the standard deviation of the derivative's value?

Answer:

$$\mu = 0.50 \cdot 10 + 0.50 \cdot (-10) = 0$$

$$\sigma^2 = 0.50 \cdot (10 - 0)^2 + 0.50 \cdot (-10 - 0)^2 = 0.5 \cdot 100 + 0.5 \cdot 100 = 100$$

$$\sigma = 10$$

where $\hat{\mu}_x$ is the sample mean from Equation 2.2. Given that we have n data points, it might seem odd that we are dividing the sum by $(n - 1)$ and not n. The reason has to do with the fact that $\hat{\mu}_x$ itself is an estimate of the true mean, which also contains a fraction of each x_i. We leave the proof for a problem at the end of the chapter, but it turns out that dividing by $(n - 1)$, not n, produces an unbiased estimate of σ^2. If the mean is known or we are calculating the population variance, then we divide by n. If instead the mean is also being estimated, then we divide by $n - 1$.

Equation 2.18 can easily be rearranged as follows (we leave the proof of this for an exercise, too):

$$\sigma^2 = E[X^2] - \mu^2 = E[X^2] - E[X]^2 \qquad \textbf{(2.20)}$$

Note that variance can be nonzero only if $E[X^2] \neq E[X]^2$.

When writing computer programs, this last version of the variance formula is often useful, since it allows you to calculate the mean and the variance in the same loop. Also, in finance it is often convenient to assume that the mean of a random variable is close to zero. For example, based on theory, we might expect the spread between two equity indexes to have a mean of zero in the long run. In this case, the variance is simply the mean of the squared returns.

As with the mean, for a continuous random variable we can calculate the variance by integrating with the probability density function. For a continuous random variable, X, with a probability density function, $f(x)$, the variance can be calculated as:

$$\sigma^2 = \int_{x_{min}}^{x_{max}} (x - \mu)^2 f(x) dx \qquad \textbf{(2.21)}$$

referring to the mean as the average. Standard deviation is a mathematically precise term, whereas volatility is a more general concept.

In the next example, we were calculating the population variance and standard deviation. *All* of the possible outcomes for the derivative were known.

To calculate the sample variance of a random variable X based on n observations, $x_1, x_2, \ldots, x_n$, we can use the following formula:

$$E[\sigma_x^2] = \hat{\sigma}_x^2 = \frac{1}{n-1} \sum_{i=1}^{n} (x_i - \hat{\mu}_x)^2 \qquad \textbf{(2.19)}$$

Sample Problem

Question:

Assume that the mean of daily Standard & Poor's (S&P) 500 returns is zero. You observe the following returns over the course of 10 days:

7%	−4%	11%	8%	3%	9%	−21%	10%	−9%	−1%

Estimate the standard deviation of daily S&P 500 returns.

Answer:

The sample mean is not exactly zero, but we are told to assume that the population mean *is* zero; therefore:

$$E[\sigma_r^2] = \hat{\sigma}_r^2 = \frac{1}{n}\sum_{i=1}^{n}(r_i^2 - 0^2) = \frac{1}{n}\sum_{i=1}^{n} r_i^2$$

$$= \frac{1}{10}0.0963 = 0.00963$$

$$\hat{\sigma}_r = 9.8\%$$

Note, because we were told to assume the mean was known, we divide by $n = 10$, not $(n - 1) = 9$.

It is not difficult to prove that, for either a discrete or a continuous random variable, multiplying by a constant will increase the standard deviation by the same factor:

$$\sigma[cX] = c\sigma[X] \qquad (2.22)$$

In other words, if you own $10 of an equity with a standard deviation of $2, then $100 of the same equity will have a standard deviation of $20.

Adding a constant to a random variable, however, does not alter the standard deviation or the variance:

$$\sigma[X + c] = \sigma[X] \qquad (2.23)$$

This is because the impact on the mean is the same as the impact on any draw of the random variable, leaving the deviation from the mean unchanged. If you own a portfolio with a standard deviation of $20, and then you add $1,000 of cash to that portfolio, the standard deviation of the portfolio will still be $20.

STANDARDIZED VARIABLES

It is often convenient to work with variables where the mean is zero and the standard deviation is one. From the preceding section it is not difficult to prove that, given a random variable X with mean μ and standard deviation σ, we can define a second random variable Y:

$$Y = \frac{X - \mu}{\sigma} \qquad (2.24)$$

such that Y will have a mean of zero and a standard deviation of one. We say that X has been standardized, or that Y is a standard random variable. In practice, if we have a data set and we want to standardize it, we first compute the sample mean and the standard deviation. Then, for each data point, we subtract the mean and divide by the standard deviation.

The inverse transformation can also be very useful when it comes to creating computer simulations. Simulations often begin with standardized variables, which need to be transformed into variables with a specific mean and standard deviation. In this case, we simply take the output from the standardized variable, multiply by the desired standard deviation, and then add the desired mean. The order is important. Adding a constant to a random variable will not change the standard deviation, but multiplying a non-mean-zero variable by a constant will change the mean.

COVARIANCE

Up until now we have mostly been looking at statistics that summarize one variable. In risk management, we often want to describe the relationship between two random variables. For example, is there a relationship between the returns of an equity and the returns of a market index?

Covariance is analogous to variance, but instead of looking at the deviation from the mean of one variable, we are going to look at the relationship between the deviations of two variables:

$$\sigma_{XY} = E[(X - \mu_X)(Y - \mu_Y)] \qquad (2.25)$$

where σ_{XY} is the covariance between two random variables, X and Y, with means μ_X and μ_Y, respectively. As you can see from the definition, variance is just a special case of covariance. Variance is the covariance of a variable with itself.

If X tends to be above μ_X when Y is above μ_Y (both deviations are positive), and X tends to be below μ_X when Y is below μ_Y (both deviations are negative), then the covariance will be positive (a positive number multiplied by a positive number is positive; likewise, for two negative numbers). If the opposite is true and the deviations tend to be of opposite sign, then the covariance will be negative. If the deviations have no discernible relationship, then the covariance will be zero.

Earlier in this chapter, we cautioned that the expectations operator is not generally multiplicative. This fact turns out to be closely related to the concept of covariance. Just as we rewrote our variance equation earlier, we can rewrite Equation 2.25 as follows:

$$\sigma_{XY} = E[(X - \mu_X)(Y - \mu_Y)] = E[XY] - \mu_X\mu_Y \quad \textbf{(2.26)}$$
$$= E[XY] - E[X]E[Y]$$

In the special case where the covariance between X and Y is zero, the expected value of XY is equal to the expected value of X multiplied by the expected value of Y:

$$\sigma_{XY} = 0 \Rightarrow E[XY] = E[X]E[Y] \quad \textbf{(2.27)}$$

If the covariance is anything other than zero, then the two sides of this equation cannot be equal. Unless we know that the covariance between two variables is zero, we cannot assume that the expectations operator is multiplicative.

In order to calculate the covariance between two random variables, X and Y, assuming the means of both variables are known, we can use the following formula:

$$\hat{\sigma}_{x,y} = \frac{1}{n}\sum_{i=1}^{n}(x_i - \mu_x)(y_i - \mu_Y)$$

If the means are unknown and must also be estimated, we replace n with $(n - 1)$:

$$\hat{\sigma}_{x,y} = \frac{1}{n-1}\sum_{i=1}^{n}(x_i - \hat{\mu}_x)(y_i - \hat{\mu}_Y)$$

If we replaced y_i in these formulas with x_i, calculating the covariance of X with itself, the resulting equations would be the same as the equations for calculating variance from the previous section.

CORRELATION

Closely related to the concept of covariance is correlation. To get the correlation of two variables, we simply divide their covariance by their respective standard deviations:

$$\rho_{XY} = \frac{\sigma_{XY}}{\sigma_X\sigma_Y} \quad \textbf{(2.28)}$$

Correlation has the nice property that it varies between −1 and +1. If two variables have a correlation of +1, then we say they are perfectly correlated. If the ratio of one variable to another is always the same and positive then the two variables will be perfectly correlated.

If two variables are highly correlated, it is often the case that one variable *causes* the other variable, or that both variables share a common underlying driver. We will see in later chapters, though, that it is very easy for two random variables with no causal link to be highly correlated. *Correlation does not prove causation.* Similarly, if two variables are uncorrelated, it does not necessarily follow that they are unrelated. For example, a random variable that is symmetrical around zero and the square of that variable will have zero correlation.

Sample Problem

Question:

X is a random variable. X has an equal probability of being −1, 0, or +1. What is the correlation between X and Y if $Y = X^2$?

Answer:

We have:

$$P[X = -1] = P[X = 0] = P[X = 1] = \frac{1}{3}$$
$$Y = X^2$$

First we calculate the mean of both variables:

$$E[X] = \frac{1}{3}(-1) + \frac{1}{3}(0) + \frac{1}{3}(1) = 0$$
$$E[Y] = \frac{1}{3}(-1^2) + \frac{1}{3}(0^2) + \frac{1}{3}(1^2) = \frac{1}{3}(1) + \frac{1}{3}(0) + \frac{1}{3}(1) = \frac{2}{3}$$

The covariance can be found as:

$$Cov[X, Y] = E[(X - E[X])(Y - E[Y])]$$
$$Cov[X, Y] = \frac{1}{3}(-1 - 0)\left(1 - \frac{2}{3}\right) + \frac{1}{3}(0 - 0)\left(0 - \frac{2}{3}\right)$$
$$+ \frac{1}{3}(1 - 0)\left(1 - \frac{2}{3}\right) = 0$$

Because the covariance is zero, the correlation is also zero. There is no need to calculate the variances or standard deviations.

As forewarned, even though X and Y are clearly related, the correlation is zero.

APPLICATION: PORTFOLIO VARIANCE AND HEDGING

If we have a portfolio of securities and we wish to determine the variance of that portfolio, all we need to know is the variance of the underlying securities and their respective correlations.

For example, if we have two securities with random returns X_A and X_B, with means μ_A and μ_B and standard deviations σ_A and σ_B, respectively, we can calculate the variance of X_A plus X_B as follows:

$$\sigma_{A+B}^2 = \sigma_A^2 + \sigma_B^2 + 2\rho_{AB}\sigma_A\sigma_B \qquad (2.29)$$

where ρ_{AB} is the correlation between X_A and X_B. The proof is left as an exercise. Notice that the last term can either increase or decrease the total variance. Both standard deviations must be positive; therefore, if the correlation is positive, the overall variance will be higher compared to the case where the correlation is negative.

If the variance of both securities is equal, then Equation 2.29 simplifies to:

$$\sigma_{A+B}^2 = 2\sigma^2(1+\rho_{AB}) \quad \text{where } \sigma_A^2 = \sigma_B^2 = \sigma^2 \qquad (2.30)$$

Now we know that the correlation can vary between −1 and +1, so, substituting into our new equation, the portfolio variance must be bound by 0 and $4\sigma^2$. If we take the square root of both sides of the equation, we see that the standard deviation is bound by 0 and 2σ. Intuitively this should make sense. If, on the one hand, we own one share of an equity with a standard deviation of $10 and then purchase another share of the *same* equity, then the standard deviation of our two-share portfolio must be $20 (trivially, the correlation of a random variable with itself must be one). On the other hand, if we own one share of this equity and then purchase another security that always generates the exact opposite return, the portfolio is perfectly balanced. The returns are always zero, which implies a standard deviation of zero.

In the special case where the correlation between the two securities is zero, we can further simplify our equation. For the standard deviation:

$$\rho_{AB} = 0 \Rightarrow \sigma_{A+B} = \sqrt{2}\sigma \qquad (2.31)$$

We can extend Equation 2.29 to any number of variables:

$$Y = \sum_{i=1}^{n} X_i$$
$$\sigma_Y^2 = \sum_{i=1}^{n}\sum_{j=1}^{n} \rho_{ij}\sigma_i\sigma_j \qquad (2.32)$$

In the case where all of the X_i's are uncorrelated and all the variances are equal to σ, Equation 2.32 simplifies to:

$$\sigma_Y = \sqrt{n}\sigma \quad iff \ \rho_{ij} = 0 \forall i \neq j \qquad (2.33)$$

This is the famous square root rule for the addition of uncorrelated variables. There are many situations in statistics in which we come across collections of random variables that are independent and have the same statistical properties. We term these variables independent and identically distributed (i.i.d.). In risk management we might have a large portfolio of securities, which can be approximated as a collection of i.i.d. variables. As we will see in subsequent chapters, this i.i.d. assumption also plays an important role in estimating the uncertainty inherent in statistics derived from sampling, and in the analysis of time series. In each of these situations, we will come back to this square root rule.

By combining Equation 2.29 with Equation 2.22, we arrive at an equation for calculating the variance of a linear combination of variables. If Y is a linear combination of X_A and X_B, such that:

$$Y = aX_A + bX_B \qquad (2.34)$$

then, using our standard notation, we have:

$$\sigma_Y^2 = a^2\sigma_A^2 + b^2\sigma_B^2 + 2ab\rho_{AB}\sigma_A\sigma_B \qquad (2.35)$$

Correlation is central to the problem of hedging. Using the same notation as before, imagine we have $1 of Security A, and we wish to hedge it with $$h$ of Security B (if h is positive, we are buying the security; if h is negative, we are shorting the security). In other words, h is the hedge ratio. We introduce the random variable P for our hedged portfolio. We can easily compute the variance of the hedge portfolio using Equation 2.35:

$$P = X_A + hX_B \qquad (2.36)$$
$$\sigma_P^2 = \sigma_A^2 + h^2\sigma_B^2 + 2h\rho_{AB}\sigma_A\sigma_B$$

As a risk manager, we might be interested to know what hedge ratio would achieve the portfolio with the least variance. To find this minimum variance hedge ratio, we simply take the derivative of our equation for the portfolio variance with respect to h, and set it equal to zero:

$$\frac{d\sigma_P^2}{dh} = 2h\sigma_B^2 + 2\rho_{AB}\sigma_A\sigma_B \qquad (2.37)$$

$$h^* = -\rho_{AB}\frac{\sigma_A}{\sigma_B}$$

You can check that this is indeed a minimum by calculating the second derivative. Substituting h^* back into our original equation, we see that the smallest variance we can achieve is:

$$\min[\sigma_P^2] = \sigma_A^2(1 - \rho_{AB}^2) \qquad (2.38)$$

At the extremes, where ρ_{AB} equals -1 or $+1$, we can reduce the portfolio volatility to zero by buying or selling the hedge asset in proportion to the standard deviation of the assets. In between these two extremes we will always be left with some positive portfolio variance. This risk that we cannot hedge is referred to as idiosyncratic risk.

If the two securities in the portfolio are positively correlated, then selling $\$h$ of Security B will reduce the portfolio's volatility to the minimum possible level. Sell any less and the portfolio will be underhedged. Sell any more and the portfolio will be overhedged. In risk management it is possible to have too much of a good thing. A common mistake made by portfolio managers is to overhedge with a low-correlation instrument.

Notice that when ρ_{AB} equals zero (i.e., when the two securities are uncorrelated), the optimal hedge ratio is zero. You cannot hedge one security with another security if they are uncorrelated. Adding an uncorrelated security to a portfolio will always increase its volatility.

This last statement is not an argument against diversification. If your entire portfolio consists of $\$100$ invested in Security A and you *add* any amount of an uncorrelated Security B to the portfolio, the dollar standard deviation of the portfolio will increase. Alternatively, if Security A and Security B are uncorrelated and have the same standard deviation, then *replacing* some of Security A with Security B will decrease the dollar standard deviation of the portfolio. For example, $\$80$ of Security A plus $\$20$ of Security B will have a lower standard deviation than $\$100$ of Security A, but $\$100$ of Security A *plus* $\$20$ of Security B will have a higher standard deviation—again, assuming Security A and Security B are uncorrelated and have the same standard deviation.

MOMENTS

Previously, we defined the mean of a variable X as:

$$\mu = E[X]$$

It turns out that we can generalize this concept as follows:

$$m_k = E[X^k] \qquad (2.39)$$

We refer to m_k as the kth moment of X. The mean of X is also the first moment of X.

Similarly, we can generalize the concept of variance as follows:

$$\mu_k = E[(X - \mu)^k] \qquad (2.40)$$

We refer to μ_k as the kth central moment of X. We say that the moment is central because it is central around the mean. Variance is simply the second central moment.

While we can easily calculate any central moment, in risk management it is very rare that we are interested in anything beyond the fourth central moment.

SKEWNESS

The second central moment, variance, tells us how spread-out a random variable is around the mean. The third central moment tells us how symmetrical the distribution is around the mean. Rather than working with the third central moment directly, by convention we first standardize the statistic. This standardized third central moment is known as skewness:

$$\text{Skewness} = \frac{E[(X - \mu)^3]}{\sigma^3} \qquad (2.41)$$

where σ is the standard deviation of X.

By standardizing the central moment, it is much easier to compare two random variables. Multiplying a random variable by a constant will not change the skewness.

A random variable that is symmetrical about its mean will have zero skewness. If the skewness of the random variable is positive, we say that the random variable exhibits positive skew. Figures 2-1 and 2-2 show examples of positive and negative skewness.

Skewness is a very important concept in risk management. If the distributions of returns of two investments are the same in all respects, with the same mean and standard

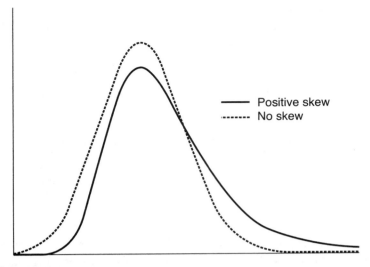

FIGURE 2-1 Positive skew.

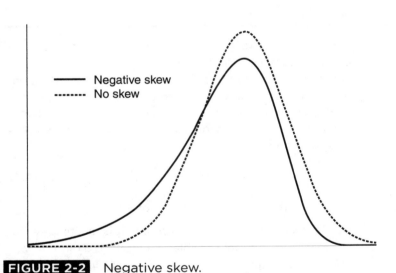

FIGURE 2-2 Negative skew.

deviation but different skews, then the investment with more negative skew is generally considered to be more risky. Historical data suggest that many financial assets exhibit negative skew.

As with variance, the equation for skewness differs depending on whether we are calculating the population skewness or the sample skewness. For the population statistic, the skewness of a random variable X, based on n observations, x_1, x_2, . . . , x_n, can be calculated as:

$$\hat{s} = \frac{1}{n}\sum_{i=1}^{n}\left(\frac{x_i - \mu}{\sigma}\right)^3 \qquad (2.42)$$

where μ is the population mean and σ is the population standard deviation. Similar to our calculation of sample variance, if we are calculating the sample skewness, there is going to be an overlap with the calculation of the sample mean and sample standard deviation. We need to correct for that. The sample skewness can be calculated as:

$$\tilde{s} = \frac{n}{(n-1)(n-2)}\sum_{i=1}^{n}\left(\frac{x_i - \hat{\mu}}{\hat{\sigma}}\right)^3 \qquad (2.43)$$

Based on Equation 2.20 for variance, it is tempting to guess that the formula for the third central moment can be written simply in terms of $E[X^3]$ and μ. Be careful, as the two sides of this equation are not equal:

$$E[(X - \mu)^k] \neq E[X^3] - \mu^3 \qquad (2.44)$$

The correct equation is:

$$E[(X - \mu)^3] = E[X^3] - 3\mu\sigma^2 - \mu^3 \qquad (2.45)$$

For many symmetrical continuous distributions, the mean, median, and mode all have the same value. Many continuous distributions with negative skew have a mean that is less than the median, which is less than the mode. For example, it might be that a certain derivative is just as likely to produce positive returns as it is to produce negative returns (the median is zero), but there are more big negative returns than big positive returns (the distribution is skewed), so the mean is less than zero. As a risk manager, understanding the impact of skew on the mean relative to the median and mode can be useful. Be careful, though, as this rule of thumb does not always work. Many practitioners mistakenly believe that this rule of thumb is in fact always true. It is not, and it is very easy to produce a distribution that violates the rule.

Sample Problem

Question:

Prove that the left-hand side of Equation 2.45 is indeed equal to the right-hand side of the equation.

Answer:

We start by multiplying out the terms inside the expectation. This is not too difficult to do, but, as a shortcut, we could use the binomial theorem:

$$E[(X - \mu)^3] = E[X^3 - 3\mu X^2 + 3\mu^2 X - \mu^3]$$

Next we separate the terms inside the expectations operator and move any constants, namely μ, outside the operator:

$$E[(X^3 - 3\mu X^2 + 3\mu^2 X - 3\mu^3]$$
$$= E[X^3] - 3\mu E[X^2] + 3\mu^2 E[X] - \mu^3$$

$E[X]$ is simply the mean, μ. For $E[X^2]$, we reorganize our equation for variance, Equation 2.20, as follows:

$$\sigma^2 = E[X^2] - \mu^2$$
$$E[X^2] = \sigma^2 + \mu^2$$

Substituting these results into our equation and collecting terms, we arrive at the final equation:

$$E[(X - \mu)^3] = E[X^3] - 3\mu(\sigma^2 + \mu^2) + 3\mu^2\mu - \mu^3$$
$$E[(X - \mu)^3] = E[X^3] - 3\mu\sigma^2 - \mu^3$$

The following two populations have the same mean, variance, and skewness. The second population has a higher kurtosis.

Population 1: $\{-17, -17, 17, 17\}$

Population 2: $\{-23, -7, 7, 23\}$

Notice, to balance out the variance, when we moved the outer two points out six units, we had to move the inner two points in 10 units. Because the random variable with higher kurtosis has points further from the mean, we often refer to distribution with high kurtosis as fat-tailed. Figures 2-3 and 2-4 show examples of continuous distributions with high and low kurtosis.

Like skewness, kurtosis is an important concept in risk management. Many financial assets exhibit high levels of kurtosis. If the distribution of returns of two assets have the same mean, variance, and skewness, but different kurtosis, then the distribution with the higher kurtosis will tend to have more extreme points, and be considered more risky.

As with variance and skewness, the equation for kurtosis differs depending on whether we are calculating the population kurtosis or the sample kurtosis. For the population

KURTOSIS

The fourth central moment is similar to the second central moment, in that it tells us how spread-out a random variable is, but it puts more weight on extreme points. As with skewness, rather than working with the central moment directly, we typically work with a standardized statistic. This standardized fourth central moment is known as the kurtosis. For a random variable X, we can define the kurtosis as K, where:

$$K = \frac{E[(X - \mu)^4]}{\sigma^4} \qquad \textbf{(2.46)}$$

where σ is the standard deviation of X, and μ is its mean.

By standardizing the central moment, it is much easier to compare two random variables. As with skewness, multiplying a random variable by a constant will not change the kurtosis.

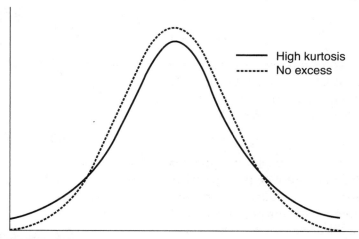

FIGURE 2-3 High kurtosis.

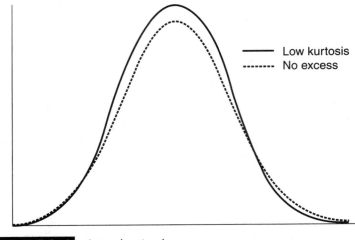

Low kurtosis
No excess

FIGURE 2-4   Low kurtosis.

statistic, the kurtosis of a random variable X can be calculated as:

$$\hat{K} = \frac{1}{n}\sum_{i=1}^{n}\left(\frac{x_i - \mu}{\sigma}\right)^4 \qquad (2.47)$$

where μ is the population mean and σ is the population standard deviation. Similar to our calculation of sample variance, if we are calculating the sample kurtosis, there is going to be an overlap with the calculation of the sample mean and sample standard deviation. We need to correct for that. The sample kurtosis can be calculated as:

$$\tilde{K} = \frac{n(n+1)}{(n-1)(n-2)(n-3)}\sum_{i=1}^{n}\left(\frac{x_i - \hat{\mu}}{\hat{\sigma}}\right)^4 \qquad (2.48)$$

In the next chapter we will study the normal distribution, which has a kurtosis of 3. Because normal distributions are so common, many people refer to "excess kurtosis," which is simply the kurtosis minus 3.

$$K_{excess} = K - 3 \qquad (2.49)$$

In this way, the normal distribution has an excess kurtosis of 0. Distributions with positive excess kurtosis are termed leptokurtotic. Distributions with negative excess kurtosis are termed platykurtotic. Be careful; by default, many applications calculate excess kurtosis.

When we are also estimating the mean and variance, calculating the sample excess kurtosis is somewhat more complicated than just subtracting 3. The correct formula is:

$$\tilde{K}_{excess} = \tilde{K} - 3\frac{(n-1)^2}{(n-2)(n-3)} \qquad (2.50)$$

where $\tilde{K}$ is the sample kurtosis from Equation 2.46. As n increases, the last term on the right-hand side converges to 3.

COSKEWNESS AND COKURTOSIS

Just as we generalized the concept of mean and variance to moments and central moments, we can generalize the concept of covariance to cross central moments. The third and fourth standardized cross central moments are referred to as coskewness and cokurtosis, respectively. Though used less frequently, higher-order cross moments can be very important in risk management.

As an example of how higher-order cross moments can impact risk assessment, take the series of returns shown in Table 2-1 for four fund managers, A, B, C, and D.

In this admittedly contrived setup, each manager has produced exactly the same set of returns; only the order in which the returns were produced is different. It follows that the mean, standard deviation, skew, and kurtosis of the returns are exactly the same for each manager. In this

TABLE 2-1   Fund Returns

Time	A	B	C	D
1	0.0%	−3.8%	−15.3%	−15.3%
2	−3.8%	−15.3%	−7.2%	−7.2%
3	−15.3%	3.8%	0.0%	−3.8%
4	−7.2%	−7.2%	−3.8%	15.3%
5	3.8%	0.0%	3.8%	0.0%
6	7.2%	7.2%	7.2%	7.2%
7	15.3%	15.3%	15.3%	3.8%

TABLE 2-2 Combined Fund Returns

Time	A + B	C + D
1	−1.9%	−15.3%
2	−9.5%	−7.2%
3	−5.8%	−1.9%
4	−7.2%	5.8%
5	1.9%	1.9%
6	7.2%	7.2%
7	15.3%	9.5%

example it is also the case that the covariance between managers A and B is the same as the covariance between managers C and D.

If we combine A and B in an equally weighted portfolio and combine C and D in a separate equally weighted portfolio, we get the returns shown in Table 2-2.

The two portfolios have the same mean and standard deviation, but the skews of the port-folios are different. Whereas the worst return for A + B is −9.5%, the worst return for C + D is −15.3%. As a risk manager, knowing that the worst outcome for portfolio C + D is more than 1.6 times as bad as the worst outcome for A + B could be very important.

So how did two portfolios whose constituents seemed so similar end up being so different? One way to understand what is happening is to graph the two sets of returns for each portfo-lio against each other, as shown in Figures 2-5 and 2-6.

The two charts share a certain symmetry, but are clearly different. In the first portfolio, A + B, the two managers' best positive returns occur during the same time period, but their worst negative returns occur in different periods. This causes the distribution of points to be skewed toward the top-right of the chart. The situation is reversed for managers C and D: their worst negative returns occur

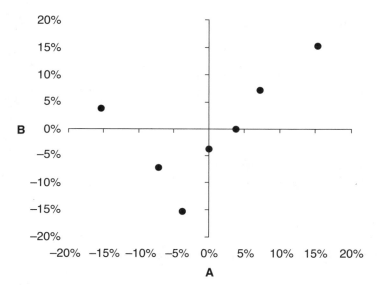

FIGURE 2-5 Funds A and B.

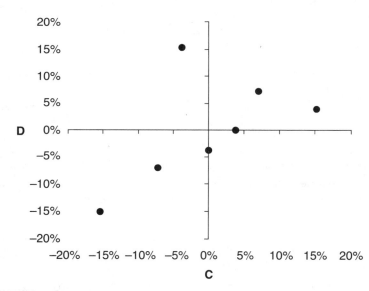

FIGURE 2-6 Funds C and D.

TABLE 2-3	Sample Coskewness	
	A + B	C + D
S_{XXY}	0.99	−0.58
S_{XYY}	0.58	−0.99

TABLE 2-4	Number of Nontrivial Cross Moments		
n	Covariance	Coskewness	Cokurtosis
2	1	2	3
5	10	30	65
10	45	210	705
20	190	1,520	8,835
30	435	4,930	40,890
100	4,950	171,600	4,421,175

in the same period, but their best positive returns occur in different periods. In the second chart, the points are skewed toward the bottom-left of the chart.

The reason the charts look different, and the reason the returns of the two portfolios are different, is because the coskewness between the managers in each of the portfolios is different. For two random variables, there are actually two nontrivial coskewness statistics. For example, for A and B, we have:

$$S_{AAB} = E[(A - \mu_A)^2(B - \mu_B)]/\sigma_A^2\sigma_B$$
$$S_{ABB} = E[(A - \mu_A)(B - \mu_B)^2]/\sigma_A\sigma_B^2 \qquad \textbf{(2.51)}$$

The complete set of sample coskewness statistics for the sets of managers is shown in Table 2-3.

Both coskewness values for A and B are positive, whereas they are both negative for C and D. Just as with skewness, negative values of coskewness tend to be associated with greater risk.

In general, for n random variables, the number of nontrivial cross-central moments of order m is:

$$k = \frac{(m + n - 1)!}{m!(n - 1)!} - n \qquad \textbf{(2.52)}$$

In this case, nontrivial means that we have excluded the cross moments that involve only one variable (i.e., our standard skewness and kurtosis). To include the nontrivial moments, we would simply add n to the preceding result.

For coskewness, Equation 2.52 simplifies to:

$$k_3 = \frac{(n + 2)(n + 1)n}{6} - n \qquad \textbf{(2.53)}$$

Despite their obvious relevance to risk management, many standard risk models do not explicitly define coskewness or cokurtosis. One reason that many models avoid these higher-order cross moments is practical. As the number of variables increases, the number of nontrivial cross moments increases rapidly. With 10 variables there are 30 coskewness parameters and 65 cokurtosis parameters.

With 100 variables, these numbers increase to 171,600 and over 4 million, respectively. Table 2-4 compares the number of nontrivial cross moments for a variety of sample sizes. In most cases there is simply not enough data to calculate all of these cross moments.

Risk models with time-varying volatility or time-varying correlation can display a wide range of behaviors with very few free parameters. Copulas can also be used to describe complex interactions between variables that go beyond covariances, and have become popular in risk management in recent years. All of these approaches capture the essence of coskewness and cokurtosis, but in a more tractable framework. As a risk manager, it is important to differentiate between these models—which address the higher-order cross moments indirectly—and models that simply omit these risk factors altogether.

BEST LINEAR UNBIASED ESTIMATOR (BLUE)

In this chapter we have been careful to differentiate between the true parameters of a distribution and estimates of those parameters based on a sample of population data. In statistics we refer to these parameter estimates, or to the method of obtaining the estimate, as an estimator. For example, at the start of the chapter, we introduced an estimator for the sample mean:

$$\hat{\mu} = \frac{1}{n}\sum_{i=1}^{n} x_i \qquad \textbf{(2.54)}$$

This formula for computing the mean is so popular that we're likely to take it for granted. Why this equation, though? One justification that we gave earlier is that this particular estimator provides an unbiased estimate of the true mean. That is:

$$E[\hat{\mu}] = \mu \qquad \textbf{(2.55)}$$

Clearly, a good estimator should be unbiased. That said, for a given data set, we could imagine any number of unbiased estimators of the mean. For example, assuming there are at least three data points in our sample, x_1, x_2, and x_3, the following equation:

$$\tilde{\mu} = 0.75x_1 + 0.25x_2 + 0.00x_3 \qquad \textbf{(2.56)}$$

is also an unbiased estimator of the mean. Intuitively, this new estimator seems strange; we have put three times as much weight on x_1 as on x_2, and we have put no weight on x_3. There is no reason, as we have described the problem, to believe that any one data point is better than any other, so equally distributing the weight might seem like a logical procedure. Still, this new estimator is unbiased, and our criteria for judging this estimator to be strange seems rather subjective. What we need is an objective measure for comparing different estimators.

As we will see in coming chapters, just as we can measure the variance of random variables, we can measure the variance of parameter estimators as well. For example, if we measure the sample mean of a random variable several times, we can get a different answer each time. Imagine rolling a die 10 times and taking the average of all the rolls. Then repeat this process again and again.

The sample mean is potentially different for each sample of 10 rolls. It turns out that this variability of the sample mean, or any other distribution parameter, is a function not only of the underlying variable, but of the form of the estimator as well.

When choosing among all the unbiased estimators, statisticians typically try to come up with the estimator with the minimum variance. If we limit ourselves to estimators that can be written as a linear equation, we can often prove that a particular candidate has the minimum variance among all the potential unbiased estimators. We call an estimator with these properties the best linear unbiased estimator, or BLUE. This is certainly one of the more amusing acronyms in statistics. All of the estimators that we produced in this chapter for the mean, variance, covariance, skew, and kurtosis are BLUE.

It is possible to have two estimators for the same parameter, one BLUE and the other biased but with lower variance. Just such a situation occurs with our sample variance estimator in Equation 2.19. Remember that, if the sample mean was also an estimate, we divided the summation by $(n - 1)$. If we had instead divided by n, this new estimator would be biased but would in fact have a lower variance. Of course, we could drive the variance of the estimator all the way to zero, simply by choosing a constant as an estimator. This would be a very poor choice. In almost all situations, for most statisticians, the BLUE estimator will be the preferred estimator.

Distributions

3

Learning Objectives

Candidates, after completing this reading, should be able to:

- Define and distinguish between parametric and nonparametric distributions.
- Describe the key properties of the following distributions: uniform distribution, Bernoulli distribution, Binomial distribution, Poisson distribution, normal distribution, lognormal distribution, Chi-squared distribution, Student's t, and F-distributions, and identify common occurrences of each distribution.

- Describe and apply the Central Limit Theorem.
- Describe the properties of independent and identically distributed (i.i.d.) random variables.
- Describe a mixture distribution and explain the creation and characteristics of mixture distributions.

Excerpt is Chapter 4 of Mathematics and Statistics for Financial Risk Management, *by Michael Miller.*

In Chapter 1, we were introduced to random variables. In nature and in finance, random variables tend to follow certain patterns, or distributions. In this chapter we will learn about some of the most widely used probability distributions in risk management.

PARAMETRIC DISTRIBUTIONS

Distributions can be divided into two broad categories: parametric distributions and nonparametric distributions. A parametric distribution can be described by a mathematical function. In the following sections we will explore a number of parametric distributions including the uniform distribution and the normal distribution. A nonparametric distribution cannot be summarized by a mathematical formula. In its simplest form, a nonparametric distribution is just a collection of data. An example of a nonparametric distribution would be a collection of historical returns for a security.

Parametric distributions are often easier to work with, but they force us to make assumptions, which may not be supported by real-world data. Nonparametric distributions can fit the observed data perfectly. The drawback of nonparametric distributions is that they are potentially too specific, which can make it difficult to draw any general conclusions.

UNIFORM DISTRIBUTION

For a continuous random variable, X, recall that the probability of an outcome occurring between b_1 and b_2 can be found by integrating as follows:

$$P[b_1 \leq X \leq b_2] = \int_{b_1}^{b_2} f(x)dx$$

where $f(x)$ is the probability density function (PDF) of X.

The uniform distribution is one of the most fundamental distributions in statistics. The probability density function is given by the following formula:

$$u(b_1,b_2) = \begin{cases} c & \forall b_1 \leq x \leq b_2 \\ 0 & \forall b_1 > x > b_2 \end{cases} \quad \text{s.t. } b_2 > b_1 \qquad (3.1)$$

In other words, the probability density is constant and equal to c between b_1 and b_2, and zero everywhere else.

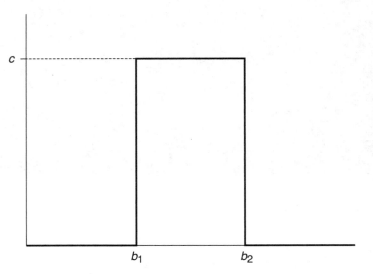

FIGURE 3-1 Probability density function of a uniform distribution.

Figure 3-1 shows the plot of a uniform distribution's probability density function.

Because the probability of any outcome occurring must be one, we can find the value of c as follows:

$$\int_{-\infty}^{+\infty} u(b_1,b_2)dx = 1 \qquad (3.2)$$

$$\int_{-\infty}^{+\infty} u(b_1,b_2)dx = \int_{-\infty}^{b_1} 0dx + \int_{b_1}^{b_2} cdx + \int_{b_2}^{+\infty} 0dx = \int_{b_1}^{b_2} cdx$$

$$\int_{b_1}^{b_2} cdx = [cx]_{b_1}^{b_2} = c(b_2 - b_1) = 1$$

$$c = \frac{1}{b_2 - b_1}$$

On reflection, this result should be obvious from the graph of the density function. That the probability of any outcome occurring must be one is equivalent to saying that the area under the probability density function must be equal to one. In Figure 3-1, we only need to know that the area of a rectangle is equal to the product of its width and its height to determine that c is equal to $1/(b_2 - b_1)$.

With the probability density function in hand, we can proceed to calculate the mean and the variance. For the mean:

$$\mu = \int_{b_1}^{b_2} cxdx = \frac{1}{2}(b_2 + b_1) \qquad (3.3)$$

In other words, the mean is just the average of the start and end values of the distribution.

Similarly, for the variance, we have:

$$\sigma^2 = \int_{b_1}^{b_2} c(x - \mu)^2 dx = \frac{1}{12}(b_2 - b_1)^2 \qquad \textbf{(3.4)}$$

This result is not as intuitive. The proof of both results is left as an exercise at the end of the chapter.

For the special case where $b_1 = 0$ and $b_2 = 1$, we refer to the distribution as a standard uniform distribution. Standard uniform distributions are extremely common. The default random number generator in most computer programs (technically a pseudo random number generator) is typically a standard uniform random variable. Because these random number generators are so ubiquitous, uniform distributions often serve as the building blocks for computer models in finance.

To calculate the cumulative distribution function (CDF) of the uniform distribution, we simply integrate the PDF. Again, assuming a lower bound of b_1 and an upper bound of b_2, we have:

$$P[X \leq a] = \int_{b_1}^{a} cdz = c[z]_{b_1}^{a} = \frac{a - b_1}{b_2 - b_1} \qquad \textbf{(3.5)}$$

As required, when a equals b_1, we are at the minimum, and the CDF is zero. When a equals b_2, we are at the maximum, the entire distribution is less than the maximum, and the CDF equals one.

As we will see later, we can use combinations of uniform distributions to approximate other more complex distributions. As we will see in the next section, uniform distributions can also serve as the basis of some of the simplest distributions, including Bernoulli distributions.

BERNOULLI DISTRIBUTION

Bernoulli's principle explains how the flow of fluids or gases leads to changes in pressure. It can be used to explain a number of phenomena, including how the wings of airplanes provide lift. Without it, modern aviation would be impossible. Bernoulli's principle is named after Daniel Bernoulli, an eighteenth-century Dutch-Swiss mathematician and scientist. Daniel came from a family of accomplished mathematicians. Daniel and his cousin Nicolas

Bernoulli first described and presented a proof for the St. Petersburg Paradox. But it is not Daniel or Nicolas, but rather their uncle, Jacob Bernoulli, for whom the Bernoulli distribution is named. In addition to the Bernoulli distribution, Jacob is credited with first describing the concept of continuously compounded returns, and, along the way, discovering Euler's number, e.

The Bernoulli distribution is incredibly simple. A Bernoulli random variable is equal to either zero or one. If we define p as the probability that X equals one, we have:

$$P[X = 1] = p \text{ and } P[X = 0] = 1 - p \qquad \textbf{(3.6)}$$

We can easily calculate the mean and variance of a Bernoulli variable:

$$\mu = p \cdot 1 + (1 - p) \cdot 0 = p \qquad \textbf{(3.7)}$$
$$\sigma^2 = p \cdot (1 - p)^2 + (1 - p) \cdot (0 - p)^2 = p(1 - p)$$

Binary outcomes are quite common in finance: a bond can default or not default; the return of a stock can be positive or negative; a central bank can decide to raise rates or not to raise rates.

In a computer simulation, one way to model a Bernoulli variable is to start with a standard uniform variable. Conveniently, both the standard uniform variable and our Bernoulli probability, p, range between zero and one. If the draw from the standard uniform variable is less than p, we set our Bernoulli variable equal to one; likewise, if the draw is greater than p, we set the Bernoulli variable to zero (see Figure 3-2).

BINOMIAL DISTRIBUTION

A binomial distribution can be thought of as a collection of Bernoulli random variables. If we have two independent bonds and the probability of default for both is 10%, then there are three possible outcomes: no bond defaults, one bond defaults, or both bonds default. Labeling the number of defaults K:

$$P[K = 0] = (1 - 10\%)^2 = 81\%$$
$$P[K = 1] = 2 \cdot 10\% \cdot (1 - 10\%) = 18\%$$
$$P[K = 2] = 10\%^2 = 1\%$$

Notice that for $K = 1$, we have multiplied the probability of a bond defaulting, 10%, and the probability of a bond not defaulting, $1 - 10\%$, by 2. This is because there are two

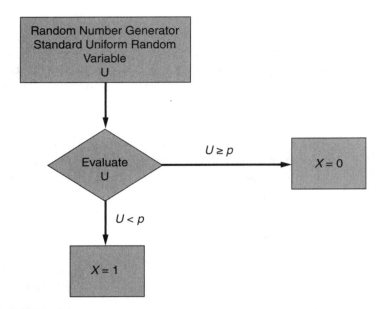

FIGURE 3-2 How to generate a Bernoulli distribution from a uniform distribution.

ways in which exactly one bond can default: the first bond defaults and the second does not, or the second bond defaults and the first does not.

If we now have three bonds, still independent and with a 10% chance of defaulting, then:

$$P[K = 0] = (1 - 10\%)^3 = 72.9\%$$

$$P[K = 1] = 3 \cdot 10\% \cdot (1 - 10\%)^2 = 24.3\%$$

$$P[K = 2] = 3 \cdot 10\%^2 \cdot (1 - 10\%) = 2.7\%$$

$$P[K = 3] = 10\%^3 = 0.1\%$$

Notice that there are three ways in which we can get exactly one default and three ways in which we can get exactly two defaults.

We can extend this logic to any number of bonds. If we have n bonds, the number of ways in which k of those bonds can default is given by the number of combinations:

$$\binom{n}{k} = \frac{n!}{k!(n - k)!} \qquad \textbf{(3.8)}$$

Similarly, if the probability of one bond defaulting is p, then the probability of any *particular* k bonds defaulting is

simply $p^k(1 - p)^{n-k}$. Putting these two together, we can calculate the probability of any k bonds defaulting as:

$$P[K = k] = \binom{n}{k}p^k(1 - p)^{n-k} \qquad \textbf{(3.9)}$$

This is the probability density function for the binomial distribution. You should check that this equation produces the same result as our examples with two and three bonds. While the general proof is somewhat complicated, it is not difficult to prove that the probabilities sum to one for $n = 2$ or $n = 3$, no matter what value p takes. It is a common mistake when calculating these probabilities to leave out the combinatorial term.

For the formulation in Equation 3.9, the mean of random variable K is equal to np. So for a bond portfolio with 40 bonds, each with a 20% chance of defaulting, we would expect eight bonds ($8 = 20 \times 0.40$) to default on average. The variance of a binomial distribution is $np(1 - p)$.

Figure 3-3 shows binomial distributions with $p = 0.50$, for $n = 4$, 16, and 64. The highest point of each distribution occurs in the middle. In other words, the most likely

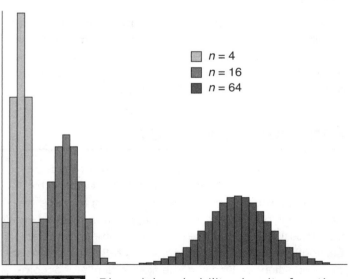

■ $n = 4$
■ $n = 16$
■ $n = 64$

FIGURE 3-3 Binomial probability density functions.

Sample Problem

Question:

Assume we have four bonds, each with a 10% probability of defaulting over the next year. The event of default for any given bond is independent of the other bonds defaulting. What is the probability that zero, one, two, three, or all of the bonds default? What is the mean number of defaults? The standard deviation?

Answer:

We can calculate the probability of each possible outcome as follows:

# of Defaults	$\binom{n}{k}$	$p^k(1-p)^{n-k}$	Probability
0	1	65.61%	65.61%
1	4	7.29%	29.16%
2	6	0.81%	4.86%
3	4	0.09%	0.36%
4	1	0.01%	0.01%
			100.00%

We can calculate the mean number of defaults two ways. The first is to use our formula for the mean:

$$\mu = np = 4 \cdot 10\% = 0.40$$

On average there are 0.40 defaults. The other way we could arrive at this result is to use the probabilities from the table. We get:

$$\mu = \sum_{i=0}^{4} p_i x_i = 65.61\% \cdot 0 + 29.16\% \cdot 1 + 4.86\% \cdot 2 + 0.36\% \cdot 3$$
$$+ \; 0.01\% \cdot 4 = 0.40$$

This is consistent with our earlier result.

To calculate the standard deviation, we also have two choices. Using our formula for variance, we have:

$$\sigma^2 = np(1-p) = 4 \cdot 10\%(1 - 10\%) = 0.36$$
$$\sigma = 0.60$$

As with the mean, we could also use the probabilities from the table:

$$\sigma^2 = \sum_{i=0}^{4} p_i (x_i - \mu)^2$$
$$\sigma^2 = 65.61\% \cdot 0.16 + 29.16\% \cdot 0.36 + 4.86\% \cdot 2.56 + 0.36\% \cdot 6.76$$
$$+ \; 0.01\% \cdot 12.96 = 0.36$$
$$\sigma = 0.60$$

Again, this is consistent with our earlier result.

---

outcome for a binomial random variable, the mode, is $n/2$ when n is even or the whole numbers either side of $n/2$ when n is odd.

POISSON DISTRIBUTION

Another useful discrete distribution is the Poisson distribution, named for the French mathematician Simeon Denis Poisson.

For a Poisson random variable X:

$$P[X = n] = \frac{\lambda^n}{n!} e^{-\lambda} \qquad \textbf{(3.10)}$$

for some constant λ. It turns out that both the mean and variance of X are equal to λ. Figure 3-4 shows the probability density function of a Poisson distribution.

The Poisson distribution is often used to model the occurrence of events over time—for example, the number of bond defaults in a portfolio or the number of crashes in equity markets. In this case, n is the number of events that occur in an interval, and λ is the expected number of events in the interval. Poisson distributions are often used to model jumps in jump diffusion models.

If the rate at which events occur over time is constant, and the probability of any one event occurring is independent of all other events, then we say that the events follow a Poisson process, where:

$$P[X = n] = \frac{(\lambda t)^n}{n!} e^{-\lambda t} \qquad \textbf{(3.11)}$$

where t is the amount of time elapsed. In other words, the expected number of events before time t is equal to λt.

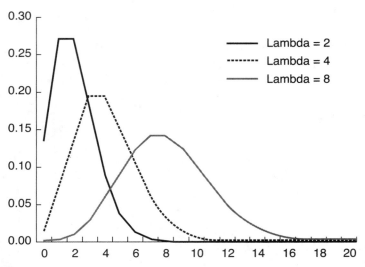

FIGURE 3-4 Poisson probability density function.

In popular literature, the normal distribution is often referred to as the bell curve because of the shape of its probability density function (see Figure 3-5).

The probability density function of the normal distribution is symmetrical, with the mean and median coinciding with the highest point of the PDF. Because it is symmetrical, the skew of a normal distribution is always zero. The kurtosis of a normal distribution is always 3. By definition, the excess kurtosis of a normal distribution is zero.

In some fields it is more common to refer to the normal distribution as the Gaussian distribution, after the famous German mathematician Johann Gauss, who is credited with some of the earliest work with the distribution. It is not the case that one name is more precise than the other as with mean and average. Both normal distribution and Gaussian distribution are acceptable terms.

For a random variable X, the probability density function for the normal distribution is:

$$f(x) = \frac{1}{\sigma\sqrt{2\pi}} e^{-\frac{1}{2}\left(\frac{x-\mu}{\sigma}\right)^2} \tag{3.12}$$

Sample Problem

Question:

Assume that defaults in a large bond portfolio follow a Poisson process. The expected number of defaults each month is four. What is the probability that there are exactly three defaults over the course of one month? Two months?

Answer:

For the first question, we solve the following:

$$P[X = 3] = \frac{(\lambda t)^n}{n!} e^{-\lambda t} = \frac{(4 \cdot 1)^3}{3!} e^{-4 \cdot 1} = 19.5\%$$

Over two months, the answer is:

$$P[X = 3] = \frac{(\lambda t)^n}{n!} e^{-\lambda t} = \frac{(4 \cdot 2)^3}{3!} e^{-4 \cdot 2} = 2.9\%$$

NORMAL DISTRIBUTION

The normal distribution is probably the most widely used distribution in statistics, and is extremely popular in finance. The normal distribution occurs in a large number of settings, and is extremely easy to work with.

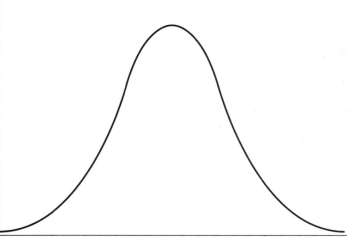

FIGURE 3-5 Normal distribution probability density function.

The distribution is described by two parameters, μ and σ; μ is the mean of the distribution and σ is the standard deviation. We leave the proofs of these statements for the exercises at the end of the chapter.

Rather than writing out the entire density function, when a variable is normally distributed it is the convention to write:

$$X \sim N(\mu, \sigma^2) \qquad \textbf{(3.13)}$$

This would be read "X is normally distributed with a mean of μ and variance of σ^2."

One reason that normal distributions are easy to work with is that any linear combination of independent normal variables is also normal. If we have two normally distributed variables, X and Y, and two constants, a and b, then Z is also normally distributed:

$$Z = aX + bY \text{ s.t. } Z \sim N(a\mu_X + b\mu_Y, a^2\sigma_X^2 + b^2\sigma_Y^2) \qquad \textbf{(3.14)}$$

This is very convenient. For example, if the log returns of individual stocks are normally distributed, then the average return of those stocks will also be normally distributed.

When a normal distribution has a mean of zero and a standard deviation of one, it is referred to as a standard normal distribution.

$$\phi = \frac{1}{\sqrt{2\pi}} e^{-\frac{1}{2}x^2} \qquad \textbf{(3.15)}$$

It is the convention to denote the standard normal PDF by ϕ, and the cumulative standard normal distribution by ϕ.

Because a linear combination of normal distributions is also normal, standard normal distributions are the building blocks of many financial models. To get a normal variable with a standard deviation of σ and a mean of μ, we simply multiply the standard normal variable by σ and add μ.

$$X = \mu + \sigma\phi \Rightarrow X \sim N(\mu, \sigma^2) \qquad \textbf{(3.16)}$$

To create two correlated normal variables, we can combine three independent standard normal variables, $X_1, X_2,$ and X_3, as follows:

$$X_A = \sqrt{\rho}X_1 + \sqrt{1-\rho}X_2 \qquad \textbf{(3.17)}$$
$$X_B = \sqrt{\rho}X_1 + \sqrt{1-\rho}X_3$$

In this formulation, X_A and X_B are also standard normal variables, but with a correlation of ρ. The proof is left for an exercise at the end of the chapter.

Normal distributions are used throughout finance and risk management. We suggested that log returns are extremely useful in financial modeling. One attribute that makes log returns particularly attractive is that they can be modeled using normal distributions. Normal distributions can generate numbers from negative infinity to positive infinity. For a particular normal distribution, the most extreme values might be extremely unlikely, but they can occur. This poses a problem for standard returns, which typically cannot be less than −100%. For log returns, though, there is no such constraint. Log returns also can range from negative to positive infinity.

Normally distributed log returns are widely used in financial simulations, and form the basis of a number of financial models, including the Black-Scholes option pricing model. As we will see in the coming chapters, while this normal assumption is often a convenient starting point, much of risk management is focused on addressing departures from this normality assumption.

There is no explicit solution for the cumulative standard normal distribution, or for its inverse. That said, most statistical packages will be able to calculate values for both functions. To calculate values for the CDF or inverse CDF for the normal distribution, there are a number of well-known numerical approximations.

Because the normal distribution is so widely used, most practitioners are expected to have at least a rough idea of how much of the distribution falls within one, two, or three standard deviations. In risk management it is also useful to know how many standard deviations are needed to encompass 95% or 99% of outcomes. Table 3-1 lists some common values. Notice that for each row in the table, there is a "one-tailed" and "two-tailed" column. If we want to know how far we have to go to encompass 95% of the mass in the density function, the one-tailed value tells us that 95% of the values are less than 1.64 standard deviations above the mean. Because the normal distribution is symmetrical, it follows that 5% of the values are less than 1.64 standard deviations below the mean. The two-tailed value, in turn, tells us that 95% of the mass is within +/−1.96 standard deviations of the mean. It follows that 2.5% of the outcomes are less than −1.96 standard deviations from the mean, and 2.5% are greater than +1.96 standard deviations from the mean. Rather than one-tailed and two-tailed, some authors refer to "one-sided" and "two-sided" values.

TABLE 3-1	Normal Distribution Confidence Intervals	
	One-Tailed	**Two-Tailed**
1.0%	−2.33	−2.58
2.5%	−1.96	−2.24
5.0%	−1.64	−1.96
10.0%	−1.28	−1.64
90.0%	1.28	1.64
95.0%	1.64	1.96
97.5%	1.96	2.24
99.0%	2.33	2.58

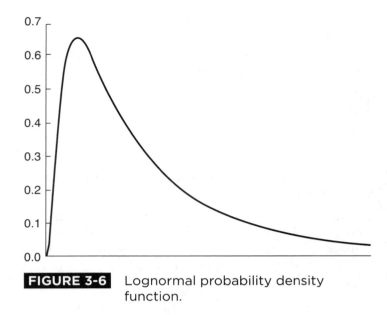

FIGURE 3-6   Lognormal probability density function.

LOGNORMAL DISTRIBUTION

It's natural to ask: if we assume that log returns are normally distributed, then how are standard returns distributed? To put it another way: rather than modeling log returns with a normal distribution, can we use another distribution and model standard returns directly?

The answer to these questions lies in the lognormal distribution, whose density function is given by:

$$f(x) = \frac{1}{x\sigma\sqrt{2\pi}} e^{-\frac{1}{2}\left(\frac{\ln x - \mu}{\sigma}\right)^2}$$ **(3.18)**

If a variable has a lognormal distribution, then the log of that variable has a normal distribution. So, if log returns are assumed to be normally distributed, then one plus the standard return will be lognormally distributed.

Unlike the normal distribution, which ranges from negative infinity to positive infinity, the lognormal distribution is undefined, or zero, for negative values. Given an asset with a standard return, R, if we model $(1 + R)$ using the lognormal distribution, then R will have a minimum value of −100%. This feature, which we associate with limited liability, is common to most financial assets. Using the lognormal distribution provides an easy way to ensure that we avoid returns less than −100%. The probability

density function for a lognormal distribution is shown in Figure 3-6.

Equation 3.18 looks almost exactly like the equation for the normal distribution, Equation 3.12, with x replaced by $\ln(x)$. Be careful, though, as there is also the x in the denominator of the leading fraction. At first it might not be clear what the x is doing there. By carefully rearranging Equation 3.18, we can get something that, while slightly longer, looks more like the normal distribution in form:

$$f(x) = e^{\frac{1}{2}\sigma^2 - \mu} \frac{1}{\sigma\sqrt{2\pi}} e^{-\frac{1}{2}\left(\frac{\ln x - (\mu - \sigma^2)}{\sigma}\right)^2}$$ **(3.19)**

While not as pretty, this starts to hint at what we've actually done. Rather than being symmetrical around μ, as in the normal distribution, the lognormal distribution is asymmetrical and peaks at $\exp(\mu - \sigma^2)$.

Given μ and σ, the mean is given by:

$$E[X] = e^{\mu + \frac{1}{2}\sigma^2}$$ **(3.20)**

This result looks very similar to the Taylor expansion of the natural logarithm around one. Remember, if R is a standard return and r the corresponding log return, then:

$$r \approx R - \frac{1}{2}R^2$$ **(3.21)**

Be careful: because these equations are somewhat similar, it is very easy to get the signs in front of σ^2 and R^2 backward.

The variance of the lognormal distribution is given by:

$$E[(X - E[X])^2] = (e^{\sigma^2} - 1)e^{2\mu + \sigma^2} \qquad \textbf{(3.22)}$$

The equations for the mean and the variance hint at the difficulty of working with lognormal distributions directly. It is convenient to be able to describe the returns of a financial instrument as being lognormally distributed, rather than having to say the log returns of that instrument are normally distributed. When it comes to modeling, though, even though they are equivalent, it is often easier to work with log returns and normal distributions than with standard returns and lognormal distributions.

CENTRAL LIMIT THEOREM

Assume we have an index made up of a large number of equities, or a bond portfolio that contains a large number of similar bonds. In these situations and many more, it is often convenient to assume that the constituent elements—the equities or bonds—are made up of statistically identical random variables, and that these variables are uncorrelated with each other. As mentioned previously, in statistics we term these variables independent and identically distributed (i.i.d.). If the constituent elements are i.i.d., it turns out we can say a lot about the distribution of the population, even if the distribution of the individual elements is unknown.

We already know that if we add two i.i.d. normal distributions together we get a normal distribution, but what happens if we add two i.i.d. uniform variables together? Looking at the graph of the uniform distribution (Figure 3-1), you might think that we would get another uniform distribution, but this isn't the case. In fact, the probability density function resembles a triangle.

Assume we have two defaulted bonds, each with a face value of $100. The recovery rate for each bond is assumed to be uniform, between $0 and $100. At best we recover the full face value of the bond; at worst we get nothing. Further, assume the recovery rate for each bond is independent of the other. In other words, the bonds are i.i.d. uniform, between $0 and $100. What is the distribution for the portfolio

of the two bonds? In the worst-case scenario, we recover $0 from both bonds, and the total recovery is $0. In the best-case scenario, we recover the full amount for both bonds, $200 for the portfolio. Because the bonds are independent, these extremes are actually very unlikely. The most likely scenario is right in the middle, where we recover $100. This could happen if we recover $40 from the first bond and $60 from the second, $90 from the first and $10 from the second, or any of an infinite number of combinations. Figure 3-7 shows the distribution of values for the portfolio of two i.i.d. bonds.

With three bonds, the distribution ranges from $0 to $300, with the mode at $150. With four bonds, the distribution ranges from $0 to $400, with the mode at $200. As we continue to add more bonds, the shape of the distribution function continues to change. Figure 3-8 shows the density functions for the sums of 4, 8, and 16 i.i.d. uniform variables, normalized to have the same range.

Oddly enough, even though we started with uniform variables, the distribution is starting to look increasingly like a normal distribution. The resemblance is not just superficial; it turns out that as we add more and more variables, the distribution actually converges to a normal distribution. What's more, this is not just true if we start out with uniform distributions; it applies to any

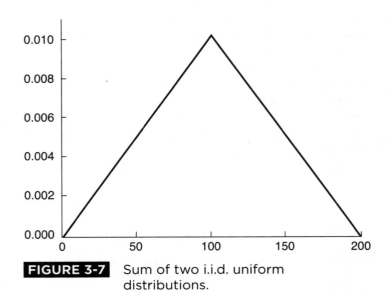

FIGURE 3-7 Sum of two i.i.d. uniform distributions.

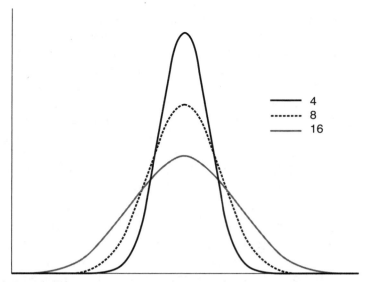

FIGURE 3-8 Sums of various i.i.d. uniform distributions.

distributions with finite variance.* This result is known as the central limit theorem.

More formally, if we have n i.i.d. random variables, X_1, X_2, . . . , X_n, each with mean μ and standard deviation σ, and we define S_n as the sum of those n variables, then:

$$\lim_{n \to \infty} S_n \sim N(n\mu, n\sigma^2) \qquad \textbf{(3.23)}$$

In other words, as n approaches infinity, the sum converges to a normal distribution. This result is one of the most important results in statistics and is the reason why the normal distribution is so ubiquitous. In risk, as in a number of other fields, we are often presented with data that either is i.i.d. by construction or is assumed to be i.i.d. Even when the underlying variables are not normal—which is rare in practice—the i.i.d. assumption, combined with the central limit theorem, allows us to approximate a large collection of data using a normal distribution. The central limit theorem is often used to justify the approximation of financial variables by a normal distribution.

---

* Even though we have not yet encountered any distributions with infinite variance, they can exist. The Cauchy distribution is an example of a parametric distribution with infinite variance. While rare in finance, it's good to know that these distributions can exist.

APPLICATION: MONTE CARLO SIMULATIONS
PART 1: CREATING NORMAL RANDOM VARIABLES

While some problems in risk management have explicit analytic solutions, many problems have no exact mathematical solution. In these cases, we can often approximate a solution by creating a Monte Carlo simulation. A Monte Carlo simulation consists of a number of trials. For each trial we feed random inputs into a system of equations. By collecting the outputs from the system of equations for a large number of trials, we can estimate the statistical properties of the output variables.

Even in cases where explicit solutions might exist, a Monte Carlo solution might be preferable in practice if the explicit solution is difficult to derive or extremely complex. In some cases a simple Monte Carlo simulation can be easier to understand, thereby reducing operational risk.

As an example of a situation where we might use a Monte Carlo simulation, pretend we are asked to evaluate the mean and standard deviation of the profits from a fixed strike arithmetic Asian option, where the value of the option, V, at expiry is:

$$V = \max\left[\frac{1}{T}\sum_{t=1}^{T} S_t - X, 0\right] \qquad \textbf{(3.24)}$$

Here X is the strike price, S_t is the closing price of the underlying asset at time t, and T is the number of periods in the life of the option. In other words, the value of the option at expiry is the greater of zero, or the average price of the underlying asset less the strike price.

Assume there are 200 days until expiry. Further, we are told that the returns of the underlying asset are lognormal, with a mean of 10% and a standard deviation of 20%. The input to our Monte Carlo simulation would be lognormal variables with the appropriate mean and standard deviation. For each trial, we would generate 200 random daily returns, use the returns to calculate a series of random prices, calculate the average of the price series, and use the average to calculate the value of the option. We would repeat this process again and again, using a different realization of the random returns each time, and each time calculating a new value for the option.

The initial step in the Monte Carlo simulation, generating the random inputs, can itself be very complex. How do we create the uncorrelated normally distributed random variables to start with? Many special-purpose statistical packages contain functions that will generate random draws from normal distributions. If the application we are using does not have this feature, but does have a standard random number generator, which generates a standard uniform distribution, there are two ways we can generate random normal variables. The first is to use an inverse normal transformation. As mentioned previously, there is no explicit formula for the inverse normal transformation, but there are a number of good approximations.

The second approach takes advantage of the central limit theorem. By adding together a large number of i.i.d. uniform distributions, and then multiplying and adding the correct constants, a good approximation to any normal variable can be formed. A classic approach is to simply add 12 standard uniform variables together, and subtract 6:

$$X = \sum_{i=1}^{12} U_i - 6 \qquad \textbf{(3.25)}$$

Because the mean of a standard uniform variable is $\frac{1}{2}$ and the variance is $\frac{1}{12}$, this produces a good approximation to a standard normal variable, with mean zero and standard deviation of one. By utilizing a greater number of uniform variables, we could increase the accuracy of our approximation, but for most applications, this approximation is more than adequate.

CHI-SQUARED DISTRIBUTION

If we have k independent standard normal variables, Z_1, Z_2, ..., Z_k, then the sum of their squares, S, has a chi-squared distribution. We write:

$$S = \sum_{i=1}^{k} Z_i^2 \qquad \textbf{(3.26)}$$
$$S \sim \chi_k^2$$

The variable k is commonly referred to as the degrees of freedom. It follows that the sum of two independent chi-squared variables, with k_1 and k_2 degrees of freedom, will follow a chi-squared distribution, with $(k_1 + k_2)$ degrees of freedom.

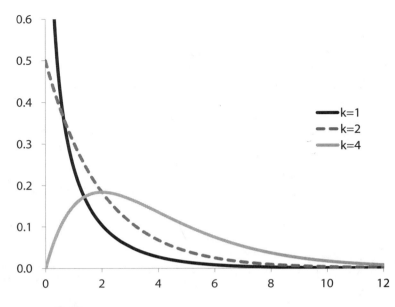

FIGURE 3-9 Chi-squared probability density function.

Because the chi-squared variable is the sum of squared values, it can only take on nonnegative values and is asymmetrical. The mean of the distribution is k, and the variance is $2k$. As k increases, the chi-squared distribution becomes increasingly symmetrical. As k approaches infinity, the chi-squared distribution converges to the normal distribution. Figure 3-9 shows the probability density functions for some chi-squared distributions with different values for k.

For positive values of x, the probability density function for the chi-squared distribution is:

$$f(x) = \frac{1}{2^{k/2}\Gamma(k/2)} x^{\frac{k}{2}-1} e^{-\frac{x}{2}} \qquad \textbf{(3.27)}$$

where Γ is the gamma function:

$$\Gamma(n) = \int_0^\infty x^{n-1} e^{-x} dx \qquad \textbf{(3.28)}$$

The chi-squared distribution is widely used in risk management, and in statistics in general, for hypothesis testing.

STUDENT'S *t* DISTRIBUTION

Another extremely popular distribution in statistics and in risk management is Student's *t* distribution. The distribution was first described in English, in 1908, by William

Sealy Gosset, an employee at the Guinness brewery in Dublin. In order to comply with his firm's policy on publishing in public journals, he submitted his work under the pseudonym Student. The distribution has been known as Student's t distribution ever since. In practice, it is often referred to simply as the t distribution.

If Z is a standard normal variable and U is a chi-square variable with k degrees of freedom, which is independent of Z, then the random variable X:

$$X = \frac{Z}{\sqrt{U/k}} \qquad (3.29)$$

follows a t distribution with k degrees of freedom.

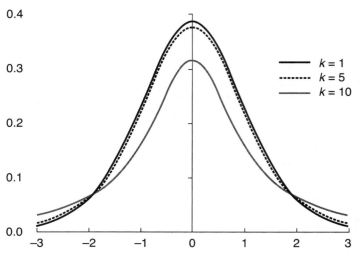

FIGURE 3-10 Student's t probability density functions.

Mathematically, the distribution is quite complicated. The probability density function can be written:

$$f(x) = \frac{\Gamma\left(\frac{k+1}{2}\right)}{\sqrt{k\pi}\,\Gamma\left(\frac{k}{2}\right)}\left(1 + \frac{x^2}{k}\right)^{-(k+1)/2} \qquad (3.30)$$

where k is the degrees of freedom and Γ is the gamma function.

Very few risk managers will memorize this PDF equation, but it is important to understand the basic shape of the distribution and how it changes with k. Figure 3-10 shows the probability density function for three Student's t distributions. Notice how changing the value of k changes the shape of the distribution, specifically the tails.

The t distribution is symmetrical around its mean, which is equal to zero. For low values of k, the t distribution looks very similar to a standard normal distribution, except that it displays excess kurtosis. As k increases, this excess kurtosis decreases. In fact, as k approaches infinity, the t distribution converges to a standard normal distribution.

The variance of the t distribution for $k > 2$ is $k/(k - 2)$. You can see that as k increases, the variance of the t distribution converges to one, the variance of the standard normal distribution.

As we will see in the following chapter, the t distribution's popularity derives mainly from its use in hypothesis testing.

The t distribution is also a popular choice for modeling the returns of financial assets, since it displays excess kurtosis.

F-DISTRIBUTION

If U_1 and U_2 are two independent chi-squared distributions with k_1 and k_2 degrees of freedom, respectively, then X:

$$X = \frac{U_1/k_1}{U_2/k_2} \sim F(k_1, k_2) \qquad (3.31)$$

follows an F-distribution with parameters k_1 and k_2.

The probability density function of the F-distribution, as with the chi-squared distribution, is rather complicated:

$$f(x) = \frac{\sqrt{\dfrac{(k_1 x)^{k_1} k_2^{k_2}}{(k_1 x + k_2)^{k_1 + k_2}}}}{xB\left(\dfrac{k_1}{2}, \dfrac{k_2}{2}\right)} \qquad (3.32)$$

where $B(x, y)$ is the beta function:

$$B(x, y) = \int_0^1 z^{x-1}(1-z)^{y-1}dz \qquad (3.33)$$

As with the chi-squared and Student's t distributions, memorizing the probability density function is probably

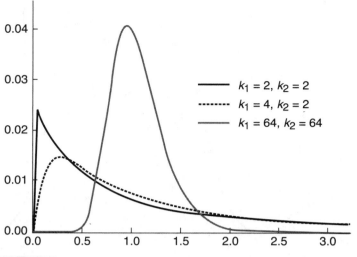

FIGURE 3-11 *F*-distribution probability density functions.

not something most risk managers would be expected to do; rather, it is important to understand the general shape and some properties of the distribution.

Figure 3-11 shows the probability density functions for several *F*-distributions. Because the chi-squared PDF is zero for negative values, the *F*-distribution's density function is also zero for negative values. The mean and variance of the *F*-distribution are as follows:

$$\mu = \frac{k_2}{k_2 - 2} \text{ for } k_2 > 2 \qquad \textbf{(3.34)}$$

$$\sigma^2 = \frac{2k_2^2(k_1 + k_2 - 2)}{k_1(k_2 - 2)^2(k_2 - 4)} \text{ for } k_2 > 4$$

As k_1 and k_2 increase, the mean and mode converge to one. As k_1 and k_2 approach infinity, the *F*-distribution converges to a normal distribution.

There is also a nice relationship between Student's *t* distribution and the *F*-distribution. From the description of the *t* distribution, Equation 3.29, it is easy to see that the square of a variable with a *t* distribution has an *F*-distribution. More specifically, if *X* is a random variable with a *t* distribution with *k* degrees of freedom, then X^2 has an *F* distribution with 1 and *k* degrees of freedom:

$$X^2 \sim F(1, k) \qquad \textbf{(3.35)}$$

MIXTURE DISTRIBUTIONS

Imagine a stock whose log returns follow a normal distribution with low volatility 90% of the time, and a normal distribution with high volatility 10% of the time. Most of the time the world is relatively dull, and the stock just bounces along. Occasionally, though—maybe there is an earnings announcement or some other news event—the stock's behavior is more extreme. We could write the combined density function as:

$$f(x) = w_L f_L(x) + w_H f_H(x) \qquad \textbf{(3.36)}$$

where $w_L = 0.90$ is the probability of the return coming from the low volatility distribution, $f_L(x)$, and $w_H = 0.10$ is the probability of the return coming from the high-volatility distribution $f_H(x)$. We can think of this as a two-step process. First, we randomly choose the high or low distribution, with a 90% chance of picking the low distribution. Second, we generate a random return from the chosen normal distribution. The final distribution, $f(x)$, is a legitimate probability distribution in its own right, and although it is equally valid to describe a random draw directly from this distribution, it is often helpful to think in terms of this two-step process.

Note that the two-step process is not the same as the process described in a previous section for adding two random variables together. An example of adding two random variables together is a portfolio of two stocks. At each point in time, each stock generates a random return, and the portfolio return is the sum of *both* returns. In the case we are describing now, the return appears to come from *either* the low-volatility distribution *or* the high-volatility distribution. Adding the probability density functions is not the same as adding random variables.

The distribution that results from a weighted average distribution of density functions is known as a mixture distribution. More generally, we can create a distribution:

$$f(x) = \sum_{i=1}^{n} w_i f_i(x) \text{ s.t. } \sum_{i=1}^{n} w_i = 1 \qquad \textbf{(3.37)}$$

where the various $f_i(x)$'s are known as the component distributions, and the w_i's are known as the mixing

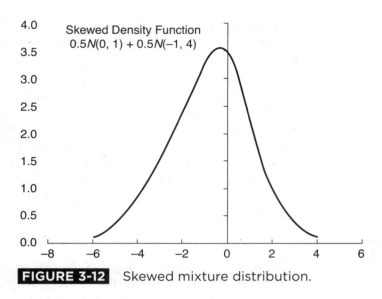

FIGURE 3-12 Skewed mixture distribution.

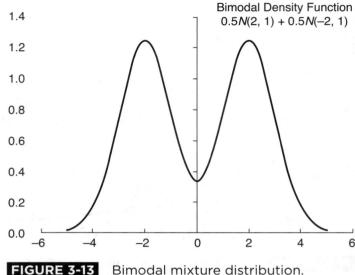

FIGURE 3-13 Bimodal mixture distribution.

proportions or weights. Notice that in order for the resulting mixture distribution to be a legitimate distribution, the sum of the component weights must equal one.

Mixture distributions are extremely flexible. In a sense they occupy a realm between parametric distributions and nonparametric distributions. In a typical mixture distribution, the component distributions are parametric, but the weights are based on empirical data, which is nonparametric. Just as there is a trade-off between parametric distributions and nonparametric distributions, there is a trade-off between using a low number and a high number of component distributions. By adding more and more component distributions, we can approximate any data set with increasing precision. At the same time, as we add more and more component distributions, the conclusions that we can draw tend to become less general in nature.

Just by adding two normal distributions together, we can develop a large number of interesting distributions. Similar to the previous example, if we combine two normal distributions with the same mean but different variances, we can get a symmetrical mixture distribution that displays excess kurtosis. By shifting the mean of one distribution,

we can also create a distribution with positive or negative skew. Figure 3-12 shows an example of a skewed mixture distribution created from two normal distributions.

Finally, if we move the means far enough apart, the resulting mixture distribution will be bimodal; that is, the PDF will have two distinct maxima, as shown in Figure 3-13.

Mixture distributions can be extremely useful in risk management. Securities whose return distributions are skewed or have excess kurtosis are often considered riskier than normal distributions, since extreme events can occur more frequently. Mixture distributions provide a ready method for modeling these attributes.

A bimodal distribution can be extremely risky. If one component of a security's returns has an extremely low mixing weight, we might be tempted to ignore that component. If the component has an extremely negative mean, though, ignoring it could lead us to severely underestimate the risk of the security. Equity market crashes are a perfect example of an extremely low probability, highly negative mean event.

Hypothesis Testing & Confidence Intervals

4

■ Learning Objectives

Candidates, after completing this reading, should be able to:

- Calculate and interpret the sample mean and sample variance.
- Define and construct a confidence interval.
- Define and construct an appropriate null and alternative hypothesis, and calculate an appropriate test statistic.
- Differentiate between a one-tailed and a two-tailed test and explain the circumstances in which to use each test.

- Interpret the results of hypothesis tests with a specific level of confidence.
- Describe and apply the principle of Chebyshev's inequality.

Excerpt is Chapter 5 of Mathematics and Statistics for Financial Risk Management, *by Michael Miller.*

In this chapter we will explore two closely related topics, confidence intervals and hypothesis testing. At the end of the chapter, we will explore applications, including value-at-risk (VaR).

THE SAMPLE MEAN REVISITED

Imagine we take the output from a standard random number generator on a computer, and multiply it by 100. The resulting data generating process (DGP) is a uniform random variable, which ranges between 0 and 100, with a mean of 50. If we generate 20 draws from this DGP and calculate the sample mean of those 20 draws, it is unlikely that the sample mean will be exactly 50. The sample mean might round to 50, say 50.03906724, but exactly 50 is next to impossible. In fact, given that we have only 20 data points, the sample mean might not even be close to the true mean.

The sample mean is actually a random variable itself. If we continue to repeat the experiment—generating 20 data points and calculating the sample mean each time—the calculated sample mean will be different every time. As we proved in Chapter 2, even though we never get exactly 50, the expected value of each sample mean is in fact 50. It might sound strange to say it, but the mean of our sample mean is the true mean of the distribution. Using our standard notation:

$$E[\hat{\mu}] = \mu \qquad (4.1)$$

Instead of 20 data points, what if we generate 1,000 data points? With 1,000 data points, the expected value of our sample mean is still 50, just as it was with 20 data points. While we still don't expect our sample mean to be exactly 50, we expect our sample mean will tend to be closer when we are using 1,000 data points. The reason is simple: a single outlier won't have nearly the impact in a pool of 1,000 data points that it will in a pool of 20. If we continue to generate sets of 1,000 data points, it stands to reason that the standard deviation of our sample mean will be lower with 1,000 data points than it would be if our sets contained only 20 data points.

It turns out that the variance of our sample mean doesn't just decrease with the sample size; it decreases in a predictable way, in proportion to the sample size. In other words, if our sample size is n and the true variance of our DGP is σ^2, then the variance of the sample mean is:

$$\sigma_{\hat{\mu}}^2 = \frac{\sigma^2}{n} \qquad (4.2)$$

It follows that the standard deviation of the sample mean decreases with the square root of n. This square root is important. In order to reduce the standard deviation of the mean by a factor of 2, we need four times as many data points. To reduce it by a factor of 10, we need 100 times as much data. This is yet another example of the famous square root rule for independent and identically distributed (i.i.d.) variables.

In our current example, because the DGP follows a uniform distribution, we can easily calculate the variance of each data point, which is 10,000/12 = 833.33 (Equation 3.4). This is equivalent to a standard deviation of approximately 28.87. For 20 data points, the standard deviation of the mean will then be $28.87/\sqrt{20} = 6.45$, and for 1,000 data points, the standard deviation will be $28.87/\sqrt{1,000} = 0.91$.

We have the mean and the standard deviation of our sample mean, but what about the shape of the distribution? You might think that the shape of the distribution would depend on the shape of the underlying distribution of the DGP. If we recast our formula for the sample mean slightly, though:

$$\hat{\mu} = \frac{1}{n} \sum_{i=1}^{n} x_i = \sum_{i=1}^{n} \frac{1}{n} x_i \qquad (4.3)$$

and regard each of the $(1/n)x_i$'s as a random variable in its own right, we see that our sample mean is equivalent to the sum of n i.i.d. random variables, each with a mean of μ/n and a standard deviation of σ/n. Using the central limit theorem, we claim that the distribution of the sample mean converges to a normal distribution. For large values of n, the distribution of the sample mean will be extremely close to a normal distribution. Practitioners will often assume that the sample mean *is* normally distributed.

SAMPLE VARIANCE REVISITED

Just as with the sample mean, we can treat the sample variance as a random variable. For a given DGP if we repeatedly calculate the sample variance, the expected value of the sample variance will equal the true variance, and the variance of the sample variance will equal:

$$E[(\hat{\sigma}^2 - \sigma^2)^2] = \sigma^4 \left(\frac{2}{n-1} + \frac{\kappa}{n} \right) \qquad (4.4)$$

where n is the sample size, and κ is the excess kurtosis.

Sample Problem

Question:

You are given 10 years of monthly returns for a portfolio manager. The mean monthly return is 2.3%, and the standard deviation of the returns series is 3.6%. What is the standard deviation of the mean?

The portfolio manager is being compared against a benchmark with a mean monthly return of 1.5%. What is the probability that the portfolio manager's mean return exceeds the benchmark? Assume the sample mean is normally distributed.

Answer:

There are a total of 120 data points in the sample (10 years × 12 months per year). The standard deviation of the mean is then 0.33%:

$$\sigma_{\hat{\mu}} = \frac{\sigma}{\sqrt{n}} = \frac{3.6\%}{\sqrt{120}} = 0.33\%$$

The distance between the portfolio manager's mean return and the benchmark is −2.43 standard deviations: (1.50% − 2.30%)/0.33% = −2.43. For a normal distribution, 99.25% of the distribution lies above −2.43 standard deviations, and only 0.75% lies below. The difference between the portfolio manager and the benchmark is highly significant.

If the DGP has a normal distribution, then we can also say something about the shape of the distribution of the sample variance. If we have n sample points and $\hat{\sigma}^2$ is the sample variance, then our estimator will follow a chi-squared distribution with $(n − 1)$ degrees of freedom:

$$(n - 1)\frac{\hat{\sigma}^2}{\sigma^2} \sim \chi^2_{n-1} \qquad \textbf{(4.5)}$$

where σ^2 is the population variance. Note that this is true only when the DGP has a normal distribution. Unfortunately, unlike the case of the sample mean, we cannot apply the central limit theorem here. Even when the sample size is large, if the underlying distribution is nonnormal, the statistic in Equation 4.5 can vary significantly from a chi-squared distribution.

CONFIDENCE INTERVALS

In our discussion of the sample mean, we assumed that the standard deviation of the underlying distribution was known. In practice, the true standard deviation is likely to be unknown. At the same time we are measuring our sample mean, we will typically be measuring a sample variance as well.

It turns out that if we first standardize our estimate of the sample mean using the sample standard deviation, the new random variable follows a Student's t distribution with $(n − 1)$ degrees of freedom:

$$t = \frac{\hat{\mu} - \mu}{\hat{\sigma}/\sqrt{n}} \qquad \textbf{(4.6)}$$

Here the numerator is simply the difference between the sample mean and the population mean, while the denominator is the sample standard deviation divided by the square root of the sample size. To see why this new variable follows a t distribution, we simply need to divide both the numerator and the denominator by the population standard deviation. This creates a standard normal variable in the numerator, and the square root of a chi-square variable in the denominator with the appropriate constant. We know from the previous chapter on distributions that this combination of random variables follows a t distribution. This standardized version of the population mean is so frequently used that it is referred to as a t-statistic, or simply a t-stat.

Technically, this result requires that the underlying distribution be normally distributed. As was the case with the sample variance, the denominator may not follow a chi-squared distribution if the underlying distribution is nonnormal. Oddly enough, for large sample sizes the overall t-statistic still converges to a t distribution. If the sample size is small and the data distribution is nonnormal, be aware that the t-statistic, as defined here, may not be well approximated by a t distribution.

By looking up the appropriate values for the t distribution, we can establish the probability that our t-statistic is contained within a certain range:

$$P\left[x_L \leq \frac{\hat{\mu} - \mu}{\hat{\sigma}/\sqrt{n}} \leq x_U\right] = 1 - \alpha \qquad \textbf{(4.7)}$$

where x_L and x_U are constants, which, respectively, define the lower and upper bounds of the range within the t distribution, and $(1 − \alpha)$ is the probability that our t-statistic will be found within that range. The right-hand side may seem a bit awkward, but, by convention, $(1 − \alpha)$ is called the confidence level, while α by itself is known as the significance level.

In practice, the population mean, μ, is often unknown. By rearranging the previous equation we come to an equation with a more interesting form:

$$P\left[\hat{\mu} - \frac{x_L\hat{\sigma}}{\sqrt{n}} \leq \mu \leq \hat{\mu} + \frac{x_U\hat{\sigma}}{\sqrt{n}}\right] = 1 - \alpha \qquad \textbf{(4.8)}$$

Looked at this way, we are now giving the probability that the population mean will be contained within the defined range. When it is formulated this way, we call this range the confidence interval for the population mean. Confidence intervals are not limited to the population mean. Though it may not be as simple, in theory we can define a confidence level for any distribution parameter.

HYPOTHESIS TESTING

One problem with confidence intervals is that they require us to settle on an arbitrary confidence level. While 95% and 99% are common choices for the confidence level in risk management, there is nothing sacred about these numbers. It would be perfectly legitimate to construct a 74.92% confidence interval. At the same time, we are often concerned with the probability that a certain variable exceeds a threshold. For example, given the observed returns of a mutual fund, what is the probability that the standard deviation of those returns is less than 20%?

In a sense, we want to turn the confidence interval around. Rather than saying there is an x% probability that the population mean is contained within a given interval, we want to know what the probability is that the population mean is greater than y. When we pose the question this way, we are in the realm of hypothesis testing.

Traditionally the question is put in the form of a null hypothesis. If we are interested in knowing if the expected return of a portfolio manager is greater than 10%, we would write:

$$H_0 : \mu_r > 10\% \qquad \textbf{(4.9)}$$

where H_0 is known as the null hypothesis. Even though the true population mean is unknown, for the hypothesis test we assume the population mean *is* 10%. In effect, we are asking, *if* the true population mean *is* 10%, what is the probability that we would see a given sample mean? With our null hypothesis in hand, we gather our data, calculate the sample mean, and form the appropriate *t*-statistic. In this case, the appropriate *t*-statistic is:

$$t = \frac{\hat{\mu} - 10\%}{\sigma/\sqrt{n}} \qquad \textbf{(4.10)}$$

We can then look up the corresponding probability from the *t* distribution.

In addition to the null hypothesis, we can offer an alternative hypothesis. In the previous example, where our null hypothesis is that the expected return is greater than 10%, the logical alternative would be that the expected return is less than or equal to 10%:

$$H_1 : \mu_r \leq 10\% \qquad \textbf{(4.11)}$$

In principle, we could test any number of hypotheses. In practice, as long as the alternative is trivial, we tend to limit ourselves to stating the null hypothesis.

Which Way to Test?

If we want to know if the expected return of a portfolio manager is greater than 10%, the obvious statement of the null hypothesis might seem to be $\mu_r > 10\%$. But there is no reason that we couldn't have started with the alternative hypothesis, that $\mu_r \leq 10\%$. Finding that the first is true and finding that the second is false are logically equivalent.

Many practitioners construct the null hypothesis so that the desired result is false. If we are an investor trying to find good portfolio managers, then we would make the null hypothesis $\mu_r \leq 10\%$. That we want the expected return to be greater than 10% but we are testing for the opposite makes us seem objective. Unfortunately, in the case where there is a high probability that the manager's expected return is greater than 10% (a good result), we have to say, "We reject the null hypothesis that the manager's returns are less than or equal to 10% at the x% level." This is very close to a double negative. Like a medical test where the good outcome is negative and the bad outcome is positive, we often find that the good outcome for a null hypothesis is rejection.

To make matters more complicated, what happens if the portfolio manager doesn't seem to be that good? If we *rejected* the null hypothesis when there was a high probability that the portfolio manager's expected return was greater than 10%, should we *accept* the null hypothesis when there is a high probability that the returns are less than 10%? In the realm of statistics, outright acceptance seems too certain. In practice, we can do two things. First, we can state that the probability of rejecting the null

Sample Problem

Question:

At the start of the year, you believed that the annualized volatility of XYZ Corporation's equity was 45%. At the end of the year, you have collected a year of daily returns, 256 business days' worth. You calculate the standard deviation, annualize it, and come up with a value of 48%. Can you reject the null hypothesis, $H_0 : \sigma = 45\%$, at the 95% confidence level?

Answer:

The appropriate test statistic is:

$$(n-1)\frac{\hat{\sigma}^2}{\sigma^2} = (256 - 1)\frac{0.48^2}{0.45^2} = 290.13 \sim \chi^2_{255}$$

Notice that annualizing the standard deviation has no impact on the test statistic. The same factor would appear in the numerator and the denominator, leaving the ratio unchanged. For a chi-squared distribution with 255 degrees of freedom, 290.13 corresponds to a probability of 6.44%. We fail to reject the null hypothesis at the 95% confidence level.

hypothesis is low (e.g., "The probability of rejecting the null hypothesis is only 4.2%"). More often we say that we *fail to reject* the null hypothesis (e.g., "We fail to reject the null hypothesis at the 95.8% level").

One Tail or Two?

Novice statisticians often get confused about the choice between one-tailed and two-tailed critical values. In many scientific fields where positive and negative deviations are equally important, two-tailed confidence levels are the more prevalent. In risk management, more often than not, we are more concerned with the probability of bad outcomes, and this concern naturally leads to one-tailed tests.

A two-tailed null hypothesis could take the form:

$$H_0 : \mu = 0 \qquad \textbf{(4.12)}$$
$$H_1 : \mu \neq 0$$

In this case, H_1 implies that extreme positive or negative values would cause us to reject the null hypothesis. If we are concerned with both sides of the distribution (both tails), we should choose a two-tailed test.

A one-tailed test could be of the form:

$$H_0 : \mu > c \qquad \textbf{(4.13)}$$
$$H_1 : \mu \leq c$$

In this case, we will reject H_0 only if the estimate of μ is significantly less than c. If we are only concerned with deviations in one direction, we should use a one-tailed test.

As long as the null hypothesis is clearly stated, the choice of a one-tailed or two-tailed confidence level should be obvious.

The 95% confidence level is a very popular choice for confidence levels, both in risk management and in the sciences. Many non-risk managers remember from their science classes that a 95% confidence level is equivalent to approximately 1.96 standard deviations. For a two-tailed test this is correct; for a normal distribution 95% of the mass is within $+/-1.96$ standard deviations. For a one-tailed test, though, 95% of the mass is within $+/-1.64$ standard deviations. Using 1.96 instead of 1.64 is a common mistake for people new to risk management.

Table 4-1 shows common critical values for *t*-tests of varying degrees of freedom and for a normal distribution. Notice that all distributions are symmetrical. For small sample sizes, extreme values are more likely, but as the sample size increases, the *t* distribution converges to the normal distribution. For 5% significance with 100 degrees of freedom, the difference between our rule of thumb based on the normal distribution, 1.64 standard deviations, is very close to the actual value of 1.66.

TABLE 4-1 Common Critical Values for Student's *t* Distribution

	t_{10}	t_{100}	$t_{1,000}$	N
1.0%	−2.76	−2.36	−2.33	−2.33
2.5%	−2.23	−1.98	−1.96	−1.96
5.0%	−1.81	−1.66	−1.65	−1.64
10.0%	−1.37	−1.29	−1.28	−1.28
90.0%	1.37	1.29	1.28	1.28
95.0%	1.81	1.66	1.65	1.64
97.5%	2.23	1.98	1.96	1.96
99.0%	2.76	2.36	2.33	2.33

The Confidence Level Returns

As we stated at the beginning of this section, one of the great things about a hypothesis test is that we are not required to choose an arbitrary confidence level. In practice, though, 95% and 99% confidence levels are such gold standards that we often end up referring back to them. If we can reject a null hypothesis at the 96.3% confidence level, some practitioners will simply say that the hypothesis was rejected at the 95% confidence level. The implication is that even though we may be more confident, 95% is enough. This convention can be convenient when testing a hypothesis repeatedly. As an example, we might want to test the validity of a risk model against new market data every day and be alerted only when the hypothesis cannot be rejected at the 95% confidence level. In the end, our inability to decide on a universal confidence level should serve as a reminder that, in statistics, there is no such thing as a sure bet; there is no such thing as absolute certainty.

CHEBYSHEV'S INEQUALITY

In the preceding sections, we were working with sample statistics where the shape of the distribution was known. Amazingly, even if we do not know the entire distribution of a random variable, we can form a confidence interval, as long as we know the variance of the variable. For a random variable, X, with a standard deviation of σ, the probability that X is within n standard deviations of μ is less than or equal to $1/n^2$:

$$P[|X - \mu| \geq n\sigma] \leq \frac{1}{n^2} \qquad \textbf{(4.14)}$$

This is a result of what is known as Chebyshev's inequality.

For a given level of variance, Chebyshev's inequality places an upper limit on the probability of a variable being more than a certain distance from its mean. For a given distribution, the actual probability may be considerably less. Take, for example, a standard normal variable. Chebyshev's inequality tells us that the probability of being greater than two standard deviations from the mean is less than or equal to 25%. The exact probability for a standard normal variable is closer to 5%, which is indeed less than 25%.

Chebyshev's inequality makes clear how assuming normality can be very anticonservative. If a variable is normally distributed, the probability of a three standard deviation event is very small, 0.27%. If we assume normality, we will assume that three standard deviation events are very rare. For other distributions, though, Chebyshev's inequality tells us that the probability could be as high as ⅑, or approximately 11%. Eleven percent is hardly a rare occurrence. Assuming normality when a random variable is in fact not normal can lead to a severe underestimation of risk. Risk managers take note!

APPLICATION: VaR

Value-at-risk (VaR) is one of the most widely used risk measures in finance. VaR was popularized by J.P. Morgan in the 1990s. The executives at J.P. Morgan wanted their risk managers to generate one statistic at the end of each day, which summarized the risk of the firm's entire portfolio. What they came up with was VaR.

Figure 4-1 provides a graphical representation of VaR. If the 95% VaR of a portfolio is $100, then we expect the portfolio will lose $100 or less in 95% of the scenarios, and lose $100 or more in 5% of the scenarios. We can define VaR for any level of confidence, but 95% has become an extremely popular choice in finance. The time horizon also needs to be specified for VaR. On trading desks, with liquid portfolios, it is common to measure the one-day 95% VaR. In other settings, in which less liquid assets may be involved, time frames of up to one year are not uncommon. VaR is decidedly a one-tailed confidence interval.

For a given confidence level, $1 - \alpha$, we can define value-at-risk more formally as:

$$P[L \leq \text{VaR}_\alpha] = \alpha \qquad \textbf{(4.15)}$$

where the random variable L is our loss.

Value-at-risk is often described as a confidence interval. As we saw earlier in this chapter, the term *confidence interval* is generally applied to the estimation of distribution parameters. In practice, when calculating VaR, the distribution is often taken as a given. Either way, the tools, concepts, and vocabulary are the same. So even though VaR may not technically be a confidence interval, we still refer to the *confidence level* of VaR.

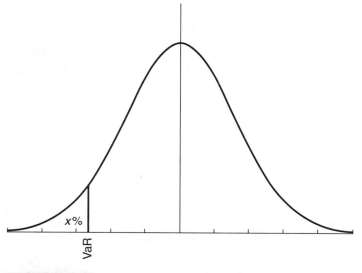

FIGURE 4-1 Value-at-risk example.

Most practitioners reverse the sign of L when quoting VaR numbers. By this convention, a 95% VaR of $400 implies that there is a 5% probability that the portfolio will *lose* $400 or more. Because this represents a loss, others would say that the VaR is −$400. The former is more popular, and is the convention used throughout the rest of the book. In practice, it is often best to avoid any ambiguity by, for example, stating that the VaR is equal to a loss of $400.

If an actual loss exceeds the predicted VaR threshold, that event is known as an exceedance. Another assumption of VaR models is that exceedance events are uncorrelated with each other. In other words, if our VaR measure is set at a one-day 95% confidence level, and there is an exceedance event today, then the probability of an exceedance event tomorrow is still 5%. An exceedance event today has no impact on the probability of future exceedance events.

Sample Problem

Question:

The probability density function (PDF) for daily profits at Triangle Asset Management can be described by the following function:

$$p = \frac{1}{10} + \frac{1}{100}\pi \quad -10 \le \pi \le 0$$

$$p = \frac{1}{10} - \frac{1}{100}\pi \quad 0 < \pi \le 10$$

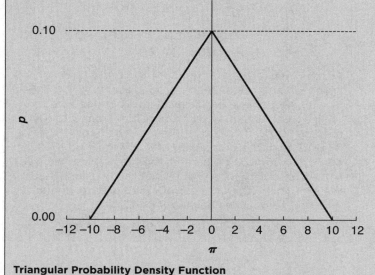

Triangular Probability Density Function

What is the one-day 95% VaR for Triangle Asset Management?

Answer:

To find the 95% VaR, we need to find *a*, such that:

$$\int_{-10}^{a} p\,d\pi = 0.05$$

By inspection, half the distribution is below zero, so we need only bother with the first half of the function:

$$\int_{-10}^{a}\left(\frac{1}{10} + \frac{1}{100}\pi\right)d\pi = \left[\frac{1}{10}\pi + \frac{1}{200}\pi^2\right]_{-10}^{a}$$

$$= \frac{1}{10}a + \frac{1}{200}a^2 + 0.50 = 0.05$$

$$a^2 + 20a + 90 = 0$$

Using the quadratic formula, we can solve for *a*:

$$a = \frac{-20 \pm \sqrt{400 - 4 \cdot 90}}{2} = -10 \pm \sqrt{10}$$

Because the distribution is not defined for $\pi < -10$, we can ignore the negative, giving us the final answer:

$$a = -10 + \sqrt{10} = -6.84$$

The one-day 95% VaR for Triangle Asset Management is a loss of approximately 6.84.

Back-Testing

An obvious concern when using VaR is choosing the appropriate confidence interval. As mentioned, 95% has become a very popular choice in risk management. In some settings there may be a natural choice for the confidence level, but most of the time the exact choice is arbitrary.

A common mistake for newcomers is to choose a confidence level that is too high. Naturally, a higher confidence level sounds more conservative. A risk manager who measures one-day VaR at the 95% confidence level will, on average, experience an exceedance event every 20 days. A risk manager who measures VaR at the 99.9% confidence level expects to see an exceedance only once every 1,000 days. Is an event that happens once every 20 days really something that we need to worry about? It is tempting to believe that the risk manager using the 99.9% confidence level is concerned with more serious, riskier outcomes, and is therefore doing a better job.

The problem is that, as we go further and further out into the tail of the distribution, we become less and less certain of the shape of the distribution. In most cases, the assumed distribution of returns for our portfolio will be based on historical data. If we have 1,000 data points, then there are 50 data points to back up our 95% confidence level, but only one to back up our 99.9% confidence level. As with any distribution parameter, the variance of our estimate of the parameter decreases with the sample size. One data point is hardly a good sample size on which to base a parameter estimate.

A related problem has to do with back-testing. Good risk managers should regularly back-test their models. Back-testing entails checking the predicted outcome of a model against actual data. Any model parameter can be back-tested.

In the case of VaR, back-testing is easy. As we saw in a problem at the end of Chapter 3, each period can be viewed as a Bernoulli trial. In the case of one-day 95% VaR, there is a 5% chance of an exceedance event each day, and a 95% chance that there is no exceedance. Because exceedance events are independent, over the course of n days, the distribution of exceedances follows a binomial distribution:

$$P[K = k] = \binom{n}{k} p^k (1 - p)^{n-k} \qquad \text{(4.16)}$$

In this case, n is the number of periods that we are using to back-test, k is the number of exceedances, and $(1 - p)$ is our confidence level.

Sample Problem

Question:

As a risk manager, you are tasked with calculating a daily 95% VaR statistic for a large fixed income portfolio. Over the past 100 days, there have been four exceedances. How many exceedances should you have expected? What was the probability of exactly four exceedances during this time? Four or less? Four or more?

Answer:

The probability of exactly four exceedances is 17.81%:

$$P[K = 4] = \binom{100}{4} 0.05^4 (1 - 0.05)^{100-4} = 0.1781$$

Remember, by convention, for a 95% VaR the probability of an exceedance is 5%, not 95%.

The probability of four or fewer exceedances is 43.60%. Here we simply do the same calculation as in the first part of the problem, but for zero, one, two, three, and four exceedances. It's important not to forget zero:

$$P[K \leq 4] = \sum_{k=0}^{4} \binom{100}{k} 0.05^k (1 - 0.05)^{100-k}$$
$$= 0.0059 + 0.0312 + 0.0812 + 0.1396$$
$$+ 0.1781 = 0.4360$$

For the final result, we could use the brute force approach and calculate the probability for $k = 4, 5, 6, \ldots, 99, 100$, a total of 97 calculations. Instead we realize that the sum of all probabilities from 0 to 100 must be 100%; therefore, if the probability of $K \leq 4$ is 43.60%, then the probability of $K > 4$ must be 100% − 43.60% = 56.40%. Be careful, though, as what we want is the probability for $K \geq 4$. To get this, we simply add the probability that $K = 4$, from the first part of our question, to get the final answer, 74.21%:

$$P[K \geq 4] = 0.5640 + 0.1781 = 0.7421$$

Subadditivity

There is a reason VaR has become so popular in risk management. The appeal of VaR is its simplicity. Because VaR can be calculated for any portfolio, it allows us to easily compare the risk of different portfolios. Because it boils risk down to a single number, VaR provides us with a convenient way to track the risk of a portfolio over time. Finally, the concept of VaR is intuitive, even to those not versed in statistics.

Because it is so popular, VaR has come under a lot of criticism. The criticism generally falls into one of three categories.

At a very high level, financial institutions have been criticized for being overly reliant on VaR. This is not so much a criticism of VaR as it is a criticism of financial institutions for trying to make risk too simple.

At the other end of the spectrum, many experts have criticized how VaR is measured in practice. This is not so much a criticism of VaR as it is a criticism of specific implementation of VaR. For example, in the early days of finance it was popular to make what is known as a delta-normal assumption. That is, when measuring VaR, you would assume that all asset returns were normally distributed, and that all options could be approximated by their delta exposures. Further, the relationship between assets was based entirely on a covariance matrix (no coskewness or cokurtosis). These assumptions made calculating VaR very easy, even for large portfolios, but the results were often disappointing. As computing power became cheaper and more widespread, this approach quickly fell out of favor. Today VaR models can be extremely complex, but many people outside of risk management still remember when delta-normal was the standard approach, and mistakenly believe that this is a fundamental shortcoming of VaR.

In between, there are more sophisticated criticisms. One such criticism is that VaR is not a subadditive risk measure. It is generally accepted that a logical risk measure should have certain properties; see, for example, Artzner, Delbaen, Eber, and Heath (1999). One such property is known as subadditivity. Subadditivity is basically a fancy way of saying that diversification is good, and a good risk measure should reflect that.

Assume our risk measure is a function f that takes as its input a random variable representing an asset or portfolio of assets. Higher values of the risk measure are associated with greater risk. If we have two risky portfolios, X and Y, then f is said to be subadditive if:

$$f(X + Y) \leq f(X) + f(Y) \qquad (4.17)$$

In other words, the risk of the combined portfolio, $(X + Y)$, is less than or equal to the sum of the risks of the separate portfolios. Variance and standard deviation are subadditive risk measures.

While there is lots to recommend VaR, unfortunately it does not always satisfy the requirement of subadditivity. The following example demonstrates a violation of subadditivity.

Sample Problem

Question:

Imagine a portfolio with two bonds, each with a 4% probability of defaulting. Assume that default events are uncorrelated and that there is a recovery rate of 0%. The bonds are currently worth $100 each. If a bond defaults, it is worth $0; if it does not, it is still worth $100. What is the 95% VaR of each bond separately? What is the 95% VaR of the bond portfolio?

Answer:

For each bond separately, the 95% VaR is $0. For an individual bond, in (over) 95% of scenarios, there is no loss.

In the combined portfolio, however, there are three possibilities, with the following probabilities:

P[x]	x
0.16%	−$200
7.68%	−$100
92.16%	$0

As we can easily see, there are no defaults in only 92.16% = $(1 − 4\%)^2$ of the scenarios. In the other 7.84% of scenarios, the loss is greater than or equal to $100. The 95% VaR of the portfolio is therefore $100.

Because the VaR of the combined portfolio is greater than the sum of the VaRs of the separate portfolios, VaR seems to suggest that there is no diversification benefit, even though the bonds are uncorrelated. It seems to suggest that holding $200 of either bond would be less risky than holding a portfolio with $100 of each. Clearly this is not correct. For this portfolio, VaR is not subadditive.

This example makes clear that when assets have payout functions that are discontinuous near the VaR critical level, we are likely to have problems with subadditivity. By the same token, if the payout functions of the assets in a portfolio are continuous, then VaR will be subadditive. In many settings this is not an onerous assumption. In between, we have large, diverse portfolios, which contain some assets with discontinuous payout functions. For these portfolios subadditivity will likely be only a minor issue.

Expected Shortfall

Another criticism of VaR is that it does not tell us anything about the tail of the distribution. Two portfolios could have the exact same 95% VaR, but very different distributions beyond the 95% confidence level.

More than VaR, then, what we really want to know is how big the loss will be when we have an exceedance event. Using the concept of conditional probability, we can define the expected value of a loss, given an exceedance, as follows:

$$E[L|L > VaR_\alpha] = S \qquad \textbf{(4.18)}$$

Sample Problem

Question:

In a previous example, the probability density function of Triangle Asset Management's daily profits could be described by the following function:

$$p = \frac{1}{10} + \frac{1}{100}\pi \quad -10 \leq \pi \leq 0$$

$$p = \frac{1}{10} - \frac{1}{100}\pi \quad 0 < \pi \leq 10$$

We calculated Triangle's one-day 95% VaR as a loss of $(10 - \sqrt{10}) = 6.84$. For the same confidence level and time horizon, what is the expected shortfall?

Answer:

Because the VaR occurs in the region where $\pi < 0$, we only need to utilize the first half of the function. Using Equation 4.19, we have:

$$S = \frac{1}{0.05}\int_{-10}^{VaR}\pi p\, d\pi = 20\int_{-10}^{VaR}\pi\left(\frac{1}{10} + \frac{1}{100}\pi\right)d\pi$$

$$= \int_{-10}^{VaR}\left(2\pi + \frac{\pi^2}{5}\right)d\pi = \left[\pi^2 + \frac{1}{15}\pi^3\right]_{-10}^{VaR}$$

$$S = \left(\left(-10 + \sqrt{10}\right)^2 + \frac{1}{15}\left(-10 + \sqrt{10}\right)^3\right) - \left((-10)^2 + \frac{1}{15}(-10)^3\right)$$

$$S = -10 + \frac{2}{3}\sqrt{10} = -7.89$$

Thus, the expected shortfall is a loss of 7.89. Intuitively this should make sense. The expected shortfall must be greater than the VaR, 6.84, but less than the minimum loss of 10. Because extreme events are less likely (the height of the PDF decreases away from the center), it also makes sense that the expected shortfall is closer to the VaR than it is to the maximum loss.

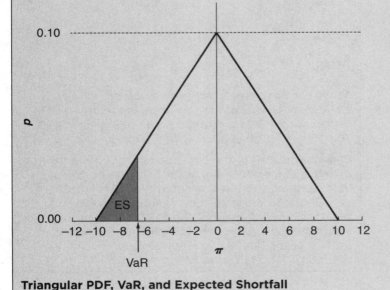

Triangular PDF, VaR, and Expected Shortfall

we refer to this conditional expected loss, S, as the expected shortfall.

If the profit function has a probability density function given by $f(x)$, and VaR is the VaR at the α confidence level, we can find the expected shortfall as:

$$S = \frac{1}{1-\alpha} \int_{-\infty}^{VaR} xf(x)dx \qquad (4.19)$$

In most cases the VaR for a portfolio will correspond to a loss, and Equation 4.19 will produce a negative value. As with VaR, it is common to reverse the sign when speaking about the expected shortfall.

Expected shortfall does answer an important question. What's more, expected shortfall turns out to be subadditive, thereby avoiding one of the major criticisms of VaR. As our discussion on back-testing suggests, though, the reliability of our expected shortfall measure may be difficult to gauge.

Linear Regression with One Regressor

5

■ Learning Objectives

Candidates, after completing this reading, should be able to:

- Explain how regression analysis in econometrics measures the relationship between dependent and independent variables.
- Define and interpret a population regression function, regression coefficients, parameters, slope, intercept, and the error term.
- Define and interpret a sample regression function, regression coefficients, parameters, slope, intercept, and the error term.
- Describe the key properties of a linear regression.
- Define an ordinary least squares (OLS) regression and calculate the intercept and slope of the regression.

- Describe the method and three key assumptions of OLS for estimation of parameters.
- Summarize the benefits of using OLS estimators.
- Describe the properties of OLS estimators and their sampling distributions, and explain the properties of consistent estimators in general.
- Define and interpret the explained sum of squares, the total sum of squares, the residual sum of squares, the standard error of the regression, and the regression R^2.
- Interpret the results of an OLS regression.

Excerpt is Chapter 4 of Introduction to Econometrics, Brief Edition *by James H. Stock and Mark W. Watson.*

A state implements tough new penalties on drunk drivers: What is the effect on highway fatalities? A school district cuts the size of its elementary school classes: What is the effect on its students' standardized test scores? You successfully complete one more year of college classes: What is the effect on your future earnings?

All three of these questions are about the unknown effect of changing one variable, X (X being penalties for drunk driving, class size, or years of schooling), on another variable, Y (Y being highway deaths, student test scores, or earnings).

This chapter introduces the linear regression model relating one variable, X, to another, Y. This model postulates a linear relationship between X and Y; the slope of the line relating X and Y is the effect of a one-unit change in X on Y. Just as the mean of Y is an unknown characteristic of the population distribution of Y, the slope of the line relating X and Y is an unknown characteristic of the population joint distribution of X and Y. The econometric problem is to estimate this slope—that is, to estimate the effect on Y of a unit change in X—using a sample of data on these two variables.

This chapter describes methods for estimating this slope using a random sample of data on X and Y. For instance, using data on class sizes and test scores from different school districts, we show how to estimate the expected effect on test scores of reducing class sizes by, say, one student per class. The slope and the intercept of the line relating X and Y can be estimated by a method called ordinary least squares (OLS).

THE LINEAR REGRESSION MODEL

The superintendent of an elementary school district must decide whether to hire additional teachers and she wants your advice. If she hires the teachers, she will reduce the number of students per teacher (the student–teacher ratio) by two. She faces a tradeoff. Parents want smaller classes so that their children can receive more individualized attention. But hiring more teachers means spending more money, which is not to the liking of those paying the bill! So she asks you: If she cuts class sizes, what will the effect be on student performance?

In many school districts, student performance is measured by standardized tests, and the job status or pay of some administrators can depend in part on how well their students do on these tests. We therefore sharpen the superintendent's question: If she reduces the average class size by two students, what will the effect be on standardized test scores in her district?

A precise answer to this question requires a quantitative statement about changes. If the superintendent *changes* the class size by a certain amount, what would she expect the *change* in standardized test scores to be? We can write this as a mathematical relationship using the Greek letter beta, $\beta_{ClassSize}$, where the subscript "ClassSize" distinguishes the effect of changing the class size from other effects. Thus,

$$\beta_{ClassSize} = \frac{\text{change in TestScore}}{\text{change in ClassSize}} = \frac{\Delta TestScore}{\Delta ClassSize} \quad \text{(5.1)}$$

where the Greek letter Δ (delta) stands for "change in." That is, $\beta_{ClassSize}$ is the change in the test score that results from changing the class size, divided by the change in the class size.

If you were lucky enough to know $\beta_{ClassSize}$, you would be able to tell the superintendent that decreasing class size by one student would change districtwide test scores by $\beta_{ClassSize}$. You could also answer the superintendent's actual question, which concerned changing class size by two students per class. To do so, rearrange Equation (5.1) so that

$$\Delta TestScore = \beta_{ClassSize} \times \Delta ClassSize \quad \text{(5.2)}$$

Suppose that $\beta_{ClassSize} = -0.6$. Then a reduction in class size of two students per class would yield a predicted change in test scores of $(-0.6) \times (-2) = 1.2$; that is, you would predict that test scores would *rise* by 1.2 points as a result of the *reduction* in class sizes by two students per class.

Equation (5.1) is the definition of the slope of a straight line relating test scores and class size. This straight line can be written

$$TestScore = \beta_0 + \beta_{ClassSize} \times ClassSize \quad \text{(5.3)}$$

where β_0 is the intercept of this straight line, and, as before, $\beta_{ClassSize}$ is the slope. According to Equation (5.3), if you knew β_0 and $\beta_{ClassSize}$, not only would you be able to determine the *change* in test scores at a district associated with a *change* in class size, but you also would be able to predict the average test score itself for a given class size.

When you propose Equation (5.3) to the superintendent, she tells you that something is wrong with this formulation.

She points out that class size is just one of many facets of elementary education, and that two districts with the same class sizes will have different test scores for many reasons. One district might have better teachers or it might use better textbooks. Two districts with comparable class sizes, teachers, and textbooks still might have very different student populations; perhaps one district has more immigrants (and thus fewer native English speakers) or wealthier families. Finally, she points out that, even if two districts are the same in all these ways, they might have different test scores for essentially random reasons having to do with the performance of the individual students on the day of the test. She is right, of course; for all these reasons, Equation (5.3) will not hold exactly for all districts. Instead, it should be viewed as a statement about a relationship that holds *on average* across the population of districts.

A version of this linear relationship that holds for *each* district must incorporate these other factors influencing test scores, including each district's unique characteristics (for example, quality of their teachers, background of their students, how lucky the students were on test day). One approach would be to list the most important factors and to introduce them explicitly into Equation (5.3) (an idea we return to in Chapter 7). For now, however, we simply lump all these "other factors" together and write the relationship for a given district as

$$TestScore = \beta_0 + \beta_{ClassSize} \times ClassSize + \text{other factors} \quad \textbf{(5.4)}$$

Thus, the test score for the district is written in terms of one component, $\beta_0 + \beta_{ClassSize} \times ClassSize$, that represents the average effect of class size on scores in the population of school districts and a second component that represents all other factors.

Although this discussion has focused on test scores and class size, the idea expressed in Equation (5.4) is much more general, so it is useful to introduce more general notation. Suppose you have a sample of n districts. Let Y_i be the average test score in the ith district, let X_i be the average class size in the ith district, and let u_i denote the other factors influencing the test score in the ith district. Then Equation (5.4) can be written more generally as

$$Y_i = \beta_0 + \beta_1 X_i + u_i \quad \textbf{(5.5)}$$

for each district, (that is, $i = 1, \ldots, n$), where β_0 is the intercept of this line and β_1 is the slope. [The general notation "β_1" is used for the slope in Equation (5.5) instead of

"$\beta_{ClassSize}$" because this equation is written in terms of a general variable X_i.]

Equation (5.5) is the **linear regression model with a single regressor**, in which Y is the **dependent variable** and X is the **independent variable** or the **regressor**.

The first part of Equation (5.5), $\beta_0 + \beta_1 X_i$, is the **population regression line** or the **population regression function**. This is the relationship that holds between Y and X on average over the population. Thus, if you knew the value of X, according to this population regression line you would predict that the value of the dependent variable, Y, is $\beta_0 + \beta_1 X$.

The **intercept** β_0 and the **slope** β_1 are the **coefficients** of the population regression line, also known as the **parameters** of the population regression line. The slope β_1 is the change in Y associated with a unit change in X. The intercept is the value of the population regression line when $X = 0$; it is the point at which the population regression line intersects the Y axis. In some econometric applications, the intercept has a meaningful economic interpretation. In other applications, the intercept has no real-world meaning; for example, when X is the class size, strictly speaking the intercept is the predicted value of test scores when there are no students in the class! When the real-world meaning of the intercept is nonsensical it is best to think of it mathematically as the coefficient that determines the level of the regression line.

The term u_i in Equation (5.5) is the **error term**. The error term incorporates all of the factors responsible for the difference between the ith district's average test score and the value predicted by the population regression line. This error term contains all the other factors besides X that determine the value of the dependent variable, Y, for a specific observation, i. In the class size example, these other factors include all the unique features of the ith district that affect the performance of its students on the test, including teacher quality, student economic background, luck, and even any mistakes in grading the test.

The linear regression model and its terminology are summarized in Box 5-1.

Figure 5-1 summarizes the linear regression model with a single regressor for seven hypothetical observations on test scores (Y) and class size (X). The population regression line is the straight line $\beta_0 + \beta_1 X$. The population regression line slopes down ($\beta_1 < 0$), which means

Terminology for the Linear Regression Model with a Single Regressor

The linear regression model is

$$Y_i = \beta_0 + \beta_1 X_i + u_i$$

where

the subscript i runs over observations, $i = 1, \ldots, n$;

Y_i is the *dependent variable*, the *regressand*, or simply the *left-hand variable*;

X_i is the *independent variable*, the *regressor*, or simply the *right-hand variable*;

$\beta_0 + \beta_1 X$ is the *population regression line* or *population regression function*;

β_0 is the *intercept* of the population regression line;

β_1 is the *slope* of the population regression line; and

u_i is the *error term*.

as mentioned earlier, it has no real-world meaning in this example.

Because of the other factors that determine test performance, the hypothetical observations in Figure 5-1 do not fall exactly on the population regression line. For example, the value of Y for district #1, Y_1, is above the population regression line. This means that test scores in district #1 were better than predicted by the population regression line, so the error term for that district, u_1, is positive. In contrast, Y_2 is below the population regression line, so test scores for that district were worse than predicted, and $u_2 < 0$.

Now return to your problem as advisor to the superintendent: What is the expected effect on test scores of reducing the student–teacher ratio by two students per teacher? The answer is easy: The expected change is $(-2) \times \beta_{ClassSize}$. But what is the value of $\beta_{ClassSize}$?

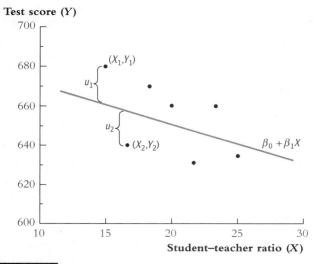

Test score (Y)

FIGURE 5-1 Scatter plot of test score vs. student–teacher ratio (hypothetical data).

The scatterplot shows hypothetical observations for seven school districts. The population regression line is $\beta_0 + \beta_1 X$. The vertical distance from the ith point to the population regression line is $Y_i - (\beta_0 + \beta_1 X_i)$, which is the population error term u_i for the ith observation.

that districts with lower student–teacher ratios (smaller classes) tend to have higher test scores. The intercept β_0 has a mathematical meaning as the value of the Y axis intersected by the population regression line, but,

ESTIMATING THE COEFFICIENTS OF THE LINEAR REGRESSION MODEL

In a practical situation, such as the application to class size and test scores, the intercept β_0 and slope β_1 of the population regression line are unknown. Therefore, we must use data to estimate the unknown slope and intercept of the population regression line.

This estimation problem is similar to others you have faced in statistics. For example, suppose you want to compare the mean earnings of men and women who recently graduated from college. Although the population mean earnings are unknown, we can estimate the population means using a random sample of male and female college graduates. Then the natural estimator of the unknown population mean earnings for women, for example, is the average earnings of the female college graduates in the sample.

The same idea extends to the linear regression model. We do not know the population value of $\beta_{ClassSize}$, the slope of the unknown population regression line relating X (class size) and Y (test scores). But just as it was possible to learn about the population mean using a sample of data drawn from that population, so is it possible to learn about the population slope $\beta_{ClassSize}$ using a sample of data.

TABLE 5-1 Summary of the Distribution of Student-Teacher Ratios and Fifth-Grade Test Scores for 420 K–8 Districts in California in 1998

	Average	Standard Deviation	Percentile						
			10%	25%	40%	50% (median)	60%	75%	90%
Student-teacher ratio	19.6	1.9	17.3	18.6	19.3	19.7	20.1	20.9	21.9
Test score	665.2	19.1	630.4	640.0	649.1	654.5	659.4	666.7	679.1

The data we analyze here consist of test scores and class sizes in 1999 in 420 California school districts that serve kindergarten through eighth grade. The test score is the districtwide average of reading and math scores for fifth graders. Class size can be measured in various ways. The measure used here is one of the broadest, which is the number of students in the district divided by the number of teachers—that is, the district-wide student-teacher ratio. These data are described in more detail in Appendix A.

Table 5-1 summarizes the distributions of test scores and class sizes for this sample. The average student-teacher ratio is 19.6 students per teacher and the standard deviation is 1.9 students per teacher. The 10th percentile of the distribution of the student-teacher ratio is 17.3 (that is, only 10% of districts have student-teacher ratios below 17.3), while the district at the 90th percentile has a student-teacher ratio of 21.9.

A scatterplot of these 420 observations on test scores and the student-teacher ratio is shown in Figure 5-2. The sample correlation is −0.23, indicating a weak negative relationship between the two variables. Although larger classes in this sample tend to have lower test scores, there are other determinants of test scores that keep the observations from falling perfectly along a straight line.

Despite this low correlation, if one could somehow draw a straight line through these data, then the slope of this line would be an estimate of $\beta_{ClassSize}$ based on these data. One way to draw the line would be to take out a pencil and a ruler and to "eyeball" the best line you could. While this method is easy, it is very unscientific and different people will create different estimated lines.

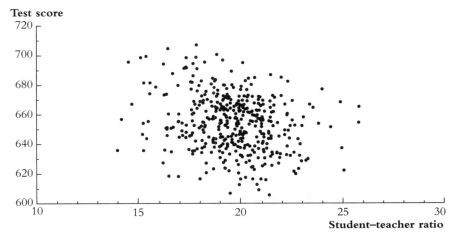

FIGURE 5-2 Scatterplot of test score vs. student–teacher ratio (California School District data).

Data from 420 California school districts. There is a weak negative relationship between the student–teacher ratio and test scores: The sample correlation is −0.23.

How, then, should you choose among the many possible lines? By far the most common way is to choose the line that produces the "least squares" fit to these data—that is, to use the ordinary least squares (OLS) estimator.

The Ordinary Least Squares Estimator

The OLS estimator chooses the regression coefficients so that the estimated regression line is as close as possible to the observed data, where closeness is measured by the sum of the squared mistakes made in predicting Y given X.

As discussed previously, the sample average, $\overline{Y}$, is the least squares estimator of the population mean, $E(Y)$; that is, $\overline{Y}$ minimizes the total squared estimation mistakes $\sum_{i=1}^{n}(Y_i - m)^2$ among all possible estimators m.

The OLS estimator extends this idea to the linear regression model. Let b_0 and b_1 be some estimators of β_0 and β_1. The regression line based on these estimators is $b_0 + b_1 X$, so the value of Y_i predicted using this line is $b_0 + b_1 X_i$. Thus, the mistake made in predicting the ith observation is $Y_i - (b_0 + b_1 X_i) = Y_i - b_0 - b_1 X_i$. The sum of these squared prediction mistakes over all n observations is

$$\sum_{i=1}^{n}(Y_i - b_0 - b_1 X_i)^2 \qquad \text{(5.6)}$$

The sum of the squared mistakes for the linear regression model in Equation (5.6) is the extension of the sum of the squared mistakes for the problem of estimating the mean. In fact, if there is no regressor, then b_1 does not enter Equation (5.6) and the two problems are identical except for the different notation, b_0 in Equation (5.6). Just as there is a unique estimator, $\overline{Y}$, so is there a unique pair of estimators of β_0 and β_1 that minimize Equation (5.6).

The estimators of the intercept and slope that minimize the sum of squared mistakes in Equation (5.6) are called the **ordinary least squares (OLS) estimators** of β_0 and β_1.

OLS has its own special notation and terminology. The OLS estimator of β_0 is denoted $\hat{\beta}_0$, and the OLS estimator of β_1 is denoted $\hat{\beta}_1$. The **OLS regression line** is the straight line constructed using the OLS estimators: $\hat{\beta}_0 + \hat{\beta}_1 X$. The **predicted value** of Y_i given X_i, based on the OLS regression line, is $\hat{Y}_i = \hat{\beta}_0 + \hat{\beta}_1 X_i$. The **residual** for the ith observation is the difference between Y_i and its predicted value: $\hat{u}_i = Y_i - \hat{Y}_i$.

You could compute the OLS estimators $\hat{\beta}_0$ and $\hat{\beta}_1$ by trying different values of b_0 and b_1 repeatedly until you find those that minimize the total squared mistakes in Equation (5.6); they are the least squares estimates. This method would be quite tedious, however. Fortunately there are formulas, derived by minimizing Equation (5.6) using calculus, that streamline the calculation of the OLS estimators.

The OLS formulas and terminology are collected in Box 5-2. These formulas are implemented in virtually all statistical and spreadsheet programs. These formulas are derived in Appendix B.

BOX 5-2 The OLS Estimator, Predicted Values, and Residuals

The OLS estimators of the slope β_1 and the intercept β_0 are

$$\hat{\beta}_1 = \frac{\sum_{i=1}^{n}(X_i - \overline{X})(Y_i - \overline{Y})}{\sum_{i=1}^{n}(X_i - \overline{X})^2} = \frac{s_{XY}}{s_X^2} \qquad \text{(5.7)}$$

$$\hat{\beta}_0 = \overline{Y} - \hat{\beta}_1 \overline{X}. \qquad \text{(5.8)}$$

The OLS predicted values $\hat{Y}_i$ and residuals $\hat{u}_i$ are

$$\hat{Y}_i = \hat{\beta}_0 + \hat{\beta}_1 X_i, \quad i = 1, \ldots, n \qquad \text{(5.9)}$$

$$\hat{u}_i = Y_i - \hat{Y}_i, \quad i = 1, \ldots, n. \qquad \text{(5.10)}$$

The estimated intercept ($\hat{\beta}_0$), slope ($\hat{\beta}_1$), and residual ($\hat{u}_i$) are computed from a sample of n observations of X_i and Y_i, $i = 1, \ldots, n$. These are estimates of the unknown true population intercept (β_0), slope (β_1), and error term (u_i).

OLS Estimates of the Relationship Between Test Scores and the Student–Teacher Ratio

When OLS is used to estimate a line relating the student–teacher ratio to test scores using the 420 observations in Figure 5-2, the estimated slope is -2.28 and the estimated intercept is 698.9. Accordingly, the OLS regression line for these 420 observations is

$$\widehat{TestScore} = 698.9 - 2.28 \times STR, \qquad \text{(5.11)}$$

where *TestScore* is the average test score in the district and *STR* is the student–teacher ratio. The symbol " ˆ " over *TestScore* in Equation (5.11) indicates that this is the predicted value based on the OLS regression line. Figure 5-3 plots this OLS regression line superimposed over the scatterplot of the data previously shown in Figure 5-2.

The slope of -2.28 means that an increase in the student–teacher ratio by one student per class is, on average, associated with a decline in districtwide test scores by 2.28 points on the test. A decrease in the student–teacher ratio by 2 students per class is, on average, associated with an increase in test scores of 4.56 points [$= -2 \times (-2.28)$].

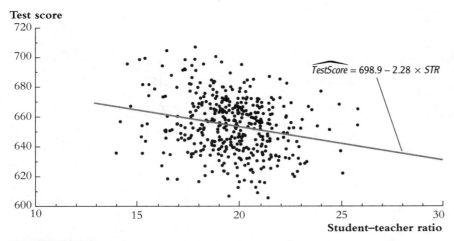

Test score

$$\widehat{TestScore} = 698.9 - 2.28 \times STR$$

FIGURE 5-3 The estimated regression line for the California data.

The estimated regression line shows a negative relationship between test scores and the student–teacher ratio. If class sizes fall by 1 student, the estimated regression predicts that test scores will increase by 2.28 points.

The negative slope indicates that more students per teacher (larger classes) is associated with poorer performance on the test.

It is now possible to predict the districtwide test score given a value of the student–teacher ratio. For example, for a district with 20 students per teacher, the predicted test score is $698.9 - 2.28 \times 20 = 653.3$. Of course, this prediction will not be exactly right because of the other factors that determine a district's performance. But the regression line does give a prediction (the OLS prediction) of what test scores would be for that district, based on their student–teacher ratio, absent those other factors.

Is this estimate of the slope large or small? To answer this, we return to the superintendent's problem. Recall that she is contemplating hiring enough teachers to reduce the student–teacher ratio by 2. Suppose her district is at the median of the California districts. From Table 5-1, the median student–teacher ratio is 19.7 and the median test score is 654.5. A reduction of 2 students per class, from 19.7 to 17.7, would move her student–teacher ratio from the 50th percentile to very near the 10th percentile. This is a big change, and she would need to hire many new teachers. How would it affect test scores?

According to Equation (5.11), cutting the student–teacher ratio by 2 is predicted to increase test scores by approximately 4.6 points; if her district's test scores are at the median, 654.5, they are predicted to increase to 659.1. Is this improvement large or small? According to Table 5-1, this improvement would move her district from the median to just short of the 60th percentile. Thus, a decrease in class size that would place her district close to the 10% with the smallest classes would move her test scores from the 50th to the 60th percentile. According to these estimates, at least, cutting the student–teacher ratio by a large amount (2 students per teacher) would help and might be worth doing depending on her budgetary situation, but it would not be a panacea.

What if the superintendent were contemplating a far more radical change, such as reducing the student–teacher ratio from 20 students per teacher to 5? Unfortunately, the estimates in Equation (5.11) would not be very useful to her. This regression was estimated using the data in Figure 5-2, and as the figure shows, the smallest student–teacher ratio in these data is 14. These data contain no information on how districts with extremely small classes perform, so these data alone are not a reliable basis for predicting the effect of a radical move to such an extremely low student–teacher ratio.

Why Use the OLS Estimator?

There are both practical and theoretical reasons to use the OLS estimators $\hat{\beta}_0$ and $\hat{\beta}_1$. Because OLS is the dominant method used in practice, it has become the common language for regression analysis throughout economics, finance (see the box), and the social sciences more generally. Presenting results using OLS (or its variants discussed later in this book) means that you are "speaking the same language" as other economists and statisticians. The OLS formulas are built into virtually all spreadsheet and statistical software packages, making OLS easy to use.

The OLS estimators also have desirable theoretical properties. These are analogous to the desirable properties

The "Beta" of a Stock

A fundamental idea of modern finance is that an investor needs a financial incentive to take a risk. Said differently, the expected return[1] on a risky investment, R, must exceed the return on a safe, or risk-free, investment, R_f. Thus the expected excess return, $R - R_f$, on a risky investment, like owning stock in a company, should be positive.

At first it might seem like the risk of a stock should be measured by its variance. Much of that risk, however, can be reduced by holding other stocks in a "portfolio"—in other words, by diversifying your financial holdings. This means that the right way to measure the risk of a stock is not by its *variance* but rather by its *covariance* with the market.

The capital asset pricing model (CAPM) formalizes this idea. According to the CAPM, the expected excess return on an asset is proportional to the expected excess return on a portfolio of all available assets (the "market portfolio"). That is, the CAPM says that

$$R - R_f = \beta(R_m - R_f) \qquad (5.12)$$

where R_m is the expected return on the market portfolio and β is the coefficient in the population regression

[1] The return on an investment is the change in its price plus any payout (dividend) from the investment as a percentage of its initial price. For example, a stock bought on January 1 for $100, which then paid a $2.50 dividend during the year and sold on December 31 for $105, would have a return of $R = [(\$105 - \$100) + \$2.50]/\$100 = 7.5\%$.

of $R - R_f$ on $R_m - R_f$. In practice, the risk-free return is often taken to be the rate of interest on short-term U.S. government debt. According to the CAPM, a stock with a $\beta < 1$ has less risk than the market portfolio and therefore has a lower expected excess return than the market portfolio. In contrast, a stock with a $\beta > 1$ is riskier than the market portfolio and thus commands a higher expected excess return.

The "beta" of a stock has become a workhorse of the investment industry, and you can obtain estimated β's for hundreds of stocks on investment firm Web sites. Those β's typically are estimated by OLS regression of the actual excess return on the stock against the actual excess return on a broad market index.

The table below gives estimated β's for six U.S. stocks. Low-risk consumer products firms like Kellogg have stocks with low β's; riskier technology stocks have high β's.

Company	Estimated β
Kellogg (breakfast cereal)	−0.03
Wal-Mart (discount retailer)	0.65
Waste Management (waste disposal)	0.70
Sprint Nextel (telecommunications)	0.78
Barnes and Noble (book retailer)	1.02
Microsoft (software)	1.27
Best Buy (electronic equipment retailer)	2.15
Amazon (online retailer)	2.65

Source: SmartMoney.com

of $\overline{Y}$ as an estimator of the population mean. Under the assumptions introduced in a later section, the OLS estimator is unbiased and consistent. The OLS estimator is also efficient among a certain class of unbiased estimators; however, this efficiency result holds under some additional special conditions, and further discussion of this result is deferred until Chapter 6.

MEASURES OF FIT

Having estimated a linear regression, you might wonder how well that regression line describes the data. Does the regressor account for much or for little of the variation in the dependent variable? Are the observations tightly clustered around the regression line, or are they spread out?

The R^2 and the standard error of the regression measure how well the OLS regression line fits the data. The R^2 ranges between 0 and 1 and measures the fraction of the variance of Y_i that is explained by X_i. The standard error of the regression measures how far Y_i typically is from its predicted value.

The R^2

The **regression R^2** is the fraction of the sample variance of Y_i explained by (or predicted by) X_i. The definitions of the predicted value and the residual (see Box 5-2) allow us to write the dependent variable Y_i as the sum of the predicted value, $\hat{Y}_i$, plus the residual $\hat{u}_i$:

$$Y_i = \hat{Y}_i + \hat{u}_i \qquad (5.13)$$

In this notation, the R^2 is the ratio of the sample variance of $\hat{Y}_i$ to the sample variance of Y_i.

Mathematically, the R^2 can be written as the ratio of the explained sum of squares to the total sum of squares. The

explained sum of squares (**ESS**) is the sum of squared deviations of the predicted values of Y_i, $\hat{Y}_i$, from their average, and the **total sum of squares** (**TSS**) is the sum of squared deviations of Y_i from its average:

$$ESS = \sum_{i=1}^{n}(\hat{Y}_i - \overline{Y})^2 \qquad \textbf{(5.14)}$$

$$TSS = \sum_{i=1}^{n}(Y_i - \overline{Y})^2 \qquad \textbf{(5.15)}$$

Equation (5.14) uses the fact that the sample average OLS predicted value equals $\overline{Y}$.

The R^2 is the ratio of the explained sum of squares to the total sum of squares:

$$R^2 = \frac{ESS}{TSS} \qquad \textbf{(5.16)}$$

Alternatively, the R^2 can be written in terms of the fraction of the variance of Y_i *not* explained by X_i. The **sum of squared residuals**, or **SSR**, is the sum of the squared OLS residuals:

$$SSR = \sum_{i=1}^{n}\hat{u}_i^2 \qquad \textbf{(5.17)}$$

It can be shown that $TSS = ESS + SSR$. Thus the R^2 also can be expressed as 1 minus the ratio of the sum of squared residuals to the total sum of squares:

$$R^2 = 1 - \frac{SSR}{TSS} \qquad \textbf{(5.18)}$$

Finally, the R^2 of the regression of Y on the single regressor X is the square of the correlation coefficient between Y and X.

The R^2 ranges between 0 and 1. If $\hat{\beta}_1 = 0$, then X_i explains none of the variation of Y_i and the predicted value of Y_i based on the regression is just the sample average of Y_i. In this case, the explained sum of squares is zero and the sum of squared residuals equals the total sum of squares; thus the R^2 is zero. In contrast, if X_i explains all of the variation of Y_i, then $Y_i = \hat{Y}_i$ for all i and every residual is zero (that is, $\hat{u}_i = 0$), so that $ESS = TSS$ and $R^2 = 1$. In general, the R^2 does not take on the extreme values of 0 or 1 but falls somewhere in between. An R^2 near 1 indicates that the regressor is good at predicting Y_i, while an R^2 near 0 indicates that the regressor is not very good at predicting Y_i.

The Standard Error of the Regression

The **standard error of the regression** (**SER**) is an estimator of the standard deviation of the regression error u_i. The units of u_i and Y_i are the same, so the SER is a measure of the spread of the observations around the regression line, measured in the units of the dependent variable. For example, if the units of the dependent variable are dollars, then the SER measures the magnitude of a typical deviation from the regression line—that is, the magnitude of a typical regression error—in dollars.

Because the regression errors $u_1, \ldots, u_n$ are unobserved, the SER is computed using their sample counterparts, the OLS residuals $\hat{u}_1, \ldots, \hat{u}_n$. The formula for the SER is

$$SER = s_{\hat{u}}, \text{ where } s_{\hat{u}}^2 = \frac{1}{n-2}\sum_{i=1}^{n}\hat{u}_i^2 = \frac{SSR}{n-2} \qquad \textbf{(5.19)}$$

where the formula for $s_{\hat{u}}^2$ uses the fact that the sample average of the OLS residuals is zero.

The formula for the SER in Equation (5.19) is similar to the formula for the sample standard deviation of Y given earlier, except that $Y_i - \overline{Y}$ is replaced by $\hat{u}_i$, and the divisor is $n - 1$, whereas here it is $n - 2$. The reason for using the divisor $n - 2$ here (instead of n) is the same as the reason for using the divisor $n - 1$: It corrects for a slight downward bias introduced because two regression coefficients were estimated. This is called a "degrees of freedom" correction; because two coefficients were estimated (β_0 and β_1), two "degrees of freedom" of the data were lost, so the divisor in this factor is $n - 2$. (The mathematics behind this is discussed in Chapter 6.) When n is large, the difference between dividing by n, by $n - 1$, or by $n - 2$ is negligible.

Application to the Test Score Data

Equation (5.11) reports the regression line, estimated using the California test score data, relating the standardized test score (*TestScore*) to the student–teacher ratio (*STR*). The R^2 of this regression is 0.051, or 5.1%, and the SER is 18.6.

The R^2 of 0.051 means that the regressor *STR* explains 5.1% of the variance of the dependent variable *TestScore*. Figure 5-3 superimposes this regression line on the scatterplot of the *TestScore* and *STR* data. As the scatterplot shows, the student–teacher ratio explains some of the variation in test scores, but much variation remains unaccounted for.

The *SER* of 18.6 means that standard deviation of the regression residuals is 18.6, where the units are points on the standardized test. Because the standard deviation is a measure of spread, the *SER* of 18.6 means that there is a large spread of the scatterplot in Figure 5-3 around the regression line as measured in points on the test. This large spread means that predictions of test scores made using only the student–teacher ratio for that district will often be wrong by a large amount.

What should we make of this low R^2 and large *SER*? The fact that the R^2 of this regression is low (and the *SER* is large) does not, by itself, imply that this regression is either "good" or "bad." What the low R^2 *does* tell us is that other important factors influence test scores. These factors could include differences in the student body across districts, differences in school quality unrelated to the student–teacher ratio, or luck on the test. The low R^2 and high *SER* do not tell us what these factors are, but they do indicate that the student–teacher ratio alone explains only a small part of the variation in test scores in these data.

THE LEAST SQUARES ASSUMPTIONS

This section presents a set of three assumptions on the linear regression model and the sampling scheme under which OLS provides an appropriate estimator of the unknown regression coefficients, β_0 and β_1. Initially these assumptions might appear abstract. They do, however, have natural interpretations, and understanding these assumptions is essential for understanding when OLS will—and will not—give useful estimates of the regression coefficients.

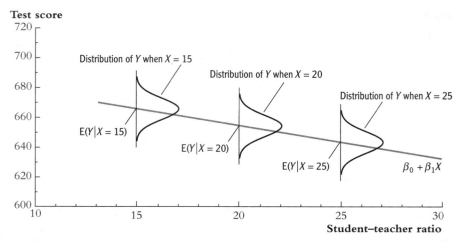

FIGURE 5-4 The conditional probability distributions and the population regression line.

The figure shows the conditional probability of test scores for districts with class sizes of 15, 20, and 25 students. The mean of the conditional distribution of test scores, given the student–teacher ratio, $E(Y|X)$, is the population regression line $\beta_0 + \beta_1 X$. At a given value of X, Y is distributed around the regression line and the error, $u = Y - (\beta_0 + \beta_1 X)$, has a conditional mean of zero for all values of X.

Assumption #1: The Conditional Distribution of u_i Given X_i Has a Mean of Zero

The first **least squares assumption** is that the conditional distribution of u_i given X_i has a mean of zero. This assumption is a formal mathematical statement about the "other factors" contained in u_i and asserts that these other factors are unrelated to X_i in the sense that, given a value of X_i, the mean of the distribution of these other factors is zero.

This is illustrated in Figure 5-4. The population regression is the relationship that holds on average between class size and test scores in the population, and the error term u_i represents the other factors that lead test scores at a given district to differ from the prediction based on the population regression line. As shown in Figure 5-4, at a given value of class size, say 20 students per class, sometimes these other factors lead to better performance than predicted ($u_i > 0$) and sometimes to worse performance ($u_i < 0$), but on average over the population the prediction is right. In other words, given $X_i = 20$, the mean of the distribution of u_i is zero. In Figure 5-4, this is shown as the distribution of u_i being centered on the population regression line at $X_i = 20$ and, more generally, at other values x of X_i as well. Said differently, the distribution of u_i, conditional on $X_i = x$, has a mean of zero; stated mathematically, $E(u_i | X_i = x) = 0$ or, in somewhat simpler notation, $E(u_i | X_i) = 0$.

As shown in Figure 5-4, the assumption that $E(u_i | X_i) = 0$ is equivalent to assuming that the population regression line is the conditional mean of Y_i given X_i (a mathematical proof of this is left as Exercise 6).

The Conditional Mean of u in a Randomized Controlled Experiment

In a randomized controlled experiment, subjects are randomly assigned to the treatment group ($X = 1$) or to the control group ($X = 0$). The random assignment typically is done using a computer program that uses no information about the subject, ensuring that X is distributed independently of all personal characteristics of the subject. Random assignment makes X and u independent, which in turn implies that the conditional mean of u given X is zero.

In observational data, X is not randomly assigned in an experiment. Instead, the best that can be hoped for is that X is *as if* randomly assigned, in the precise sense that $E(u_i | X_i) = 0$. Whether this assumption holds in a given empirical application with observational data requires careful thought and judgment, and we return to this issue repeatedly.

Correlation and Conditional Mean

Recall that if the conditional mean of one random variable given another is zero, then the two random variables have zero covariance and thus are uncorrelated. Thus, the conditional mean assumption $E(u_i | X_i) = 0$ implies that X_i and u_i are uncorrelated, or $\text{corr}(X_i, u_i) = 0$. Because correlation is a measure of linear association, this implication does not go the other way; even if X_i and u_i are uncorrelated, the conditional mean of u_i given X_i might be nonzero. However, if X_i and u_i are correlated, then it must be the case that $E(u_i | X_i)$ is nonzero. It is therefore often convenient to discuss the conditional mean assumption in terms of possible correlation between X_i and u_i. If X_i and u_i are correlated, then the conditional mean assumption is violated.

Assumption #2: (X_i, Y_i), $i = 1, \ldots, n$ Are Independently and Identically Distributed

The second least squares assumption is that (X_i, Y_i), $i = 1, \ldots, n$ are independently and identically distributed (i.i.d.) across observations. This is a statement about how the sample is drawn. If the observations are drawn by simple random sampling from a single large population, then (X_i, Y_i), $i = 1, \ldots, n$ are i.i.d. For example, let X be the age of a worker and Y be his or her earnings, and imagine drawing a person at random from the population of workers. That randomly drawn person will have a certain age and earnings (that is, X and Y will take on some values). If a sample of n workers is drawn from this population, then (X_i, Y_i), $i = 1, \ldots, n$, necessarily have the same distribution. If they are drawn at random they are also distributed independently from one observation to the next; that is, they are i.i.d.

The i.i.d. assumption is a reasonable one for many data collection schemes. For example, survey data from a randomly chosen subset of the population typically can be treated as i.i.d.

Not all sampling schemes produce i.i.d. observations on (X_i, Y_i), however. One example is when the values of X are not drawn from a random sample of the population but rather are set by a researcher as part of an experiment. For example, suppose a horticulturalist wants to study the effects of different organic weeding methods (X) on tomato production (Y) and accordingly grows different plots of tomatoes using different organic weeding techniques. If she picks the techniques (the level of X) to be used on the ith plot and applies the same technique to the ith plot in all repetitions of the experiment, then the value of X_i does not change from one sample to the next. Thus X_i is nonrandom (although the outcome Y_i is random), so the sampling scheme is not i.i.d. The results presented in this chapter developed for i.i.d. regressors are also true if the regressors are nonrandom. The case of a nonrandom regressor is, however, quite special. For example, modern experimental protocols would have the horticulturalist assign the level of X to the different plots using a computerized random number generator, thereby circumventing any possible bias by the horticulturalist (she might use her favorite weeding method for the tomatoes in the sunniest plot). When this modern experimental protocol is used, the level of X is random and (X_i, Y_i) are i.i.d.

Another example of non-i.i.d. sampling is when observations refer to the same unit of observation over time. For example, we might have data on inventory levels (Y) at a firm and the interest rate at which the firm can borrow (X), where these data are collected over time from a specific firm; for example, they might be recorded four times a year (quarterly) for 30 years. This is an example of time series data, and a key feature of time series data is that observations falling close to each other in time are not independent but rather tend to be correlated with each other; if interest rates are low now, they are likely to be low next quarter. This pattern of correlation violates the "independence" part of the i.i.d. assumption. Time series data introduce a set of complications that are best handled after developing the basic tools of regression analysis.

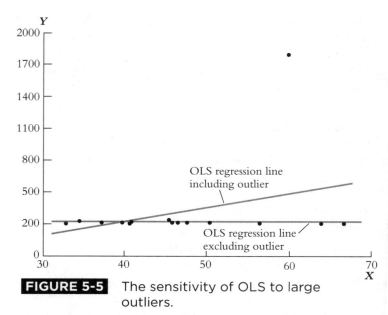

FIGURE 5-5 The sensitivity of OLS to large outliers.

This hypothetical data set has one outlier. The OLS regression line estimated with the outlier shows a strong positive relationship between X and Y, but the OLS regression line estimated without the outlier shows no relationship.

Assumption #3: Large Outliers Are Unlikely

The third least squares assumption is that large outliers—that is, observations with values of X_i and/or Y_i far outside the usual range of the data—are unlikely. Large outliers can make OLS regression results misleading. This potential sensitivity of OLS to extreme outliers is illustrated in Figure 5-5 using hypothetical data.

In this book, the assumption that large outliers are unlikely is made mathematically precise by assuming that X and Y have nonzero finite fourth moments: $0 < E(X_i^4) < \infty$ and $0 < E(Y_i^4) < \infty$. Another way to state this assumption is that X and Y have finite kurtosis.

The assumption of finite kurtosis is used in the mathematics that justify the large-sample approximations to the distributions of the OLS test statistics. We encountered this assumption when discussing the consistency of the sample variance. Specifically, the sample variance s_Y^2 is a consistent estimator of the population variance σ_Y^2 ($s_Y^2 \xrightarrow{p} \sigma_Y^2$). If $Y_1, \ldots, Y_n$ are i.i.d. and the fourth moment of Y_i is finite, then the law of large numbers applies to the average, $\frac{1}{n}\sum_{i=1}^{n}(Y_i - \mu_Y)^2$, a key step in the proof, showing that s_Y^2 is consistent.

One source of large outliers is data entry errors, such as a typographical error or incorrectly using different units for different observations: Imagine collecting data on the height of students in meters, but inadvertently recording one student's height in centimeters instead. One way to find outliers is to plot your data. If you decide that an outlier is due to a data entry error, then you can either correct the error or, if that is impossible, drop the observation from your data set.

Data entry errors aside, the assumption of finite kurtosis is a plausible one in many applications with economic data. Class size is capped by the physical capacity of a classroom; the best you can do on a standardized test is to get all the questions right and the worst you can do is to get all the questions wrong. Because class size and test scores have a finite range, they necessarily have finite kurtosis. More generally, commonly used distributions such as the normal distribution have four moments. Still, as a mathematical matter, some distributions have infinite fourth moments, and this assumption rules out those distributions. If this assumption holds then it is unlikely that statistical inferences using OLS will be dominated by a few observations.

BOX 5-3 The Least Squares Assumptions

$Y_i = \beta_0 + \beta_1 X_i + u_i$, $i = 1, \ldots, n$, where

1. The error term u_i has conditional mean zero given X_i: $E(u_i | X_i) = 0$;
2. (X_i, Y_i), $i = 1, \ldots, n$ are independent and identically distributed (i.i.d.) draws from their joint distribution; and
3. Large outliers are unlikely: X_i and Y_i have nonzero finite fourth moments.

Use of the Least Squares Assumptions

The three least squares assumptions for the linear regression model are summarized in Box 5-3. The least squares assumptions play twin roles, and we return to them repeatedly throughout this textbook.

Their first role is mathematical: If these assumptions hold, then, as is shown in the next section, in large samples the OLS estimators have sampling distributions that are normal. In turn, this large-sample normal distribution lets us develop methods for hypothesis testing and constructing confidence intervals using the OLS estimators.

Their second role is to organize the circumstances that pose difficulties for OLS regression. As we will see, the first least squares assumption is the most important to consider in practice. One reason why the first least squares assumption might not hold in practice is discussed in Chapter 7.

It is also important to consider whether the second assumption holds in an application. Although it plausibly holds in many cross-sectional data sets, the independence assumption is inappropriate for time series data. Therefore, the regression methods developed under assumption 2 require modification for some applications with time series data.

The third assumption serves as a reminder that OLS, just like the sample mean, can be sensitive to large outliers. If your data set contains large outliers, you should examine those outliers carefully to make sure those observations are correctly recorded and belong in the data set.

SAMPLING DISTRIBUTION OF THE OLS ESTIMATORS

Because the OLS estimators $\hat{\beta}_0$ and $\hat{\beta}_1$ are computed from a randomly drawn sample, the estimators themselves are random variables with a probability distribution—the sampling distribution—that describes the values they could take over different possible random samples. This section presents these sampling distributions. In small samples, these distributions are complicated, but in large samples, they are approximately normal because of the central limit theorem.

The Sampling Distribution of the OLS Estimators

Review of the Sampling Distribution of $\overline{Y}$

Recall the discussion about the sampling distribution of the sample average, $\overline{Y}$, an estimator of the unknown population mean of Y, μ_Y. Because $\overline{Y}$ is calculated using a randomly drawn sample, $\overline{Y}$ is a random variable that takes on different values from one sample to the next; the probability of these different values is summarized in its sampling distribution. Although the sampling distribution of $\overline{Y}$ can be complicated when the sample size is small, it is possible to make certain statements about it that hold for all n. In particular, the mean of the sampling distribution is μ_Y, that is, $E(\overline{Y}) = \mu_Y$, so $\overline{Y}$ is an unbiased estimator of μ_Y. If n is large, then more can be said about the sampling distribution. In particular, the central limit theorem states that this distribution is approximately normal.

The Sampling Distribution of $\hat{\beta}_0$ and $\hat{\beta}_1$

These ideas carry over to the OLS estimators $\hat{\beta}_0$ and $\hat{\beta}_1$ of the unknown intercept β_0 and slope β_1 of the population regression line. Because the OLS estimators are calculated using a random sample, $\hat{\beta}_0$ and $\hat{\beta}_1$ are random variables that take on different values from one sample to the next; the probability of these different values is summarized in their sampling distributions.

Although the sampling distribution of $\hat{\beta}_0$ and $\hat{\beta}_1$ can be complicated when the sample size is small, it is possible to make certain statements about it that hold for all n. In particular, the mean of the sampling distributions of $\hat{\beta}_0$ and

$\hat{\beta}_1$ are β_0 and β_1. In other words, under the least squares assumptions in Box 5-3,

$$E(\hat{\beta}_0) = \beta_0 \text{ and } E(\hat{\beta}_1) = \beta_1, \qquad \textbf{(5.20)}$$

that is, $\hat{\beta}_0$ and $\hat{\beta}_1$ are unbiased estimators of β_0 and β_1.

If the sample is sufficiently large, by the central limit theorem the sampling distribution of $\hat{\beta}_0$ and $\hat{\beta}_1$ is well approximated by the bivariate normal distribution. This implies that the marginal distributions of $\hat{\beta}_0$ and $\hat{\beta}_1$ are normal in large samples.

This argument invokes the central limit theorem. Technically, the central limit theorem concerns the distribution of averages (like $\overline{Y}$). If you examine the numerator in Equation (5.7) for $\hat{\beta}_1$, you will see that it, too, is a type of average—not a simple average, like $\overline{Y}$, but an average of the product, $(Y_i - \overline{Y})(X_i - \overline{X})$. The central limit theorem applies to this average so that, like the simpler average $\overline{Y}$, it is normally distributed in large samples.

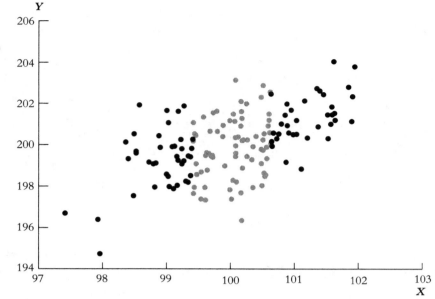

FIGURE 5-6 The variance of $\hat{\beta}_1$ and the variance of X.

The lighter dots represent a set of X_i's with a small variance. The black dots represent a set of X_i's with a large variance. The regression line can be estimated more accurately with the black dots than with the lighter dots.

The normal approximation to the distribution of the OLS estimators in large samples is summarized in Box 5-4. A relevant question in practice is how large n must be for these approximations to be reliable. We suggested that $n = 100$ is sufficiently large for the sampling distribution of $\overline{Y}$ to be well approximated by a normal distribution, and sometimes smaller n suffices. This criterion carries over to the more complicated averages appearing in regression analysis. In virtually all modern econometric applications $n > 100$, so we will treat the normal approximations to the distributions of the OLS estimators as reliable unless there are good reasons to think otherwise.

The results in Box 5-4 imply that the OLS estimators are consistent—that is, when the sample size is large, $\hat{\beta}_0$ and $\hat{\beta}_1$ will be close to the true population coefficients β_0 and β_1 with high probability. This is because the variances $\sigma^2_{\hat{\beta}_0}$ and $\sigma^2_{\hat{\beta}_1}$ of the estimators decrease to zero as n increases (n appears in the denominator of the formulas for the variances), so the distribution of the OLS estimators will be tightly concentrated around their means, β_0 and β_1, when n is large.

Another implication of the distributions in Box 5-4 is that, in general, the larger the variance of X_i, the smaller the variance $\sigma^2_{\hat{\beta}_1}$ of $\hat{\beta}_1$. Mathematically, this arises because the variance of $\hat{\beta}_1$ in Equation (5.21) is inversely proportional to the square of the variance of X_i: the larger is var(X_i), the larger is the denominator in Equation (5.21) so the smaller is $\sigma^2_{\hat{\beta}_1}$. To get a better sense of why this is so, look

---

BOX 5-4 Large-Sample Distributions of $\hat{\beta}_0$ and $\hat{\beta}_1$

If the least squares assumptions in Box 5-3 hold, then in large samples $\hat{\beta}_0$ and $\hat{\beta}_1$ have a jointly normal sampling distribution. The large-sample normal distribution of $\hat{\beta}_1$ is $N(\beta_1, \sigma^2_{\hat{\beta}_1})$, where the variance of this distribution, $\sigma^2_{\hat{\beta}_1}$, is

$$\sigma^2_{\hat{\beta}_1} = \frac{1}{n} \frac{\text{var}[(X_i - \mu_X)u_i]}{[\text{var}(X_i)]^2}. \qquad \textbf{(5.21)}$$

The large-sample normal distribution of $\hat{\beta}_0$ is $N(\beta_0, \sigma^2_{\hat{\beta}_0})$, where

$$\sigma^2_{\hat{\beta}_0} = \frac{1}{n} \frac{\text{var}(H_i u_i)}{[E(H_i^2)]^2}, \text{ where } H_i = 1 - \left(\frac{\mu_X}{E(X_i^2)}\right)X_i. \qquad \textbf{(5.22)}$$

---

at Figure 5-6, which presents a scatterplot of 150 artificial data points on X and Y. The data points indicated by the colored dots are the 75 observations closest to $\overline{X}$. Suppose you were asked to draw a line as accurately as possible through *either* the colored or the black dots—which would you choose? It would be easier to draw a precise line through the black dots, which have a larger variance than the colored dots. Similarly, the larger the variance of X, the more precise is $\hat{\beta}_1$.

The normal approximation to the sampling distribution of $\hat{\beta}_0$ and $\hat{\beta}_1$ is a powerful tool. With this approximation in hand, we are able to develop methods for making inferences about the true population values of the regression coefficients using only a sample of data.

CONCLUSION

This chapter has focused on the use of ordinary least squares to estimate the intercept and slope of a population regression line using a sample of n observations on a dependent variable, Y, and a single regressor, X. There are many ways to draw a straight line through a scatterplot, but doing so using OLS has several virtues. If the least squares assumptions hold, then the OLS estimators of the slope and intercept are unbiased, are consistent, and have a sampling distribution with a variance that is inversely proportional to the sample size n. Moreover, if n is large, then the sampling distribution of the OLS estimator is normal.

These important properties of the sampling distribution of the OLS estimator hold under the three least squares assumptions.

The first assumption is that the error term in the linear regression model has a conditional mean of zero, given the regressor X. This assumption implies that the OLS estimator is unbiased.

The second assumption is that (X_i, Y_i) are i.i.d., as is the case if the data are collected by simple random sampling. This assumption yields the formula, presented in Box 5-4, for the variance of the sampling distribution of the OLS estimator.

The third assumption is that large outliers are unlikely. Stated more formally, X and Y have finite fourth moments (finite kurtosis). The reason for this assumption is that OLS can be unreliable if there are large outliers.

The results in this chapter describe the sampling distribution of the OLS estimator. By themselves, however, these results are not sufficient to test a hypothesis about the value of β_1 or to construct a confidence interval for β_1. Doing so requires an estimator of the standard deviation of the sampling distribution—that is, the standard error of the OLS estimator. This step—moving from the sampling distribution of $\hat{\beta}_1$ to its standard error, hypothesis tests, and confidence intervals—is taken in the next chapter.

SUMMARY

1. The population regression line, $\beta_0 + \beta_1 X$, is the mean of Y as a function of the value of X. The slope, β_1, is the expected change in Y associated with a 1-unit change in X. The intercept, β_0, determines the level (or height) of the regression line. Box 5-1 summarizes the terminology of the population linear regression model.

2. The population regression line can be estimated using sample observations (Y_i, X_i), $i = 1, \ldots, n$ by ordinary least squares (OLS). The OLS estimators of the regression intercept and slope are denoted by $\hat{\beta}_0$ and $\hat{\beta}_1$.

3. The R^2 and standard error of the regression (SER) are measures of how close the values of Y_i are to the estimated regression line. The R^2 is between 0 and 1, with a larger value indicating that the Y_i's are closer to the line. The standard error of the regression is an estimator of the standard deviation of the regression error.

4. There are three key assumptions for the linear regression model: (1) The regression errors, u_i, have a mean of zero conditional on the regressors X_i; (2) the sample observations are i.i.d. random draws from the population; and (3) large outliers are unlikely. If these assumptions hold, the OLS estimators $\hat{\beta}_0$ and $\hat{\beta}_1$ are (1) unbiased; (2) consistent; and (3) normally distributed when the sample is large.

Key Terms

linear regression model with a single regressor (61)
dependent variable (61)
independent variable (61)
regressor (61)
population regression line (61)
population regression function (61)

APPENDIX A

The California Test Score Data Set

The California Standardized Testing and Reporting data set contains data on test performance, school characteristics, and student demographic backgrounds. The data used here are from all 420 K–6 and K–8 districts in California with data available for 1998 and 1999. Test scores are the average of the reading and math scores on the Stanford 9 Achievement Test, a standardized test administered to fifth-grade students. School characteristics (averaged across the district) include enrollment, number of teachers (measured as "full-time equivalents"), number of computers per classroom, and expenditures per student. The student–teacher ratio used here is the number of students in the district, divided by the number of full-time equivalent teachers. Demographic variables for the students also are averaged across the district. The demographic variables include the percentage of students who are in the public assistance program CalWorks (formerly AFDC), the percentage of students who qualify for a reduced price lunch, and the percentage of students who are English learners (that is, students for whom English is a second language). All of these data were obtained from the California Department of Education (www.cde.ca.gov).

APPENDIX B

Derivation of the OLS Estimators

This appendix uses calculus to derive the formulas for the OLS estimators given in Box 5-2. To minimize the sum of squared prediction mistakes $\sum_{i=1}^{n}(Y_i - b_0 - b_1 X_i)^2$ [Equation (5.6)], first take the partial derivatives with respect to b_0 and b_1:

$$\frac{\partial}{\partial b_0}\sum_{i=1}^{n}(Y_i - b_0 - b_1 X_i)^2 = -2\sum_{i=1}^{n}(Y_i - b_0 - b_1 X_i) \text{ and} \quad \textbf{(5.23)}$$

$$\frac{\partial}{\partial b_1}\sum_{i=1}^{n}(Y_i - b_0 - b_1 X_i)^2 = -2\sum_{i=1}^{n}(Y_i - b_0 - b_1 X_i)X_i. \quad \textbf{(5.24)}$$

The OLS estimators, $\hat{\beta}_0$ and $\hat{\beta}_1$, are the values of b_0 and b_1 that minimize $\sum_{i=1}^{n}(Y_i - b_0 - b_1 X_i)^2$ or, equivalently, the values of b_0 and b_1 for which the derivatives in Equations (5.23) and (5.24) equal zero. Accordingly, setting these derivatives equal to zero, collecting terms, and dividing by n shows that the OLS estimators, $\hat{\beta}_0$ and $\hat{\beta}_1$, must satisfy the two equations,

$$\bar{Y} - \hat{\beta}_0 - \hat{\beta}_1\bar{X} = 0 \text{ and} \quad \textbf{(5.25)}$$

$$\frac{1}{n}\sum_{i=1}^{n}X_i Y_i - \hat{\beta}_0\bar{X} - \hat{\beta}_1\frac{1}{n}\sum_{i=1}^{n}X_i^2 = 0 \quad \textbf{(5.26)}$$

Solving this pair of equations for $\hat{\beta}_0$ and $\hat{\beta}_1$ yields

$$\hat{\beta}_1 = \frac{\frac{1}{n}\sum_{i=1}^{n}X_i Y_i - \bar{X}\bar{Y}}{\frac{1}{n}\sum_{i=1}^{n}X_i^2 - (\bar{X})^2} = \frac{\sum_{i=1}^{n}(X_i - \bar{X})(Y_i - \bar{Y})}{\sum_{i=1}^{n}(X_i - \bar{X})^2} \quad \textbf{(5.27)}$$

$$\hat{\beta}_0 = \bar{Y} - \hat{\beta}_1\bar{X} \quad \textbf{(5.28)}$$

Equations (5.27) and (5.28) are the formulas for $\hat{\beta}_0$ and $\hat{\beta}_1$ given in Box 5-2; the formula $\hat{\beta}_1 = s_{XY}/s_X^2$ is obtained by dividing the numerator and denominator in Equation (5.27) by $n - 1$.

Regression with a Single Regressor
Hypothesis Tests and Confidence Intervals

6

■ Learning Objectives

Candidates, after completing this reading, should be able to:

- Define, calculate, and interpret confidence intervals for regression coefficients.
- Define and interpret the *p*-value.
- Define and interpret hypothesis tests about regression coefficients.
- Define and describe the implications of homoskedasticity and heteroskedasticity.

- Describe the conditions under which the OLS is the best linear conditionally unbiased estimator.
- Explain the Gauss-Markov Theorem and its limitations, and alternatives to the OLS.
- Define, describe, apply, and interpret the *t*-statistic when the sample size is small.

Excerpt is Chapter 5 of Introduction to Econometrics, *Brief Edition, by James H. Stock and Mark W. Watson.*

This chapter continues the treatment of linear regression with a single regressor. Chapter 5 explained how the OLS estimator $\hat{\beta}_1$ of the slope coefficient β_1 differs from one sample to the next—that is, how $\hat{\beta}_1$ has a sampling distribution. In this chapter, we show how knowledge of this sampling distribution can be used to make statements about β_1 that accurately summarize the sampling uncertainty. The starting point is the standard error of the OLS estimator, which measures the spread of the sampling distribution of $\hat{\beta}_1$. The first section provides an expression for this standard error (and for the standard error of the OLS estimator of the intercept), then shows how to use $\hat{\beta}_1$ and its standard error to test hypotheses. The next section explains how to construct confidence intervals for β_1. The third section takes up the special case of a binary regressor.

The first three sections assume that the three least squares assumptions of Chapter 5 hold. If, in addition, some stronger conditions hold, then some stronger results can be derived regarding the distribution of the OLS estimator. One of these stronger conditions is that the errors are homoskedastic, a concept introduced later. The Gauss-Markov theorem, which states that, under certain conditions, OLS is efficient (has the smallest variance) among a certain class of estimators is also discussed. The final section discusses the distribution of the OLS estimator when the population distribution of the regression errors is normal.

TESTING HYPOTHESES ABOUT ONE OF THE REGRESSION COEFFICIENTS

Your client, the superintendent, calls you with a problem. She has an angry taxpayer in her office who asserts that cutting class size will not help boost test scores, so that reducing them further is a waste of money. Class size, the taxpayer claims, has no effect on test scores.

The taxpayer's claim can be rephrased in the language of regression analysis. Because the effect on test scores of a unit change in class size is $\beta_{ClassSize}$, the taxpayer is asserting that the population regression line is flat—that is, the slope $\beta_{ClassSize}$ of the population regression line is zero. Is there, the superintendent asks, evidence in your sample of 420 observations on California school districts that this

slope is nonzero? Can you reject the taxpayer's hypothesis that $\beta_{ClassSize} = 0$, or should you accept it, at least tentatively pending further new evidence?

This section discusses tests of hypotheses about the slope β_1 or intercept β_0 of the population regression line. We start by discussing two-sided tests of the slope β_1 in detail, then turn to one-sided tests and to tests of hypotheses regarding the intercept β_0.

Two-Sided Hypotheses Concerning β_1

The general approach to testing hypotheses about these coefficients is the same as to testing hypotheses about the population mean, so we begin with a brief review.

Testing Hypotheses About the Population Mean

Recall that the null hypothesis that the mean of Y is a specific value $\mu_{Y,0}$ can be written as $H_0: E(Y) = \mu_{Y,0}$, and the two-sided alternative is $H_1: E(Y) \neq \mu_{Y,0}$.

The test of the null hypothesis H_0 against the two-sided alternative proceeds as in the three steps summarized. The first is to compute the standard error of $\overline{Y}$, $SE(\overline{Y})$, which is an estimator of the standard deviation of the sampling distribution of $\overline{Y}$. The second step is to compute the t-statistic, which has the general form given in Box 6-1; applied here, the t-statistic is $t = (\overline{Y} - \mu_{Y,0})/SE(\overline{Y})$.

The third step is to compute the p-value, which is the smallest significance level at which the null hypothesis could be rejected, based on the test statistic actually observed; equivalently, the p-value is the probability of obtaining a statistic, by random sampling variation, at least as different from the null hypothesis value as is the statistic actually observed, assuming that the null hypothesis is correct. Because the t-statistic has a standard normal distribution in large samples under the null hypothesis, the p-value for a two-sided hypothesis test is $2\Phi(-|t^{act}|)$, where t^{act} is the value of the t-statistic

---

BOX 6-1   General Form of the t-Statistic

In general, the t-statistic has the form

$$t = \frac{\text{estimator} - \text{hypothesized value}}{\text{standard error of the estimator}} \qquad (6.1)$$

actually computed and Φ is the cumulative standard normal distribution. Alternatively, the third step can be replaced by simply comparing the t-statistic to the critical value appropriate for the test with the desired significance level. For example, a two-sided test with a 5% significance level would reject the null hypothesis if $|t^{act}| > 1.96$. In this case, the population mean is said to be statistically significantly different than the hypothesized value at the 5% significance level.

Testing Hypotheses About the Slope β_1

At a theoretical level, the critical feature justifying the foregoing testing procedure for the population mean is that, in large samples, the sampling distribution of $\overline{Y}$ is approximately normal. Because $\hat{\beta}_1$ also has a normal sampling distribution in large samples, hypotheses about the true value of the slope β_1 can be tested using the same general approach.

The null and alternative hypotheses need to be stated precisely before they can be tested. The angry taxpayer's hypothesis is that $\beta_{ClassSize} = 0$. More generally, under the null hypothesis the true population slope β_1 takes on some specific value, $\beta_{1,0}$. Under the two-sided alternative, β_1 does not equal $\beta_{1,0}$. That is, the **null hypothesis** and the **two-sided alternative hypothesis** are

$$H_0: \beta_1 = \beta_{1,0} \text{ vs. } H_1: \beta_1 \neq \beta_{1,0} \qquad (6.2)$$
$$\text{(two-sided alternative)}$$

To test the null hypothesis H_0, we follow the same three steps as for the population mean.

The first step is to compute the **standard error of $\hat{\beta}_1$,** $SE(\hat{\beta}_1)$. The standard error of $\hat{\beta}_1$ is an estimator of $\sigma_{\hat{\beta}_1}$, the standard deviation of the sampling distribution of $\hat{\beta}_1$. Specifically,

$$SE(\hat{\beta}_1) = \sqrt{\hat{\sigma}_{\hat{\beta}_1}^2} \qquad (6.3)$$

where

$$\hat{\sigma}_{\hat{\beta}_1}^2 = \frac{1}{n} \times \frac{\frac{1}{n-2} \sum_{i=1}^{n} (X_i - \overline{X})^2 \hat{u}_i^2}{\left[\frac{1}{n} \sum_{i=1}^{n} (X_i - \overline{X})^2\right]^2} \qquad (6.4)$$

Although the formula for $\hat{\sigma}_{\hat{\beta}_1}^2$ is complicated, in applications the standard error is computed by regression software so that it is easy to use in practice.

The second step is to compute the **t-statistic,**

$$t = \frac{\hat{\beta}_1 - \beta_{1,0}}{SE(\hat{\beta}_1)} \qquad (6.5)$$

The third step is to compute the **p-value**, the probability of observing a value of $\hat{\beta}_1$ at least as different from $\beta_{1,0}$ as the estimate actually computed ($\hat{\beta}_1^{act}$), assuming that the null hypothesis is correct. Stated mathematically,

$$p\text{-value} = Pr_{H_0}[|\hat{\beta}_1 - \beta_{1,0}| > |\hat{\beta}_1^{act} - \beta_{1,0}|] \qquad (6.6)$$

$$= Pr_{H_0}\left[\left|\frac{\hat{\beta}_1 - \beta_{1,0}}{SE(\hat{\beta}_1)}\right| > \left|\frac{\hat{\beta}_1^{act} - \beta_{1,0}}{SE(\hat{\beta}_1)}\right|\right]$$

$$= Pr_{H_0}(|t| > |t^{act}|)$$

where Pr_{H_0} denotes the probability computed under the null hypothesis, the second equality follows by dividing by $SE(\hat{\beta}_1)$, and t^{act} is the value of the t-statistic actually computed. Because $\hat{\beta}_1$ is approximately normally distributed in large samples, under the null hypothesis the t-statistic is approximately distributed as a standard normal random variable, so in large samples,

$$p\text{-value} = Pr(|Z| > |t^{act}|) = 2\Phi(-|t^{act}|) \qquad (6.7)$$

A small value of the p-value, say less than 5%, provides evidence against the null hypothesis in the sense that the chance of obtaining a value of $\hat{\beta}_1$ by pure random variation from one sample to the next is less than 5% if, in fact, the null hypothesis is correct. If so, the null hypothesis is rejected at the 5% significance level.

Alternatively, the hypothesis can be tested at the 5% significance level simply by comparing the value of the t-statistic to ± 1.96, the critical value for a two-sided test, and rejecting the null hypothesis at the 5% level if $|t^{act}| > 1.96$.

These steps are summarized in Box 6-2.

Reporting Regression Equations and Application to Test Scores

The OLS regression of the test score against the student–teacher ratio, reported in Equation (5.11), yielded $\hat{\beta}_0 = 698.9$ and $\hat{\beta}_1 = -2.28$. The standard errors of these estimates are $SE(\hat{\beta}_0) = 10.4$ and $SE(\hat{\beta}_1) = 0.52$.

Because of the importance of the standard errors, by convention they are included when reporting the estimated OLS coefficients. One compact way to report the standard

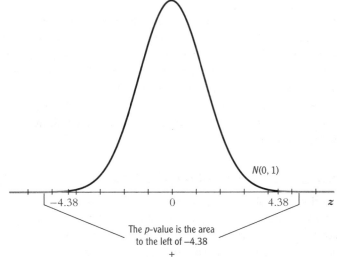

The p-value is the area
to the left of −4.38
+
the area to the right of +4.38.

FIGURE 6-1 Calculating the p-value of a two-sided test when $t^{act} = -4.38$.

The p-value of a two-sided test is the probability that $|Z| > |t^{act}|$, where Z is a standard normal random variable and t^{act} is the value of the t-statistic calculated from the sample. When $t^{act} = -4.38$, the p-value is only 0.00001.

errors is to place them in parentheses below the respective coefficients of the OLS regression line:

$$\widehat{TestScore} = 698.9 - 2.28 \times STR, \ R^2 = 0.051, \ SER = 18.6.$$
$$(10.4) \quad (0.52) \tag{6.8}$$

Equation (6.8) also reports the regression R^2 and the standard error of the regression (SER) following the estimated regression line. Thus Equation (6.8) provides the estimated regression line, estimates of the sampling uncertainty of the slope and the intercept (the standard errors), and two measures of the fit of this regression line (the R^2 and the SER). This is a common format for reporting a single regression equation, and it will be used throughout the rest of this book.

Suppose you wish to test the null hypothesis that the slope β_1 is zero in the population counterpart of Equation (6.8) at the 5% significance level. To do so, construct the t-statistic and compare it to 1.96, the 5% (two-sided) critical value taken from the standard normal distribution. The t-statistic is constructed by substituting the hypothesized value of β_1 under the null hypothesis (zero), the estimated slope, and its standard error from Equation (6.8) into the general formula in Equation (6.5); the result is $t^{act} = (-2.28 - 0)/0.52 = -4.38$. This t-statistic exceeds (in absolute value) the 5% two-sided critical value of 1.96, so the null hypothesis is rejected in favor of the two-sided alternative at the 5% significance level.

Alternatively, we can compute the p-value associated with $t^{act} = -4.38$. This probability is the area in the tails of standard normal distribution, as shown in Figure 6-1. This probability is extremely small, approximately 0.00001, or 0.001%. That is, if the null hypothesis $\beta_{ClassSize} = 0$ is true, the probability of obtaining a value of $\hat{\beta}_1$ as far from the

null as the value we actually obtained is extremely small, less than 0.001%. Because this event is so unlikely, it is reasonable to conclude that the null hypothesis is false.

One-Sided Hypotheses Concerning β_1

The discussion so far has focused on testing the hypothesis that $\beta_1 = \beta_{1,0}$ against the hypothesis that $\beta_1 \neq \beta_{1,0}$. This is a two-sided hypothesis test, because under the alternative β_1 could be either larger or smaller than $\beta_{1,0}$. Sometimes, however, it is appropriate to use a one-sided hypothesis test. For example, in the student–teacher ratio/test score problem, many people think that smaller classes provide a better learning environment. Under that hypothesis, β_1 is negative: Smaller classes lead to higher scores. It might make sense, therefore, to test the null hypothesis that $\beta_1 = 0$ (no effect) against the one-sided alternative that $\beta_1 < 0$.

For a one-sided test, the null hypothesis and the one-sided alternative hypothesis are

$$H_0: \beta_1 = \beta_{1,0} \ \text{vs.} \ H_1: \beta_1 < \beta_{1,0}, \quad \text{(one-sided alternative)} \tag{6.9}$$

where $\beta_{1,0}$ is the value of β_1 under the null (0 in the student–teacher ratio example) and the alternative is that

β_1 is less than $\beta_{1,0}$. If the alternative is that β_1 is greater than $\beta_{1,0}$, the inequality in Equation (6.9) is reversed.

Because the null hypothesis is the same for a one- and a two-sided hypothesis test, the construction of the t-statistic is the same. The only difference between a one- and two-sided hypothesis test is how you interpret the t-statistic. For the one-sided alternative in Equation (6.9), the null hypothesis is rejected against the one-sided alternative for large negative, but not large positive, values of the t-statistic: Instead of rejecting if $|t^{act}| > 1.96$, the hypothesis is rejected at the 5% significance level if $t^{act} < -1.645$.

The p-value for a one-sided test is obtained from the cumulative standard normal distribution as

$$p\text{-value} = Pr(Z < t^{act}) \qquad \textbf{(6.10)}$$
$$= \Phi(t^{act}) \ (p\text{-value, one-sided left-tail test})$$

If the alternative hypothesis is that β_1 is greater than $\beta_{1,0}$, the inequalities in Equations (6.9) and (6.10) are reversed, so the p-value is the right-tail probability, $Pr(Z > t^{act})$.

When Should a One-Sided Test Be Used?

In practice, one-sided alternative hypotheses should be used only when there is a clear reason for doing so. This reason could come from economic theory, prior empirical evidence, or both. However, even if it initially seems that the relevant alternative is one-sided, upon reflection this might not necessarily be so. A newly formulated drug undergoing clinical trials actually could prove harmful because of previously unrecognized side effects. In the class size example, we are reminded of the graduation joke that a university's secret of success is to admit talented students and then make sure that the faculty stays out of their way and does as little damage as possible. In practice, such ambiguity often leads econometricians to use two-sided tests.

Application to Test Scores

The t-statistic testing the hypothesis that there is no effect of class size on test scores [so $\beta_{1,0} = 0$ in Equation (6.9)] is $t^{act} = -4.38$. This is less than -2.33 (the critical value for a one-sided test with a 1% significance level), so the null hypothesis is rejected against the one-sided alternative at the 1% level. In fact, the p-value is less than 0.0006%. Based on these data, you can reject the angry taxpayer's assertion that the negative estimate of the

slope arose purely because of random sampling variation at the 1% significance level.

Testing Hypotheses about the Intercept β_0

This discussion has focused on testing hypotheses about the slope, β_1. Occasionally, however, the hypothesis concerns the intercept, β_0. The null hypothesis concerning the intercept and the two-sided alternative are

$$H_0: \beta_0 = \beta_{0,0} \text{ vs. } H_1: \beta_0 \neq \beta_{0,0} \qquad \textbf{(6.11)}$$
$$\text{(two-sided alternative)}$$

The general approach to testing this null hypothesis consists of the three steps in Box 6-2, applied to β_0. If the alternative is one-sided, this approach is modified as was discussed in the previous subsection for hypotheses about the slope.

Hypothesis tests are useful if you have a specific null hypothesis in mind (as did our angry taxpayer). Being able to accept or to reject this null hypothesis based on the statistical evidence provides a powerful tool for coping with the uncertainty inherent in using a sample to learn about the population. Yet, there are many times that no single hypothesis about a regression coefficient is dominant, and instead one would like to know a range of values of the coefficient that are consistent with the data. This calls for constructing a confidence interval.

CONFIDENCE INTERVALS FOR A REGRESSION COEFFICIENT

Because any statistical estimate of the slope β_1 necessarily has sampling uncertainty, we cannot determine the true value of β_1 exactly from a sample of data. It is, however, possible to use the OLS estimator and its standard error to construct a confidence interval for the slope β_1 or for the intercept β_0.

Confidence Interval for β_1

Recall that a 95% **confidence interval for β_1** has two equivalent definitions. First, it is the set of values that cannot be rejected using a two-sided hypothesis test with a 5% significance level. Second, it is an interval that has a

95% probability of containing the true value of β_1; that is, in 95% of possible samples that might be drawn, the confidence interval will contain the true value of β_1. Because this interval contains the true value in 95% of all samples, it is said to have a **confidence level** of 95%.

The reason these two definitions are equivalent is as follows. A hypothesis test with a 5% significance level will, by definition, reject the true value of β_1 in only 5% of all possible samples; that is, in 95% of all possible samples the true value of β_1 will *not* be rejected. Because the 95% confidence interval (as defined in the first definition) is the set of all values of β_1 that are *not* rejected at the 5% significance level, it follows that the true value of β_1 will be contained in the confidence interval in 95% of all possible samples.

As in the case of a confidence interval for the population mean, in principle a 95% confidence interval can be computed by testing all possible values of β_1 (that is, testing the null hypothesis $\beta_1 = \beta_{1,0}$ for all values of $\beta_{1,0}$) at the 5% significance level using the t-statistic. The 95% confidence interval is then the collection of all the values of β_1 that are not rejected. But constructing the t-statistic for all values of β_1 would take forever.

An easier way to construct the confidence interval is to note that the t-statistic will reject the hypothesized value $\beta_{1,0}$ whenever $\beta_{1,0}$ is outside the range $\hat{\beta}_1 \pm 1.96SE(\hat{\beta}_1)$. That is, the 95% confidence interval for β_1 is the interval $[\hat{\beta}_1 - 1.96SE(\hat{\beta}_1), \hat{\beta}_1 + 1.96SE(\hat{\beta}_1)]$. This argument parallels the argument used to develop a confidence interval for the population mean.

The construction of a confidence interval for β_1 is summarized in Box 6-3.

BOX 6-3 Confidence Interval for β_1

A 95% two-sided confidence interval for β_1 is an interval that contains the true value of β_1 with a 95% probability; that is, it contains the true value of β_1 in 95% of all possible randomly drawn samples. Equivalently, it is the set of values of β_1 that cannot be rejected by a 5% two-sided hypothesis test. When the sample size is large, it is constructed as

$$\text{95\% confidence interval for } \beta_1 = \quad \text{(6.12)}$$
$$[\hat{\beta}_1 - 1.96SE(\hat{\beta}_1), \hat{\beta}_1 + 1.96SE(\hat{\beta}_1)].$$

Confidence Interval for β_0

A 95% confidence interval for β_0 is constructed as in Box 6-3, with $\hat{\beta}_0$ and $SE(\hat{\beta}_0)$ replacing $\hat{\beta}_1$ and $SE(\hat{\beta}_1)$.

Application to Test Scores

The OLS regression of the test score against the student–teacher ratio, reported in Equation (6.8), yielded $\hat{\beta}_1 = -2.28$ and $SE(\hat{\beta}_1) = 0.52$. The 95% two-sided confidence interval for β_1 is $\{-2.28 \pm 1.96 \times 0.52\}$, or $-3.30 \le \beta_1 \le -1.26$. The value $\beta_1 = 0$ is not contained in this confidence interval, so (as we knew already) the hypothesis $\beta_1 = 0$ can be rejected at the 5% significance level.

Confidence Intervals for Predicted Effects of Changing X

The 95% confidence interval for β_1 can be used to construct a 95% confidence interval for the predicted effect of a general change in X.

Consider changing X by a given amount, Δx. The predicted change in Y associated with this change in X is $\beta_1 \Delta x$. The population slope β_1 is unknown, but because we can construct a confidence interval for β_1, we can construct a confidence interval for the predicted effect $\beta_1 \Delta x$. Because one end of a 95% confidence interval for β_1 is $\hat{\beta}_1 - 1.96SE(\hat{\beta}_1)$, the predicted effect of the change Δx using this estimate of β_1 is $[\hat{\beta}_1 - 1.96SE(\hat{\beta}_1)] \times \Delta x$. The other end of the confidence interval is $\hat{\beta}_1 + 1.96SE(\hat{\beta}_1)$, and the predicted effect of the change using that estimate is $[\hat{\beta}_1 + 1.96SE(\hat{\beta}_1)] \times \Delta x$. Thus a 95% confidence interval for the effect of changing x by the amount Δx can be expressed as

$$\text{95\% confidence interval for } \beta_1 \Delta x = \quad \text{(6.13)}$$
$$[\hat{\beta}_1 \Delta x - 1.96SE(\hat{\beta}_1) \times \Delta x, \ \hat{\beta}_1 \Delta x + 1.96SE(\hat{\beta}_1) \times \Delta x]$$

For example, our hypothetical superintendent is contemplating reducing the student–teacher ratio by 2. Because the 95% confidence interval for β_1 is $[-3.30, -1.26]$, the effect of reducing the student–teacher ratio by 2 could be as great as $-3.30 \times (-2) = 6.60$, or as little as $-1.26 \times (-2) = 2.52$. Thus decreasing the student–teacher ratio by 2 is predicted to increase test scores by between 2.52 and 6.60 points, with a 95% confidence level.

REGRESSION WHEN X IS A BINARY VARIABLE

The discussion so far has focused on the case that the regressor is a continuous variable. Regression analysis can also be used when the regressor is binary—that is, when it takes on only two values, 0 or 1. For example, X might be a worker's gender (= 1 if female, = 0 if male), whether a school district is urban or rural (= 1 if urban, = 0 if rural), or whether the district's class size is small or large (= 1 if small, = 0 if large). A binary variable is also called an **indicator variable** or sometimes a **dummy variable**.

Interpretation of the Regression Coefficients

The mechanics of regression with a binary regressor are the same as if it is continuous. The interpretation of β_1, however, is different, and it turns out that regression with a binary variable is equivalent to performing a difference of means analysis, as described previously.

To see this, suppose you have a variable D_i that equals either 0 or 1, depending on whether the student–teacher ratio is less than 20:

$$D_i = \begin{cases} 1 \text{ if the student–teacher ratio in } i^{\text{th}} \text{ district} < 20 \\ 0 \text{ if the student–teacher ratio in } i^{\text{th}} \text{ district} \geq 20 \end{cases}$$
(6.14)

The population regression model with D_i as the regressor is

$$Y_i = \beta_0 + \beta_1 D_i + u_i, \quad i = 1, \ldots, n \qquad \textbf{(6.15)}$$

This is the same as the regression model with the continuous regressor X_i, except that now the regressor is the binary variable D_i. Because D_i is not continuous, it is not useful to think of β_1 as a slope; indeed, because D_i can take on only two values, there is no "line" so it makes no sense to talk about a slope. Thus we will not refer to β_1 as the slope in Equation (6.15); instead we will simply refer to β_1 as the **coefficient multiplying D_i** in this regression or, more compactly, the **coefficient on D_i**.

If β_1 in Equation (6.15) is not a slope, then what is it? The best way to interpret β_0 and β_1 in a regression with a binary regressor is to consider, one at a time, the two possible cases, $D_i = 0$ and $D_i = 1$. If the student–teacher ratio is high, then $D_i = 0$ and Equation (6.15) becomes

$$Y_i = \beta_0 + u_i \quad (D_i = 0) \qquad \textbf{(6.16)}$$

Because $E(u_i | D_i) = 0$, the conditional expectation of Y_i when $D_i = 0$ is $E(Y_i | D_i = 0) = \beta_0$; that is, β_0 is the population mean value of test scores when the student–teacher ratio is high. Similarly, when $D_i = 1$,

$$Y_i = \beta_0 + \beta_1 + u_i \quad (D_i = 1) \qquad \textbf{(6.17)}$$

Thus, when $D_i = 1$, $E(Y_i | D_i = 1) = \beta_0 + \beta_1$; that is, $\beta_0 + \beta_1$ is the population mean value of test scores when the student–teacher ratio is low.

Because $\beta_0 + \beta_1$ is the population mean of Y_i when $D_i = 1$ and β_0 is the population mean of Y_i when $D_i = 0$, the difference $(\beta_0 + \beta_1) - \beta_0 = \beta_1$ is the difference between these two means. In other words, β_1 is the difference between the conditional expectation of Y_i when $D_i = 1$ and when $D_i = 0$, or $\beta_1 = E(Y_i | D_i = 1) - E(Y_i | D_i = 0)$. In the test score example, β_1 is the difference between mean test score in districts with low student–teacher ratios and the mean test score in districts with high student–teacher ratios.

Because β_1 is the difference in the population means, it makes sense that the OLS estimator β_1 is the difference between the sample averages of Y_i in the two groups, and in fact this is the case.

Hypothesis Tests and Confidence Intervals

If the two population means are the same, then β_1 in Equation (6.15) is zero. Thus, the null hypothesis that the two population means are the same can be tested against the alternative hypothesis that they differ by testing the null hypothesis $\beta_1 = 0$ against the alternative $\beta_1 \neq 0$. This hypothesis can be tested using the procedure outlined in the first section of this chapter. Specifically, the null hypothesis can be rejected at the 5% level against the two-sided alternative when the OLS t-statistic $t = \hat{\beta}_1 / SE(\hat{\beta}_1)$ exceeds 1.96 in absolute value. Similarly, a 95% confidence interval for β_1, constructed as $\hat{\beta}_1 \pm 1.96 SE(\hat{\beta}_1)$ as described earlier, provides a 95% confidence interval for the difference between the two population means.

Application to Test Scores

As an example, a regression of the test score against the student–teacher ratio binary variable D defined in Equation (6.14) estimated by OLS using the 420 observations in Figure 5-2, yields

$$\widehat{TestScore} = 650.0 + 7.4D, \ R^2 = 0.037, \ \textbf{(6.18)}$$
$$\ (1.3) \ \ (1.8)$$

$$SER = 18.7$$

where the standard errors of the OLS estimates of the coefficients β_0 and β_1 are given in parentheses below the OLS estimates. Thus the average test score for the subsample with student–teacher ratios greater than or equal to 20 (that is, for which $D = 0$) is 650.0, and the average test score for the subsample with student–teacher ratios less than 20 (so $D = 1$) is 650.0 + 7.4 = 657.4. The difference between the sample average test scores for the two groups is 7.4. This is the OLS estimate of β_1, the coefficient on the student–teacher ratio binary variable D.

Is the difference in the population mean test scores in the two groups statistically significantly different from zero at the 5% level? To find out, construct the t-statistic on β_1: $t = 7.4/1.8 = 4.04$. This exceeds 1.96 in absolute value, so the hypothesis that the population mean test scores in districts with high and low student–teacher ratios is the same can be rejected at the 5% significance level.

The OLS estimator and its standard error can be used to construct a 95% confidence interval for the true difference in means. This is $7.4 \pm 1.96 \times 1.8 = (3.9, 10.9)$. This confidence interval excludes $\beta_1 = 0$, so that (as we know from the previous paragraph) the hypothesis $\beta_1 = 0$ can be rejected at the 5% significance level.

HETEROSKEDASTICITY AND HOMOSKEDASTICITY

Our only assumption about the distribution of u_i conditional on X_i is that it has a mean of zero (the first least squares assumption). If, furthermore, the *variance* of this conditional distribution does not depend on X_i, then the errors are said to be homoskedastic. This section discusses homoskedasticity, its theoretical implications, the simplified formulas for the standard errors of the OLS estimators that arise if the errors are homoskedastic, and the risks you run if you use these simplified formulas in practice.

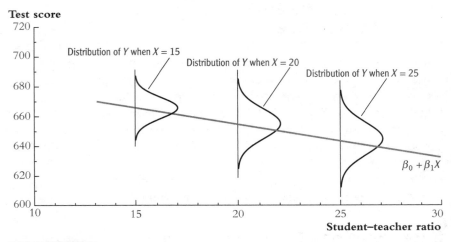

FIGURE 6-2 An example of heteroskedasticity.

Like Figure 5-4, this shows the conditional distribution of test scores for three different class sizes. Unlike Figure 5-4, these distributions become more spread out (have a larger variance) for larger class sizes. Because the variance of the distribution of u given X, var($u|X$), depends on X, u is heteroskedastic.

What Are Heteroskedasticity and Homoskedasticity?

Definitions of Heteroskedasticity and Homoskedasticity

The error term u_i is **homoskedastic** if the variance of the conditional distribution of u_i given X_i is constant for $i = 1, \ldots, n$ and in particular does not depend on X_i. Otherwise, the error term is **heteroskedastic**.

As an illustration, return to Figure 5-4. The distribution of the errors u_i is shown for various values of x. Because this distribution applies specifically for the indicated value of x, this is the conditional distribution of u_i given $X_i = x$. As drawn in that figure, all these conditional distributions have the same spread; more precisely, the variance of these distributions is the same for the various values of x. That is, in Figure 5-4, the conditional variance of u_i given $X_i = x$ does not depend on x, so the errors illustrated in Figure 5-4 are homoskedastic.

In contrast, Figure 6-2 illustrates a case in which the conditional distribution of u_i spreads out as x increases. For small values of x, this distribution is tight, but for larger values of x, it has a greater spread. Thus, in Figure 6-2 the variance of u_i given $X_i = x$ increases with x, so that the errors in Figure 6-2 are heteroskedastic.

Heteroskedasticity and Homoskedasticity

The error term u_i is homoskedastic if the variance of the conditional distribution of u_i given X_i, $\text{var}(u_i|X_i = x)$, is constant for $i = 1, \ldots, n$, and in particular does not depend on x. Otherwise, the error term is heteroskedastic.

The definitions of heteroskedasticity and homoskedasticity are summarized in Box 6-4.

Example

These terms are a mouthful and the definitions might seem abstract. To help clarify them with an example, we digress from the student–teacher ratio/test score problem and instead return to the example of earnings of male versus female college graduates. Let $MALE_i$ be a binary variable that equals 1 for male college graduates and equals 0 for female graduates. The binary variable regression model relating someone's earnings to his or her gender is

$$Earnings_i = \beta_0 + \beta_1 MALE_i + u_i \qquad \textbf{(6.19)}$$

for $i = 1, \ldots, n$. Because the regressor is binary, β_1 is the difference in the population means of the two groups—in this case, the difference in mean earnings between men and women who graduated from college.

The definition of homoskedasticity states that the variance of u_i does not depend on the regressor. Here the regressor is $MALE_i$, so at issue is whether the variance of the error term depends on $MALE_i$. In other words, is the variance of the error term the same for men and for women? If so, the error is homoskedastic; if not, it is heteroskedastic.

Deciding whether the variance of u_i depends on $MALE_i$ requires thinking hard about what the error term actually is. In this regard, it is useful to write Equation (6.19) as two separate equations, one for men and one for women:

$$Earnings_i = \beta_0 + u_i \quad \text{(women) and} \qquad \textbf{(6.20)}$$

$$Earnings_i = \beta_0 + \beta_1 + u_i \quad \text{(men)} \qquad \textbf{(6.21)}$$

Thus, for women, u_i is the deviation of the ith woman's earnings from the population mean earnings for women (β_0), and for men, u_i is the deviation of the ith man's earnings from the population mean earnings for men $(\beta_0 + \beta_1)$. It follows that the statement, "the variance of u_i does not depend on $MALE$," is equivalent to the statement, "the variance of earnings is the same for men as it is for women." In other words, in this example, the error term is homoskedastic if the variance of the population distribution of earnings is the same for men and women; if these variances differ, the error term is heteroskedastic.

Mathematical Implications of Homoskedasticity

The OLS Estimators Remain Unbiased and Asymptotically Normal

Because the least squares assumptions in Box 5-3 place no restrictions on the conditional variance, they apply to both the general case of heteroskedasticity and the special case of homoskedasticity. Therefore, the OLS estimators remain unbiased and consistent even if the errors are homoskedastic. In addition, the OLS estimators have sampling distributions that are normal in large samples even if the errors are homoskedastic. Whether the errors are homoskedastic or heteroskedastic, the OLS estimator is unbiased, consistent, and asymptotically normal.

Efficiency of the OLS Estimator When the Errors Are Homoskedastic

If the least squares assumptions in Box 5-3 hold and the errors are homoskedastic, then the OLS estimators $\hat{\beta}_0$ and $\hat{\beta}_1$ are efficient among all estimators that are linear in $Y_1, \ldots, Y_n$ and are unbiased, conditional on $X_1, \ldots, X_n$. This result, which is called the Gauss-Markov theorem, is discussed in the next section.

Homoskedasticity-Only Variance Formula

If the error term is homoskedastic, then the formulas for the variances of $\hat{\beta}_0$ and $\hat{\beta}_1$ in Box 5-4 simplify. Consequently, if the errors are homoskedastic, then there is a specialized formula that can be used for the standard errors of $\hat{\beta}_0$ and $\hat{\beta}_1$. The **homoskedasticity-only standard error** of $\hat{\beta}_1$ is $SE(\hat{\beta}_1) = \sqrt{\tilde{\sigma}^2_{\hat{\beta}_1}}$, where $\tilde{\sigma}^2_{\hat{\beta}_1}$ is the homoskedasticity-only estimator of the variance of $\hat{\beta}_1$:

$$\tilde{\sigma}^2_{\hat{\beta}_1} = \frac{s^2_{\hat{u}}}{\sum_{i=1}^{n}(X_i - \bar{X})^2} \qquad \text{(homoskedasticity-only)} \qquad \textbf{(6.22)}$$

where $s_{\hat{u}}^2$ is given in Equation (5.19). In the special case that X is a binary variable, the estimator of the variance of $\hat{\beta}_1$ under homoskedasticity (that is, the square of the standard error of $\hat{\beta}_1$ under homoskedasticity) is the so-called pooled variance formula for the difference in means.

Because these alternative formulas are derived for the special case that the errors are homoskedastic and do not apply if the errors are heteroskedastic, they will be referred to as the "homoskedasticity-only" formulas for the variance and standard error of the OLS estimators. As the name suggests, if the errors are heteroskedastic, then the homoskedasticity-only standard errors are inappropriate. Specifically, if the errors are heteroskedastic, then the t-statistic computed using the homoskedasticity-only standard error does not have a standard normal distribution, even in large samples. In fact, the correct critical values to use for this homoskedasticity-only t-statistic depend on the precise nature of the heteroskedasticity, so those critical values cannot be tabulated. Similarly, if the errors are heteroskedastic but a confidence interval is constructed as ±1.96 homoskedasticity-only standard errors, in general the probability that this interval contains the true value of the coefficient is not 95%, even in large samples.

In contrast, because homoskedasticity is a special case of heteroskedasticity, the estimators $\hat{\sigma}_{\hat{\beta}_1}^2$ and $\hat{\sigma}_{\hat{\beta}_0}^2$ of the variances of $\hat{\beta}_1$ and $\hat{\beta}_0$ given in Equations (6.4) and (6.26) produce valid statistical inferences whether the errors are heteroskedastic or homoskedastic. Thus hypothesis tests and confidence intervals based on those standard errors are valid whether or not the errors are heteroskedastic. Because the standard errors we have used so far [i.e., those based on Equations (6.4) and (6.26)] lead to statistical inferences that are valid whether or not the errors are heteroskedastic, they are called **heteroskedasticity-robust standard errors**. Because such formulas were proposed by Eicker (1967), Huber (1967), and White (1980), they are also referred to as Eicker-Huber-White standard errors.

What Does This Mean in Practice?

Which Is More Realistic, Heteroskedasticity or Homoskedasticity?

The answer to this question depends on the application. However, the issues can be clarified by returning to the example of the gender gap in earnings among college graduates. Familiarity with how people are paid in the world around us gives some clues as to which assumption is more sensible. For many years—and, to a lesser extent, today—women were not found in the top-paying jobs: There have always been poorly paid men, but there have rarely been highly paid women. This suggests that the distribution of earnings among women is tighter than among men. In other words, the variance of the error term in Equation (6.20) for women is plausibly less than the variance of the error term in Equation (6.21) for men. Thus, the presence of a "glass ceiling" for women's jobs and pay suggests that the error term in the binary variable regression model in Equation (6.19) is heteroskedastic. Unless there are compelling reasons to the contrary—and we can think of none—it makes sense to treat the error term in this example as heteroskedastic.

As this example of modeling earnings illustrates, heteroskedasticity arises in many econometric applications. At a general level, economic theory rarely gives any reason to believe that the errors are homoskedastic. It therefore is prudent to assume that the errors might be heteroskedastic unless you have compelling reasons to believe otherwise.

Practical Implications

The main issue of practical relevance in this discussion is whether one should use heteroskedasticity-robust or homoskedasticity-only standard errors. In this regard, it is useful to imagine computing both, then choosing between them. If the homoskedasticity-only and heteroskedasticity-robust standard errors are the same, nothing is lost by using the heteroskedasticity-robust standard errors; if they differ, however, then you should use the more reliable ones that allow for heteroskedasticity. The simplest thing, then, is always to use the heteroskedasticity-robust standard errors.

For historical reasons, many software programs use the homoskedasticity-only standard errors as their default setting, so it is up to the user to specify the option of heteroskedasticity-robust standard errors. The details of how to implement heteroskedasticity-robust standard errors depend on the software package you use.

The Economic Value of a Year of Education: Homoskedasticity or Heteroskedasticity?

On average, workers with more education have higher earnings than workers with less education. But if the best-paying jobs mainly go to the college educated, it might also be that the *spread* of the distribution of earnings is greater for workers with more education. Does the distribution of earnings spread out as education increases?

This is an empirical question, so answering it requires analyzing data. Figure 6-3 is a scatterplot of the hourly earnings and the number of years of education for a sample of 2950 full-time workers in the United States in 2004, ages 29 and 30, with between 6 and 18 years of education. The data come from the March 2005 Current Population Survey.

Figure 6-3 has two striking features. The first is that the mean of the distribution of earnings increases with the number of years of education. This increase is summarized by the OLS regression line,

$$\widehat{Earnings} = -3.13 + 1.47 \; Years \; Education, \quad \textbf{(6.23)}$$
$$(0.93) \; (0.07)$$

$$R^2 = 0.130, \; SER = 8.77.$$

This line is plotted in Figure 6-3. The coefficient of 1.47 in the OLS regression line means that, on average, hourly earnings increase by $1.47 for each additional year of education. The 95% confidence interval for this coefficient is $1.47 \pm 1.96 \times 0.07$, or 1.33 to 1.61.

The second striking feature of Figure 6-3 is that the spread of the distribution of earnings increases with the years of education. While some workers with many years of education have low-paying jobs, very few workers with low levels of education have high-paying jobs. This can be stated more precisely by looking at the spread of the residuals around the OLS regression line. For workers with ten years of education, the standard deviation of the residuals is $5.46; for workers with a high school diploma, this standard deviation is $7.43; and for workers with a college degree, this standard deviation increases to $10.78. Because these standard deviations differ for different levels of education, the variance of the residuals in the regression of Equation (6.23) depends on the value of the regressor (the years of education); in other words, the regression errors are heteroskedastic. In real-world terms, not all college graduates will be earning $50/hour by the time they are 29, but some will, and workers with only ten years of education have no shot at those jobs.

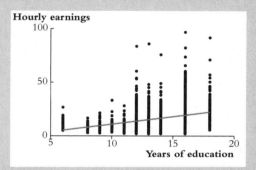

FIGURE 6-3 Scatterplot of hourly earnings and years of education for 29- to 30-year-olds in the United States in 2004.

Hourly earnings are plotted against years of education for 2950 full-time, 29- to 30-year-old workers. The spread around the regression line increases with the years of education, indicating that the regression errors are heteroskedastic.

All of the empirical examples in this book employ heteroskedasticity-robust standard errors unless explicitly stated otherwise.[1]

---

[1] In case this book is used in conjunction with other texts, it might be helpful to note that some textbooks add homoskedasticity to the list of least squares assumptions. As just discussed, however, this additional assumption is not needed for the validity of OLS regression analysis as long as heteroskedasticity-robust standard errors are used.

THE THEORETICAL FOUNDATIONS OF ORDINARY LEAST SQUARES*

As discussed in Chapter 5, the OLS estimator is unbiased, is consistent, has a variance that is inversely proportional to *n*, and has a normal sampling distribution when the sample size is large. In addition, under certain conditions the OLS estimator is more efficient than

---

* This section is optional and is not used in later chapters.

some other candidate estimators. Specifically, if the least squares assumptions hold and if the errors are homoskedastic, then the OLS estimator has the smallest variance of all conditionally unbiased estimators that are linear functions of $Y_1, \ldots, Y_n$. This section explains and discusses this result, which is a consequence of the Gauss-Markov theorem. The section concludes with a discussion of alternative estimators that are more efficient than OLS when the conditions of the Gauss-Markov theorem do not hold.

Linear Conditionally Unbiased Estimators and the Gauss-Markov Theorem

If the three least squares assumptions (Box 5-3) hold and if the error is homoskedastic, then the OLS estimator has the smallest variance, conditional on $X_1, \ldots, X_n$, among all estimators in the class of linear conditionally unbiased estimators. In other words, the OLS estimator is the **B**est **L**inear conditionally **U**nbiased **E**stimator—that is, it is BLUE. This result extends to regression the result that the sample average $\overline{Y}$ is the most efficient estimator of the population mean among the class of all estimators that are unbiased and are linear functions (weighted averages) of $Y_1, \ldots, Y_n$.

Linear Conditionally Unbiased Estimators

The class of linear conditionally unbiased estimators consists of all estimators of β_1 that are linear functions of $Y_1, \ldots, Y_n$ and that are unbiased, conditional on $X_1, \ldots, X_n$. That is, if $\tilde{\beta}_1$ is a linear estimator, then it can be written as

$$\tilde{\beta}_1 = \sum_{i=1}^{n} a_i Y_i \quad (\tilde{\beta}_1 \text{ is linear}) \qquad \textbf{(6.24)}$$

where the weights $a_1, \ldots, a_n$ can depend on $X_1, \ldots, X_n$ but *not* on $Y_1, \ldots, Y_n$. The estimator $\tilde{\beta}_1$ is conditionally unbiased if the mean of its conditional sampling distribution, given $X_1, \ldots, X_n$, is β_1. That is, the estimator $\tilde{\beta}_1$ is conditionally unbiased if

$$E(\tilde{\beta}_1 | X_1, \ldots, X_n) = \beta_1 \quad (\tilde{\beta}_1 \text{ is conditionally unbiased}) \textbf{ (6.25)}$$

The estimator $\tilde{\beta}_1$ is a linear conditionally unbiased estimator if it can be written in the form of Equation (6.24) (it is linear) and if Equation (6.25) holds (it is conditionally unbiased). It can be shown that the OLS estimator is linear and conditionally unbiased.

The Gauss-Markov Theorem

The **Gauss-Markov** theorem states that, under a set of conditions known as the Gauss-Markov conditions, the OLS estimator $\hat{\beta}_1$ has the smallest conditional variance, given $X_1, \ldots, X_n$, of all linear conditionally unbiased estimators of β_1; that is, the OLS estimator is BLUE. The Gauss-Markov conditions, which are stated in the chapter Appendix, are implied by the three least squares assumptions plus the assumption that the errors are homoskedastic. Consequently, if the three least squares assumptions hold and the errors are homoskedastic, then OLS is BLUE.

Limitations of the Gauss-Markov Theorem

The Gauss-Markov theorem provides a theoretical justification for using OLS. However, the theorem has two important limitations. First, its conditions might not hold in practice. In particular, if the error term is heteroskedastic—as it often is in economic applications—then the OLS estimator is no longer BLUE. As discussed previously, the presence of heteroskedasticity does not pose a threat to inference based on heteroskedasticity-robust standard errors, but it does mean that OLS is no longer the efficient linear conditionally unbiased estimator. An alternative to OLS when there is heteroskedasticity of a known form, called the weighted least squares estimator, is discussed below.

The second limitation of the Gauss-Markov theorem is that even if the conditions of the theorem hold, there are other candidate estimators that are not linear and conditionally unbiased; under some conditions, these other estimators are more efficient than OLS.

Regression Estimators Other than OLS

Under certain conditions, some regression estimators are more efficient than OLS.

The Weighted Least Squares Estimator

If the errors are heteroskedastic, then OLS is no longer BLUE. If the nature of the heteroskedastic is known—specifically, if the conditional variance of u_i given X_i is known up to a constant factor of proportionality—then it is possible to construct an estimator that has a smaller variance than the OLS estimator. This method, called **weighted least squares** (WLS), weights the ith observation by the inverse of the square root of the conditional variance of u_i given X_i. Because of this weighting, the errors in this weighted regression are homoskedastic, so OLS, when applied to the weighted data, is BLUE. Although theoretically elegant, the practical problem with weighted least squares is that you must know how the conditional variance of u_i depends on X_i—something that is rarely known in applications.

The Least Absolute Deviations Estimator

As discussed earlier, the OLS estimator can be sensitive to outliers. If extreme outliers are not rare, then other estimators can be more efficient than OLS and can produce inferences that are more reliable. One such estimator is the least absolute deviations (LAD) estimator, in which the regression coefficients β_0 and β_1 are obtained by solving a minimization like that in Equation (5.6), except that the absolute value of the prediction "mistake" is used instead of its square. That is, the least absolute deviations estimators of β_0 and β_1 are the values of b_0 and b_1 that minimize $\sum_{i=1}^{n} |Y_i - b_0 - b_1 X_i|$. In practice, this estimator is less sensitive to large outliers in u than is OLS.

In many economic data sets, severe outliers in u are rare, so use of the LAD estimator, or other estimators with reduced sensitivity to outliers, is uncommon in applications. Thus the treatment of linear regression throughout the remainder of this text focuses exclusively on least squares methods.

USING THE *t*-STATISTIC IN REGRESSION WHEN THE SAMPLE SIZE IS SMALL*

When the sample size is small, the exact distribution of the *t*-statistic is complicated and depends on the

_____
* This section is optional and is not used in later chapters.

unknown population distribution of the data. If, however, the three least squares assumptions hold, the regression errors are homoskedastic, *and* the regression errors are normally distributed, then the OLS estimator is normally distributed and the homoskedasticity-only *t*-statistic has a Student *t* distribution. These five assumptions—the three least squares assumptions, that the errors are homoskedastic, and that the errors are normally distributed—are collectively called the **homoskedastic normal regression assumptions**.

The *t*-Statistic and the Student *t* Distribution

The Student *t* distribution with m degrees of freedom is defined to be the distribution of $Z/\sqrt{W/m}$, where Z is a random variable with a standard normal distribution, W is a random variable with a chi-squared distribution with m degrees of freedom, and Z and W are independent. Under the null hypothesis, the *t*-statistic computed using the homoskedasticity-only standard error can be written in this form.

The homoskedasticity-only *t*-statistic testing $\beta_1 = \beta_{1,0}$ is $\tilde{t} = (\hat{\beta}_1 - \beta_{1,0})/\tilde{\sigma}_{\hat{\beta}_1}$, where $\tilde{\sigma}^2_{\hat{\beta}_1}$ is defined in Equation (6.22). Under the homoskedastic normal regression assumptions, Y has a normal distribution, conditional on $X_1, \ldots, X_n$. As discussed previously, the OLS estimator is a weighted average of $Y_1, \ldots, Y_n$, where the weights depend on $X_1, \ldots, X_n$. Because a weighted average of independent normal random variables is normally distributed, $\hat{\beta}_1$ has a normal distribution, conditional on $X_1, \ldots, X_n$. Thus $(\hat{\beta}_1 - \beta_{1,0})$ has a normal distribution under the null hypothesis, conditional on $X_1, \ldots, X_n$. In addition, the (normalized) homoskedasticity-only variance estimator has a chi-squared distribution with $n - 2$ degrees of freedom, divided by $n - 2$, and $\tilde{\sigma}^2_{\hat{\beta}_1}$ and $\hat{\beta}_1$ are independently distributed. Consequently, the homoskedasticity-only *t*-statistic has a Student *t* distribution with $n - 2$ degrees of freedom.

This result is closely related to a result discussed in the context of testing for the equality of the means in two samples. In that problem, if the two population distributions are normal with the same variance and if the *t*-statistic is constructed using the pooled standard error formula, then the (pooled) *t*-statistic has a Student *t* distribution. When X is binary, the homoskedasticity-only standard error for $\hat{\beta}_1$ simplifies to the pooled standard error formula for the difference of means. It follows that the result is a special case of the result that, if the homoskedastic normal regression assumptions hold, then the homoskedasticity-only regression t-statistic has a Student t distribution (see Exercise 10).

Use of the Student t Distribution in Practice

If the regression errors are homoskedastic and normally distributed and if the homoskedasticity-only t-statistic is used, then critical values should be taken from the Student t distribution instead of the standard normal distribution. Because the difference between the Student t distribution and the normal distribution is negligible if n is moderate or large, this distinction is relevant only if the sample size is small.

In econometric applications, there is rarely a reason to believe that the errors are homoskedastic and normally distributed. Because sample sizes typically are large, however, inference can proceed as described earlier—that is, by first computing heteroskedasticity-robust standard errors, and then using the standard normal distribution to compute p-values, hypothesis tests, and confidence intervals.

CONCLUSION

Return for a moment to the problem that started Chapter 5: the superintendent who is considering hiring additional teachers to cut the student–teacher ratio. What have we learned that she might find useful?

Our regression analysis, based on the 420 observations for 1998 in the California test score data set, showed that there was a negative relationship between the student–teacher ratio and test scores: Districts with smaller classes have higher test scores. The coefficient is moderately large, in a practical sense: Districts with 2 fewer students per teacher have, on average, test scores that are 4.6 points higher. This corresponds to moving a district at the 50th percentile of the distribution of test scores to approximately the 60th percentile.

The coefficient on the student–teacher ratio is statistically significantly different from 0 at the 5% significance level. The population coefficient might be 0, and we might simply have estimated our negative coefficient by random sampling variation. However, the probability of doing so (and of obtaining a t-statistic on β_1 as large as we did) purely by random variation over potential samples is exceedingly small, approximately 0.001%. A 95% confidence interval for β_1 is $-3.30 \le \beta_1 \le -1.26$.

This represents considerable progress toward answering the superintendent's question. Yet, a nagging concern remains. There is a negative relationship between the student–teacher ratio and test scores, but is this relationship necessarily the *causal* one that the superintendent needs to make her decision? Districts with lower student–teacher ratios have, on average, higher test scores. But does this mean that reducing the student–teacher ratio will, in fact, increase scores?

There is, in fact, reason to worry that it might not. Hiring more teachers, after all, costs money, so wealthier school districts can better afford smaller classes. But students at wealthier schools also have other advantages over their poorer neighbors, including better facilities, newer books, and better-paid teachers. Moreover, students at wealthier schools tend themselves to come from more affluent families, and thus have other advantages not directly associated with their school. For example, California has a large immigrant community; these immigrants tend to be poorer than the overall population and, in many cases, their children are not native English speakers. It thus might be that our negative estimated relationship between test scores and the student–teacher ratio is a consequence of large classes being found in conjunction with many other factors that are, in fact, the real cause of the lower test scores.

These other factors, or "omitted variables," could mean that the OLS analysis done so far has little value to the superintendent. Indeed, it could be misleading: Changing the student–teacher ratio alone would not change these other factors that determine a child's performance at school. To address this problem, we need a method that will allow us to isolate the effect on test scores of changing the student–teacher ratio, *holding these other factors constant*. That method is multiple regression analysis, the topic of Chapter 7 and 8.

SUMMARY

1. Hypothesis testing for regression coefficients is analogous to hypothesis testing for the population mean: Use the t-statistic to calculate the p-values and either accept or reject the null hypothesis. Like a confidence interval for the population mean, a 95% confidence interval for a regression coefficient is computed as the estimator ± 1.96 standard errors.

2. When X is binary, the regression model can be used to estimate and test hypotheses about the difference between the population means of the "$X = 0$" group and the "$X = 1$" group.

3. In general the error u_i is heteroskedastic—that is, the variance of u_i at a given value of X_i, $\text{var}(u_i | X_i = x)$ depends on x. A special case is when the error is homoskedastic, that is, $\text{var}(u_i | X_i = x)$ is constant. Homoskedasticity-only standard errors do not produce valid statistical inferences when the errors are heteroskedastic, but heteroskedasticity-robust standard errors do.

4. If the three least squares assumption hold *and* if the regression errors are homoskedastic, then, as a result of the Gauss-Markov theorem, the OLS estimator is BLUE.

5. If the three least squares assumptions hold, if the regression errors are homoskedastic, *and* if the regression errors are normally distributed, then the OLS t-statistic computed using homoskedasticity-only standard errors has a Student t distribution when the null hypothesis is true. The difference between the Student t distribution and the normal distribution is negligible if the sample size is moderate or large.

Key Terms

APPENDIX

The Gauss-Markov Conditions and a Proof of the Gauss-Markov Theorem

As discussed earlier, the Gauss-Markov theorem states that if the Gauss-Markov conditions hold, then the OLS estimator is the best (most efficient) conditionally linear unbiased estimator (is BLUE). This appendix begins by stating the Gauss-Markov conditions and showing that they are implied by the three least squares condition plus homoskedasticity.

The Gauss-Markov Conditions

The three **Gauss-Markov conditions** are

   (i) $E(u_i | X_1, \ldots, X_n) = 0$ **(6.26)**

   (ii) $\text{var}(u_i | X_1, \ldots, X_n) = \sigma_u^2, \; 0 < \sigma_u^2 < \infty$

   (iii) $E(u_i u_j | X_1, \ldots, X_n) = 0, i \neq j$

where the conditions hold for $i, j = 1, \ldots, n$. The three conditions, respectively, state that u_i has mean zero, that u_i has a constant variance, and that the errors are uncorrelated for different observations, where all these statements hold conditionally on all observed X's ($X_1, \ldots, X_n$).

The Gauss-Markov conditions are implied by the three least squares assumptions (Box 5-3), plus the additional assumptions that the errors are homoskedastic. Because the observations are i.i.d. (Assumption 2), $E(u_i | X_1, \ldots, X_n) = E(u_i | X_i)$, and by Assumption 1, $E(u_i | X_i) = 0$; thus condition (i) holds. Similarly, by Assumption 2, $\text{var}(u_i | X_1, \ldots, X_n) = \text{var}(u_i | X_i)$, and because the errors are assumed to be homoskedastic, $\text{var}(u_i | X_i) = \sigma_u^2$, which is constant. Assumption 3 (nonzero finite fourth moments) ensures that $0 < \sigma_u^2 < \infty$, so condition (ii) holds. To show that condition (iii) is implied by the least squares assumptions, note that $E(u_i u_j | X_1, \ldots, X_n) = E(u_i u_j | X_i, X_j)$ because (X_i, Y_i) are i.i.d. by Assumption 2. Assumption 2 also implies that $E(u_i u_j | X_i, X_j) = E(u_i | X_i) E(u_j | X_j)$ for $i \neq j$; because $E(u_i | X_i) = 0$ for all i, it follows that $E(u_i u_j | X_1, \ldots, X_n) = 0$ for all $i \neq j$, so condition (iii) holds. Thus, the least squares assumptions in Box 5-3, plus homoskedasticity of the errors, imply the Gauss-Markov conditions in Equation (6.26).

The Sample Average Is the Efficient Linear Estimator of $E(Y)$

An implication of the Gauss-Markov theorem is that the sample average, $\overline{Y}$, is the most efficient linear estimator of $E(Y_i)$ when $Y_i, \ldots, Y_n$ are i.i.d. To see this, consider the case of regression without an "X," so that the only regressor is the constant regressor $X_{0i} = 1$. Then the OLS estimator $\hat{\beta}_0 = \overline{Y}$. It follows that, under the Gauss-Markov assumptions, $\overline{Y}$ is BLUE. Note that the Gauss-Markov requirement that the error be homoskedastic is irrelevant in this case because there is no regressor, so it follows that $\overline{Y}$ is BLUE if $Y_1, \ldots, Y_n$ are i.i.d.

Linear Regression with Multiple Regressors

7

■ Learning Objectives

Candidates, after completing this reading, should be able to:

- Define and interpret omitted variable bias, and describe the methods for addressing this bias.
- Distinguish between single and multiple regression.
- Define and interpret the slope coefficient in a multiple regression.
- Describe homoskedasticity and heteroskedasticity in a multiple regression.

- Describe the OLS estimator in a multiple regression.
- Define, calculate, and interpret measures of fit in multiple regression.
- Explain the assumptions of the multiple linear regression model.
- Explain the concepts of imperfect and perfect multicollinearity and their implications.

Excerpt is Chapter 6 of Introduction to Econometrics, *Brief Edition, by James H. Stock and Mark W. Watson.*

Chapter 6 ended on a worried note. Although school districts with lower student–teacher ratios tend to have higher test scores in the California data set, perhaps students from districts with small classes have other advantages that help them perform well on standardized tests. Could this have produced misleading results and, if so, what can be done?

Omitted factors, such as student characteristics, can in fact make the ordinary least squares (OLS) estimator of the effect of class size on test scores misleading or, more precisely, biased. This chapter explains this "omitted variable bias" and introduces multiple regression, a method that can eliminate omitted variable bias. The key idea of multiple regression is that, if we have data on these omitted variables, then we can include them as additional regressors and thereby estimate the effect of one regressor (the student–teacher ratio) while holding constant the other variables (such as student characteristics).

This chapter explains how to estimate the coefficients of the multiple linear regression model. Many aspects of multiple regression parallel those of regression with a single regressor, studied in Chapters 5 and 6. The coefficients of the multiple regression model can be estimated from data using OLS; the OLS estimators in multiple regression are random variables because they depend on data from a random sample; and in large samples the sampling distributions of the OLS estimators are approximately normal.

OMITTED VARIABLE BIAS

By focusing only on the student–teacher ratio, the empirical analysis in Chapters 5 and 6 ignored some potentially important determinants of test scores by collecting their influences in the regression error term. These omitted factors include school characteristics, such as teacher quality and computer usage, and student characteristics, such as family background. We begin by considering an omitted student characteristic that is particularly relevant in California because of its large immigrant population: the prevalence in the school district of students who are still learning English.

By ignoring the percentage of English learners in the district, the OLS estimator of the slope in the regression of test scores on the student–teacher ratio could be biased; that is, the mean of the sampling distribution of the OLS estimator might not equal the true effect on test scores of a unit change in the student–teacher ratio. Here is the reasoning. Students who are still learning English might perform worse on standardized tests than native English speakers. If districts with large classes also have many students still learning English, then the OLS regression of test scores on the student–teacher ratio could erroneously find a correlation and produce a large estimated coefficient, when in fact the true causal effect of cutting class sizes on test scores is small, even zero. Accordingly, based on the analysis of Chapters 5 and 6, the superintendent might hire enough new teachers to reduce the student–teacher ratio by two, but her hoped-for improvement in test scores will fail to materialize if the true coefficient is small or zero.

A look at the California data lends credence to this concern. The correlation between the student–teacher ratio and the percentage of English learners (students who are not native English speakers and who have not yet mastered English) in the district is 0.19. This small but positive correlation suggests that districts with more English learners tend to have a higher student–teacher ratio (larger classes). If the student–teacher ratio were unrelated to the percentage of English learners, then it would be safe to ignore English proficiency in the regression of test scores against the student–teacher ratio. But because the student–teacher ratio and the percentage of English learners are correlated, it is possible that the OLS coefficient in the regression of test scores on the student–teacher ratio reflects that influence.

Definition of Omitted Variable Bias

If the regressor (the student–teacher ratio) is correlated with a variable that has been omitted from the analysis (the percentage of English learners) and that determines, in part, the dependent variable (test scores), then the OLS estimator will have **omitted variable bias**.

Omitted variable bias occurs when two conditions are true: (1) the omitted variable is correlated with the included regressor; and (2) the omitted variable is a determinant of the dependent variable. To illustrate these conditions, consider three examples of variables that are omitted from the regression of test scores on the student–teacher ratio.

Example #1: Percentage of English Learners

Because the percentage of English learners is correlated with the student–teacher ratio, the first condition for omitted variable bias holds. It is plausible that students who are still learning English will do worse on standardized tests than native English speakers, in which case the percentage of English learners is a determinant of test scores and the second condition for omitted variable bias holds. Thus, the OLS estimator in the regression of test scores on the student–teacher ratio could incorrectly reflect the influence of the omitted variable, the percentage of English learners. That is, omitting the percentage of English learners may introduce omitted variable bias.

Example #2: Time of Day of the Test

Another variable omitted from the analysis is the time of day that the test was administered. For this omitted variable, it is plausible that the first condition for omitted variable bias does not hold but the second condition does. For example, if the time of day of the test varies from one district to the next in a way that is unrelated to class size, then the time of day and class size would be uncorrelated so the first condition does not hold. Conversely, the time of day of the test could affect scores (alertness varies through the school day), so the second condition holds. However, because in this example the time that the test is administered is uncorrelated with the student–teacher ratio, the student–teacher ratio could not be incorrectly picking up the "time of day" effect. Thus omitting the time of day of the test does not result in omitted variable bias.

Example #3: Parking Lot Space per Pupil

Another omitted variable is parking lot space per pupil (the area of the teacher parking lot divided by the number of students). This variable satisfies the first but not the second condition for omitted variable bias. Specifically, schools with more teachers per pupil probably have more teacher parking space, so the first condition would be satisfied. However, under the assumption that learning takes place in the classroom, not the parking lot, parking lot space has no direct effect on learning; thus the second condition does not hold. Because parking lot space per pupil is not a determinant of test scores, omitting it from the analysis does not lead to omitted variable bias.

Omitted variable bias is summarized in Box 7-1.

BOX 7-1 **Omitted Variable Bias in Regression with a Single Regressor**

Omitted variable bias is the bias in the OLS estimator that arises when the regressor, X, is correlated with an omitted variable. For omitted variable bias to occur, two conditions must be true:

1. X is correlated with the omitted variable.
2. The omitted variable is a determinant of the dependent variable, Y.

Omitted Variable Bias and the First Least Squares Assumption

Omitted variable bias means that the first least squares assumption—that $E(u_i \mid X_i) = 0$, as listed in Box 5-3—is incorrect. To see why, recall that the error term u_i in the linear regression model with a single regressor represents all factors, other than X_i, that are determinants of Y_i. If one of these other factors is correlated with X_i, this means that the error term (which contains this factor) is correlated with X_i. In other words, if an omitted variable is a determinant of Y_i, then it is in the error term, and if it is correlated with X_i, then the error term is correlated with X_i. Because u_i and X_i are correlated, the conditional mean of u_i given X_i is nonzero. This correlation therefore violates the first least squares assumption, and the consequence is serious: The OLS estimator is biased. This bias does not vanish even in very large samples, and the OLS estimator is inconsistent.

A Formula for Omitted Variable Bias

The discussion of the previous section about omitted variable bias can be summarized mathematically by a formula for this bias. Let the correlation between X_i and u_i be $\text{corr}(X_i, u_i) = \rho_{Xu}$. Suppose that the second and third least squares assumptions hold, but the first does not because ρ_{Xu} is nonzero. Then the OLS estimator has the limit

$$\hat{\beta}_1 \xrightarrow{p} \beta_1 + \rho_{Xu}\frac{\sigma_u}{\sigma_X} \qquad (7.1)$$

That is, as the sample size increases, $\hat{\beta}_1$ is close to $\beta_1 + \rho_{Xu}(\sigma_u/\sigma_X)$ with increasingly high probability.

The Mozart Effect: Omitted Variable Bias?

A study published in *Nature* in 1993 (Rauscher, Shaw and Ky, 1993) suggested that listening to Mozart for 10-15 minutes could temporarily raise your IQ by 8 or 9 points. That study made big news—and politicians and parents saw an easy way to make their children smarter. For a while, the state of Georgia even distributed classical music CDs to all infants in the state.

What is the evidence for the "Mozart effect"? A review of dozens of studies found that students who take optional music or arts courses in high school do in fact have higher English and math test scores than those who don't.[1] A closer look at these studies, however, suggests that the real reason for the better test performance has little to do with those courses. Instead, the authors of the review suggested that the correlation between testing well and taking art or music could arise from any number of things. For example, the academically better students

might have more time to take optional music courses or more interest in doing so, or those schools with a deeper music curriculum might just be better schools across the board.

In the terminology of regression, the estimated relationship between test scores and taking optional music courses appears to have omitted variable bias. By omitting factors such as the student's innate ability or the overall quality of the school, studying music appears to have an effect on test scores when in fact it has none.

So is there a Mozart effect? One way to find out is to do a randomized controlled experiment. (As discussed in Chapter 5, randomized controlled experiments eliminate omitted variable bias by randomly assigning participants to "treatment" and "control" groups.) Taken together, the many controlled experiments on the Mozart effect fail to show that listening to Mozart improves IQ or general test performance. For reasons not fully understood, however, it seems that listening to classical music *does* help temporarily in one narrow area: folding paper and visualizing shapes. So the next time you cram for an origami exam, try to fit in a little Mozart, too.

---

[1] See the *Journal of Aesthetic Education* 34: 3-4 (Fall/Winter 2000), especially the article by Ellen Winner and Monica Cooper, (pp. 11-76) and the one by Lois Hetland (pp. 105-148).

The formula in Equation (7.1) summarizes several of the ideas discussed above about omitted variable bias:

1. Omitted variable bias is a problem whether the sample size is large or small. Because $\hat{\beta}_1$ does not converge in probability to the true value β_1, $\hat{\beta}_1$ is inconsistent; that is, $\hat{\beta}_1$ is not a consistent estimator of β_1 when there is omitted variable bias. The term $\rho_{Xu}(\sigma_u/\sigma_x)$ in Equation (7.1) is the bias in $\hat{\beta}_1$ that persists even in large samples.

2. Whether this bias is large or small in practice depends on the correlation ρ_{Xu} between the regressor and the error term. The larger is $|\rho_{Xu}|$, the larger is the bias.

3. The direction of the bias in $\hat{\beta}_1$ depends on whether X and u are positively or negatively correlated. For example, we speculated that the percentage of students learning English has a *negative* effect on district test scores (students still learning English have lower scores), so that the percentage of English learners enters the error term with a negative sign. In our data, the fraction of English learners is *positively* correlated with the student–teacher ratio (districts with more English learners have larger classes). Thus the student–teacher ratio (X) would be *negatively* correlated with

the error term (u), so $\rho_{Xu} < 0$ and the coefficient on the student–teacher ratio $\hat{\beta}_1$ would be biased toward a negative number. In other words, having a small percentage of English learners is associated both with *high* test scores and *low* student–teacher ratios, so one reason that the OLS estimator suggests that small classes improve test scores may be that the districts with small classes have fewer English learners.

Addressing Omitted Variable Bias by Dividing the Data into Groups

What can you do about omitted variable bias? Our superintendent is considering increasing the number of teachers in her district, but she has no control over the fraction of immigrants in her community. As a result, she is interested in the effect of the student–teacher ratio on test scores, *holding constant* other factors, including the percentage of English learners. This new way of posing her question suggests that, instead of using data for all districts, perhaps we should focus on districts with percentages of English learners comparable to hers. Among this subset of districts, do those with smaller classes do better on standardized tests?

TABLE 7-1 Differences in Test Scores for California School Districts with Low and High Student–Teacher Ratios, by the Percentage of English Learners in the District

| | Student–Teacher Ratio < 20 | | Student–Teacher Ratio ≥ 20 | | Difference in Test Scores, Low vs. High STR | |
	Average Test Score	n	Average Test Score	n	Difference	t-Statistic
All districts	657.4	238	650.0	182	7.4	4.04
Percentage of English learners						
< 1.9%	664.5	76	665.4	27	−0.9	−0.30
1.9–8.8%	665.2	64	661.8	44	3.3	1.13
8.8–23.0%	654.9	54	649.7	50	5.2	1.72
> 23.0%	636.7	44	634.8	61	1.9	0.68

Table 7-1 reports evidence on the relationship between class size and test scores within districts with comparable percentages of English learners. Districts are divided into eight groups. First, the districts are broken into four categories that correspond to the quartiles of the distribution of the percentage of English learners across districts. Second, within each of these four categories, districts are further broken down into two groups, depending on whether the student–teacher ratio is small ($STR < 20$) or large ($STR \geq 20$).

The first row in Table 7-1 reports the overall difference in average test scores between districts with low and high student–teacher ratios, that is, the difference in test scores between these two groups without breaking them down further into the quartiles of English learners. (Recall that this difference was previously reported in regression form in Equation (6.18) as the OLS estimate of the coefficient on D_i in the regression of *TestScore* on D_i, where D_i is a binary regressor that equals 1 if $STR_i < 20$ and equals 0 otherwise.) Over the full sample of 420 districts, the average test score is 7.4 points higher in districts with a low student–teacher ratio than a high one; the t-statistic is 4.04, so the null hypothesis that the mean test score is the same in the two groups is rejected at the 1% significance level.

The final four rows in Table 7-1 report the difference in test scores between districts with low and high student–teacher ratios, broken down by the quartile of the percentage of English learners. This evidence presents a different picture. Of the districts with the fewest English learners (< 1.9%), the average test score for those 76 with low student–teacher ratios is 664.5 and the average for the 27 with high student–teacher ratios is 665.4. Thus, for the districts with the fewest English learners, test scores were on average 0.9 points *lower* in the districts with low student–teacher ratios! In the second quartile, districts with low student–teacher ratios had test scores that averaged 3.3 points higher than those with high student–teacher ratios; this gap was 5.2 points for the third quartile and only 1.9 points for the quartile of districts with the most English learners. Once we hold the percentage of English learners constant, the difference in performance between districts with high and low student–teacher ratios is perhaps half (or less) of the overall estimate of 7.4 points.

At first this finding might seem puzzling. How can the overall effect of test scores be twice the effect of test scores within any quartile? The answer is that the districts with the most English learners tend to have *both* the highest student–teacher ratios *and* the lowest test scores. The difference in the average test score between districts in the lowest and highest quartile of the percentage of English learners is large, approximately 30 points. The districts with few English learners tend to have lower student–teacher ratios: 74% (76 of 103) of the districts in the first quartile of English learners have small classes ($STR < 20$), while only 42% (44 of 105) of the districts in the quartile with the most English learners have small classes. So, the districts with the most English learners have both lower test scores and higher student–teacher ratios than the other districts.

This analysis reinforces the superintendent's worry that omitted variable bias is present in the regression of test scores against the student–teacher ratio. By looking within quartiles of the percentage of English learners, the test score differences in the second part of Table 7-1 improve upon the simple difference-of-means analysis in the first line of Table 7-1. Still, this analysis does not yet provide the superintendent with a useful estimate of the effect on test scores of changing class size, holding constant the fraction of English learners. Such an estimate can be provided, however, using the method of multiple regression.

THE MULTIPLE REGRESSION MODEL

The **multiple regression model** extends the single variable regression model of Chapters 5 and 6 to include additional variables as regressors. This model permits estimating the effect on Y_i of changing one variable (X_{1i}) while holding the other regressors (X_{2i}, X_{3i}, and so forth) constant. In the class size problem, the multiple regression model provides a way to isolate the effect on test scores (Y_i) of the student–teacher ratio (X_{1i}) while holding constant the percentage of students in the district who are English learners (X_{2i}).

The Population Regression Line

Suppose for the moment that there are only two independent variables, X_{1i} and X_{2i}. In the linear multiple regression model, the average relationship between these two independent variables and the dependent variable, Y, is given by the linear function

$$E(Y_i \mid X_{1i} = x_1, X_{2i} = x_2) = \beta_0 + \beta_1 x_1 + \beta_2 x_2 \qquad \textbf{(7.2)}$$

where $E(Y_i \mid X_{1i} = x_1, X_{2i} = x_2)$ is the conditional expectation of Y_i given that $X_{1i} = x_1$ and $X_{2i} = x_2$. That is, if the student–teacher ratio in the ith district (X_{1i}) equals some value x_1 and the percentage of English learners in the ith district (X_{2i}) equals x_2, then the expected value of Y_i given the student–teacher ratio and the percentage of English learners is given by Equation (7.2).

Equation (7.2) is the **population regression line** or **population regression function** in the multiple regression model. The coefficient β_0 is the **intercept**, the coefficient β_1 is the **slope coefficient of X_{1i}** or, more simply, the **coefficient on X_{1i}**, and the coefficient β_2 is the **slope coefficient of X_{2i}** or, more simply, the **coefficient on X_{2i}**. One or more of the independent variables in the multiple regression model are sometimes referred to as **control variables**.

The interpretation of the coefficient β_1 in Equation (7.2) is different than it was when X_{1i} was the only regressor: In Equation (7.2), β_1 is the effect on Y of a unit change in X_1, **holding X_2 constant** or **controlling for X_2**.

This interpretation of β_1 follows from the definition that the expected effect on Y of a change in X_1, ΔX_1, holding X_2 constant, is the difference between the expected value of Y when the independent variables take on the values $X_1 + \Delta X_1$ and X_2 and the expected value of Y when the independent variables take on the values X_1 and X_2. Accordingly, write the population regression function in Equation (7.2) as $Y = \beta_0 + \beta_1 X_1 + \beta_2 X_2$, and imagine changing X_1 by the amount ΔX_1 while not changing X_2, that is, while holding X_2 constant. Because X_1 has changed, Y will change by some amount, say ΔY. After this change, the new value of Y, $Y + \Delta Y$, is

$$Y + \Delta Y = \beta_0 + \beta_1(X_1 + \Delta X_1) + \beta_2 X_2 \qquad \textbf{(7.3)}$$

An equation for ΔY in terms of ΔX_1 is obtained by subtracting the equation $Y = \beta_0 + \beta_1 X_1 + \beta_2 X_2$ from Equation (7.3), yielding $\Delta Y = \beta_1 \Delta X_1$. That is,

$$\beta_1 = \frac{\Delta Y}{\Delta X_1}, \text{ holding } X_2 \text{ constant} \qquad \textbf{(7.4)}$$

The coefficient β_1 is the effect on Y (the expected change in Y) of a unit change in X_1, holding X_2 fixed. Another phrase used to describe β_1 is the **partial effect** on Y of X_1, holding X_2 fixed.

The interpretation of the intercept in the multiple regression model, β_0, is similar to the interpretation of the intercept in the single-regressor model: It is the expected value of Y_i when X_{1i} and X_{2i} are zero. Simply put, the intercept β_0 determines how far up the Y axis the population regression line starts.

The Population Multiple Regression Model

The population regression line in Equation (7.2) is the relationship between Y and X_1 and X_2 that holds on average in the population. Just as in the case of regression with a single regressor, however, this relationship does not hold exactly because many other factors influence the dependent variable. In addition to the student–teacher ratio and the fraction of students still learning English, for example, test scores are influenced by school characteristics, other student characteristics, and luck. Thus the population regression function in Equation (7.2) needs to be augmented to incorporate these additional factors.

Just as in the case of regression with a single regressor, the factors that determine Y_i in addition to X_{1i} and X_{2i} are incorporated into Equation (7.2) as an "error" term u_i. This error term is the deviation of a particular observation (test scores in the ith district in our example) from the average population relationship. Accordingly, we have

$$Y_i = \beta_0 + \beta_1 X_{1i} + \beta_2 X_{2i} + u_i, i = 1, \ldots, n \qquad \textbf{(7.5)}$$

where the subscript i indicates the ith of the n observations (districts) in the sample.

Equation (7.5) is the **population multiple regression model** when there are two regressors, X_{1i} and X_{2i}.

In regression with binary regressors it can be useful to treat β_0 as the coefficient on a regressor that always equals 1; think of β_0 as the coefficient on X_{0i}, where $X_{0i} = 1$ for $i = 1, \ldots, n$. Accordingly, the population multiple regression model in Equation (7.5) can alternatively be written as

$$Y_i = \beta_0 X_{0i} + \beta_1 X_{1i} + \beta_2 X_{2i} + u_i \qquad \textbf{(7.6)}$$
$$\text{where } X_{0i} = 1, i = 1, \ldots, n$$

The variable X_{0i} is sometimes called the **constant regressor** because it takes on the same value—the value 1—for all observations. Similarly, the intercept, β_0, is sometimes called the **constant term** in the regression.

The two ways of writing the population regression model, Equations (7.5) and (7.6), are equivalent.

The discussion so far has focused on the case of a single additional variable, X_2. In practice, however, there might be multiple factors omitted from the single-regressor model. For example, ignoring the students' economic background might result in omitted variable bias, just as ignoring the fraction of English learners did. This reasoning leads us to consider a model with three regressors or, more generally, a model that includes k regressors. The multiple regression model with k regressors, $X_{1i}, X_{2i}, \ldots, X_{ki}$, is summarized as Box 7-2.

BOX 7-2 The Multiple Regression Model

The multiple regression model is

$$Y_i = \beta_0 + \beta_1 X_{1i} + \beta_2 X_{2i} + \cdots + \beta_k X_{ki} + u_i, i = 1, \ldots, n \qquad \textbf{(7.7)}$$

where

- Y_i is i^{th} observation on the dependent variable; $X_{1i}, X_{2i}, \ldots, X_{ki}$ are the ith observations on each of the k regressors; and u_i is the error term.

- The population regression line is the relationship that holds between Y and the X's on average in the population:

$$E(Y \mid X_{1i} = x_1, X_{2i} = x_2, \ldots, X_{ki} = x_k)$$
$$= \beta_0 + \beta_1 x_1 + \beta_2 x_2 + \cdots + \beta_k x_k$$

- β_1 is the slope coefficient on X_1, β_2 is the coefficient on X_2, and so on. The coefficient β_1 is the expected change in Y_i resulting from changing X_{1i} by one unit, holding constant $X_{2i}, \ldots, X_{ki}$. The coefficients on the other X's are interpreted similarly.

- The intercept β_0 is the expected value of Y when all the X's equal 0. The intercept can be thought of as the coefficient on a regressor, X_{0i}, that equals 1 for all i.

The definitions of homoskedasticity and heteroskedasticity in the multiple regression model are extensions of their definitions in the single-regressor model. The error term u_i in the multiple regression model is **homoskedastic** if the variance of the conditional distribution of u_i given $X_{1i}, \ldots, X_{ki}$, var$(u_i \mid X_{1i}, \ldots, X_{ki})$, is constant for $i = 1, \ldots, n$ and thus does not depend on the values of $X_{1i}, \ldots, X_{ki}$. Otherwise, the error term is **heteroskedastic**.

The multiple regression model holds out the promise of providing just what the superintendent wants to know: the effect of changing the student–teacher ratio, holding constant other factors that are beyond her control. These factors include not just the percentage of English learners, but other measurable factors that might affect test performance, including the economic background of the students. To be of practical help to the superintendent, however, we need to provide her with estimates of the unknown population coefficients $\beta_0, \ldots, \beta_k$ of the population regression model calculated using a sample of data. Fortunately, these coefficients can be estimated using ordinary least squares.

THE OLS ESTIMATOR IN MULTIPLE REGRESSION

This section describes how the coefficients of the multiple regression model can be estimated using OLS.

The OLS Estimator

Chapter 5 shows how to estimate the intercept and slope coefficients in the single-regressor model by applying OLS to a sample of observations of Y and X. The key idea is that these coefficients can be estimated by minimizing the sum of squared prediction mistakes, that is, by choosing the estimators b_0 and b_1 so as to minimize $\sum_{i=1}^{n}(Y_i - b_0 - b_1 X_i)^2$. The estimators that do so are the OLS estimators, $\hat{\beta}_0$ and $\hat{\beta}_1$.

The method of OLS also can be used to estimate the coefficients $\beta_0, \beta_1, \ldots, \beta_k$ in the multiple regression model. Let $b_0, b_1, \ldots, b_k$ be estimators of $\beta_0, \beta_1, \ldots, \beta_k$. The predicted value of Y_i, calculated using these estimators, is $b_0 + b_1 X_{1i} + \cdots + b_k X_{ki}$, and the mistake in predicting Y_i is $Y_i - (b_0 + b_1 X_{1i} + \cdots + b_k X_{ki}) = Y_i - b_0 - b_1 X_{1i} - \cdots - b_k X_{ki}$. The sum of these squared prediction mistakes over all n observations thus is

$$\sum_{i=1}^{n}(Y_i - b_0 - b_1 X_{1i} - \cdots - b_k X_{ki})^2 \qquad \textbf{(7.8)}$$

The sum of the squared mistakes for the linear regression model in Equation (7.8) is the extension of the sum of the squared mistakes given in Equation (5.6) for the linear regression model with a single regressor.

The estimators of the coefficients $\beta_0, \beta_1, \ldots, \beta_k$ that minimize the sum of squared mistakes in Equation (7.8) are called the **ordinary least squares (OLS) estimators** of $\beta_0, \beta_1, \ldots, \beta_k$. The OLS estimators are denoted $\hat{\beta}_0, \hat{\beta}_1, \ldots, \hat{\beta}_k$.

The terminology of OLS in the linear multiple regression model is the same as in the linear regression model with a single regressor. The **OLS regression line** is the straight line constructed using the OLS estimators: $\hat{\beta}_0 + \hat{\beta}_1 X_1 + \cdots + \hat{\beta}_k X_k$. The **predicted value** of Y_i given $X_{1i}, \ldots, X_{ki}$, based on the OLS regression line, is $\hat{Y}_i = \hat{\beta}_0 + \hat{\beta}_1 X_{1i} + \cdots + \hat{\beta}_k X_{ki}$. The **OLS residual** for the ith observation is the difference between Y_i and its OLS predicted value, that is, the OLS residual is $\hat{u}_i = Y_i - \hat{Y}_i$.

The OLS estimators could be computed by trial and error, repeatedly trying different values of $b_0, \ldots, b_k$ until you

are satisfied that you have minimized the total sum of squares in Equation (7.8). It is far easier, however, to use explicit formulas for the OLS estimators that are derived using calculus. The formulas for the OLS estimators in the multiple regression model are similar to those in Box 5-2 for the single-regressor model. These formulas are incorporated into modern statistical software. In the multiple regression model, the formulas for general k are best expressed and discussed using matrix notation, so their presentation is omitted.

The definitions and terminology of OLS in multiple regression are summarized in Box 7-3.

Application to Test Scores and the Student–Teacher Ratio

Earlier, we used OLS to estimate the intercept and slope coefficient of the regression relating test scores (*TestScore*) to the student–teacher ratio (*STR*), using our 420 observations for California school districts; the estimated OLS regression line, reported in Equation (5.11), is

$$\widehat{TestScore} = 698.9 - 2.28 \times STR \qquad \textbf{(7.11)}$$

Our concern has been that this relationship is misleading because the student–teacher ratio might be picking up the effect of having many English learners in districts with large classes. That is, it is possible that the OLS estimator is subject to omitted variable bias.

We are now in a position to address this concern by using OLS to estimate a multiple regression in which the dependent variable is the test score (Y_i) and there are two regressors: the student–teacher ratio (X_{1i}) and the percentage of English learners in the school district (X_{2i}) for our 420 districts ($i = 1, \ldots, 420$). The estimated OLS regression line for this multiple regression is

$$\widehat{TestScore} = 686.0 - 1.10 \times STR - 0.65 \times PctEL \qquad \textbf{(7.12)}$$

where *PctEL* is the percentage of students in the district who are English learners. The OLS estimate of the intercept ($\hat{\beta}_0$) is 686.0, the OLS estimate of the coefficient on the student–teacher ratio ($\hat{\beta}_1$) is −1.10, and the OLS estimate of the coefficient on the percentage English learners ($\hat{\beta}_2$) is −0.65.

The estimated effect on test scores of a change in the student–teacher ratio in the multiple regression is approximately half as large as when the student–teacher ratio is the only regressor: in the single-regressor equation [Equation (7.11)], a unit decrease in the *STR* is estimated to increase test scores by 2.28 points, but in the multiple regression equation [Equation (7.12)], it is estimated to increase test scores by only 1.10 points. This difference occurs because the coefficient on *STR* in the multiple regression is the effect of a change in *STR*, holding constant (or controlling for) *PctEL*, whereas in the single-regressor regression, *PctEL* is not held constant.

These two estimates can be reconciled by concluding that there is omitted variable bias in the estimate in the single-regressor model in Equation (7.11). Previously, we saw that districts with a high percentage of English learners tend to have not only low test scores but also a high student–teacher ratio. If the fraction of English learners is omitted from the regression, reducing the student–teacher ratio is estimated to have a larger effect on test scores, but this estimate reflects *both* the effect of a change in the student–teacher ratio *and* the omitted effect of having fewer English learners in the district.

We have reached the same conclusion that there is omitted variable bias in the relationship between test scores and the student–teacher ratio by two different paths: the tabular approach of dividing the data into groups and the multiple regression approach [Equation (7.12)]. Of these two methods, multiple regression has two important advantages. First, it provides a quantitative estimate of the effect of a unit decrease in the student–teacher ratio, which is what the superintendent needs to make her decision. Second, it readily extends to more than two regressors, so that multiple regression can be used to control for measurable factors other than just the percentage of English learners.

The rest of this chapter is devoted to understanding and to using OLS in the multiple regression model. Much of what you learned about the OLS estimator with a single regressor carries over to multiple regression with few or no modifications, so we will focus on that which is new with multiple regression. We begin by discussing measures of fit for the multiple regression model.

MEASURES OF FIT IN MULTIPLE REGRESSION

Three commonly used summary statistics in multiple regression are the standard error of the regression, the regression R^2, and the adjusted R^2 (also known as $\overline{R}^2$). All three statistics measure how well the OLS estimate of the multiple regression line describes, or "fits," the data.

The Standard Error of the Regression (*SER*)

The standard error of the regression (*SER*) estimates the standard deviation of the error term u_i. Thus, the *SER* is a measure of the spread of the distribution of *Y* around the regression line. In multiple regression, the *SER* is

$$SER = s_{\hat{u}}, \text{ where } s_{\hat{u}}^2 = \frac{1}{n-k-1}\sum_{i=1}^{n}\hat{u}_i^2 = \frac{SSR}{n-k-1} \qquad \textbf{(7.13)}$$

where the *SSR* is the sum of squared residuals, $SSR = \sum_{i=1}^{n}\hat{u}_i^2$.

The only difference between the definition in Equation (7.13) and the definition of the *SER* in Chapter 5 for the single-regressor model is that here the divisor is $n - k - 1$ rather than $n - 2$. In Chapter 5, the divisor $n - 2$ (rather than n) adjusts for the downward bias introduced by estimating two coefficients (the slope and intercept of the regression line). Here, the divisor $n - k - 1$ adjusts for the downward bias introduced by estimating $k + 1$ coefficients (the k slope coefficients plus the intercept). As in Chapter 5, using $n - k - 1$ rather than n is called a degrees-of-freedom adjustment. If there is a single regressor, then $k = 1$, so the formula in Chapter 5 is the same as in Equation (7.13). When n is large, the effect of the degrees-of-freedom adjustment is negligible.

The R^2

The regression R^2 is the fraction of the sample variance of Y_i explained by (or predicted by) the regressors. Equivalently, the R^2 is 1 minus the fraction of the variance of Y_i not explained by the regressors.

The mathematical definition of the R^2 is the same as for regression with a single regressor:

$$R^2 = \frac{ESS}{TSS} = 1 - \frac{SSR}{TSS} \qquad \text{(7.14)}$$

where the explained sum of squares is $ESS = \sum_{i=1}^{n}(\hat{Y}_i - \overline{Y})^2$ and the total sum of squares is $TSS = \sum_{i=1}^{n}(Y_i - \overline{Y})^2$. In multiple regression, the R^2 increases whenever a regressor is added, unless the estimated coefficient on the added regressor is exactly zero. To see this, think about starting with one regressor and then adding a second. When you use OLS to estimate the model with both regressors, OLS finds the values of the coefficients that minimize the sum of squared residuals. If OLS happens to choose the coefficient on the new regressor to be exactly zero, then the SSR will be the same whether or not the second variable is included in the regression. But if OLS chooses any value other than zero, then it must be that this value reduced the SSR relative to the regression that excludes this regressor. In practice it is extremely unusual for an estimated coefficient to be exactly zero, so in general the SSR will decrease when a new regressor is added. But this means that the R^2 generally increases (and never decreases) when a new regressor is added.

The "Adjusted R^2"

Because the R^2 increases when a new variable is added, an increase in the R^2 does not mean that adding a variable actually improves the fit of the model. In this sense, the R^2 gives an inflated estimate of how well the regression fits the data. One way to correct for this is to deflate or reduce the R^2 by some factor, and this is what the adjusted R^2, or $\overline{R}^2$, does.

The **adjusted R^2**, or $\overline{R}^2$, is a modified version of the R^2 that does not necessarily increase when a new regressor is added. The $\overline{R}^2$ is

$$\overline{R}^2 = 1 - \frac{n-1}{n-k-1}\frac{SSR}{TSS} = 1 - \frac{s_{\hat{u}}^2}{s_Y^2} \qquad \text{(7.15)}$$

The difference between this formula and the second definition of the R^2 in Equation (7.14) is that the ratio of the sum of squared residuals to the total sum of squares is multiplied by the factor $(n-1)/(n-k-1)$. As the second expression in Equation (7.15) shows, this means that the adjusted R^2 is 1 minus the ratio of the sample variance of the OLS residuals [with the degrees-of-freedom correction in Equation (7.13)] to the sample variance of Y. There are three useful things to know about the $\overline{R}^2$. First, $(n-1)/(n-k-1)$ is always greater than 1, so $\overline{R}^2$ is always less than R^2.

Second, adding a regressor has two opposite effects on the $\overline{R}^2$. On the one hand, the SSR falls, which increases the $\overline{R}^2$. On the other hand, the factor $(n-1)/(n-k-1)$ increases. Whether the $\overline{R}^2$ increases or decreases depends on which of these two effects is stronger.

Third, the $\overline{R}^2$ can be negative. This happens when the regressors, taken together, reduce the sum of squared residuals by such a small amount that this reduction fails to offset the factor $(n-1)/(n-k-1)$.

Application to Test Scores

Equation (7.12) reports the estimated regression line for the multiple regression relating test scores (*TestScore*) to the student–teacher ratio (*STR*) and the percentage of English learners (*PctEL*). The R^2 for this regression line is $R^2 = 0.426$, the adjusted R^2 is $\overline{R}^2 = 0.424$, and the standard error of the regression is $SER = 14.5$.

Comparing these measures of fit with those for the regression in which *PctEL* is excluded [Equation (7.11)] shows that including *PctEL* in the regression increased the R^2 from 0.051 to 0.426. When the only regressor is *STR*, only a small fraction of the variation in *TestScore* is explained, however, when *PctEL* is added to the regression, more than two-fifths (42.6%) of the variation in test scores is explained. In this sense, including the percentage of English learners substantially improves the fit of the regression. Because n is large and only two regressors appear in Equation (7.12), the difference between R^2 and adjusted R^2 is very small ($R^2 = 0.426$ versus $\overline{R}^2 = 0.424$).

The *SER* for the regression excluding *PctEL* is 18.6; this value falls to 14.5 when *PctEL* is included as a second regressor. The units of the *SER* are points on the standardized test. The reduction in the *SER* tells us that predictions about standardized test scores are substantially more precise if they are made using the regression with both *STR* and *PctEL* than if they are made using the regression with only *STR* as a regressor.

Using the R^2 and Adjusted R^2

The $\overline{R}^2$ is useful because it quantifies the extent to which the regressors account for, or explain, the variation in the dependent variable. Nevertheless, heavy reliance on the $\overline{R}^2$ (or R^2) can be a trap. In applications, "maximize the $\overline{R}^2$" is rarely the answer to any economically or statistically meaningful question. Instead, the decision about whether to include a variable in a multiple regression should be based on whether including that variable allows you better to estimate the causal effect of interest. We return to the issue of how to decide which variables to include—and which to exclude—in Chapter 8. First, however, we need to develop methods for quantifying the sampling uncertainty of the OLS estimator. The starting point for doing so is extending the least squares assumptions of Chapter 5 to the case of multiple regressors.

THE LEAST SQUARES ASSUMPTIONS IN MULTIPLE REGRESSION

There are four least squares assumptions in the multiple regression model. The first three are those of Chapter 5 for the single regressor model (Box 5-3), extended to allow for multiple regressors, and these are discussed only briefly. The fourth assumption is new and is discussed in more detail.

Assumption #1: The Conditional Distribution of u_i Given X_{1i}, X_{2i}, . . . , X_{ki} Has a Mean of Zero

The first assumption is that the conditional distribution of u_i given $X_{1i}, \ldots, X_{ki}$ has a mean of zero. This assumption extends the first least squares assumption with a single regressor to multiple regressors. This assumption means that sometimes Y_i is above the population regression line and sometimes Y_i is below the population regression line, but on average over the population Y_i falls on the population regression line. Therefore, for any value of the regressors, the expected value of u_i is zero. As is the case for regression with a single regressor, this is the key assumption that makes the OLS estimators unbiased. We return to omitted variable bias in multiple regression in Chapter 8.

Assumption #2: $(X_{1i}, X_{2i}, \ldots, X_{ki}, Y_i)$, $i = 1, \ldots, n$ Are i.i.d.

The second assumption is that $(X_{1i}, \ldots, X_{ki}, Y_i)$, $i = 1, \ldots, n$ are independently and identically distributed (i.i.d.) random variables. This assumption holds automatically if the data are collected by simple random sampling. The comments on this assumption appearing in Chapter 5 for a single regressor also apply to multiple regressors.

Assumption #3: Large Outliers Are Unlikely

The third least squares assumption is that large outliers—that is, observations with values far outside the usual range of the data—are unlikely. This assumption serves as a reminder that, as in single-regressor case, the OLS estimator of the coefficients in the multiple regression model can be sensitive to large outliers.

The assumption that large outliers are unlikely is made mathematically precise by assuming that $X_{1i}, \ldots, X_{ki}$, and Y_i have nonzero finite fourth moments: $0 < E(X_{1i}^4) < \infty, \ldots,$ $0 < E(X_{ki}^4) < \infty$ and $0 < E(Y_i^4) < \infty$. Another way to state this assumption is that the dependent variable and regressors have finite kurtosis. This assumption is used to derive the properties of OLS regression statistics in large samples.

Assumption #4: No Perfect Multicollinearity

The fourth assumption is new to the multiple regression model. It rules out an inconvenient situation, called perfect multicollinearity, in which it is impossible to compute the OLS estimator. The regressors are said to be **perfectly multicollinear** (or to exhibit **perfect multicollinearity**) if one of the regressors is a perfect linear function of the other regressors. The fourth least squares assumption is that the regressors are not perfectly multicollinear.

Why does perfect multicollinearity make it impossible to compute the OLS estimator? Suppose you want to estimate the coefficient on *STR* in a regression of $TestScore_i$ on STR_i and $PctEL_i$, except that you make a typographical error and accidentally type in STR_i a second time instead of $PctEL_i$; that is, you regress $TestScore_i$ on STR_i and STR_i. This is a case of perfect multicollinearity because one of the regressors (the first occurrence of *STR*) is a perfect linear function of another regressor (the second occurrence of *STR*). Depending on how your software package handles perfect multicollinearity, if you try to estimate this regression the software will do one of three things: (1) It will drop one of the occurrences of *STR*; (2) it will refuse to calculate the OLS estimates and give an error message; or (3) it will crash the computer. The mathematical reason for this failure is that perfect multicollinearity produces division by zero in the OLS formulas.

At an intuitive level, perfect multicollinearity is a problem because you are asking the regression to answer an illogical question. In multiple regression, the coefficient on one of the regressors is the effect of a change in that regressor, holding the other regressors constant. In the hypothetical regression of *TestScore* on *STR* and *STR*, the coefficient on the first occurrence of *STR* is the effect on test scores of a change in *STR*, holding constant *STR*. This makes no sense, and OLS cannot estimate this nonsensical partial effect.

The solution to perfect multicollinearity in this hypothetical regression is simply to correct the typo and to replace one of the occurrences of *STR* with the variable you originally wanted to include. This example is typical: When perfect multicollinearity occurs, it often reflects a logical mistake in choosing the regressors or some previously unrecognized feature of the data set. In general, the solution to perfect multicollinearity is to modify the regressors to eliminate the problem.

Additional examples of perfect multicollinearity are given later in this chapter, which also defines and discusses imperfect multicollinearity.

The least squares assumptions for the multiple regression model are summarized in Box 7-4.

BOX 7-4 **The Least Squares Assumptions in the Multiple Regression Model**

$Y_i = \beta_0 + \beta_1 X_{1i} + \beta_2 X_{2i} + \ldots + \beta_k X_{ki} + u_i$, $i = 1, \ldots, n$, where

1. u_i has conditional mean zero given $X_{1i}, X_{2i}, \ldots, X_{ki}$; that is,

$$E(u_i \mid X_{1i}, X_{2i}, \ldots, X_{ki}) = 0$$

2. $(X_{1i}, X_{2i}, \ldots, X_{ki}, Y_i)$, $i = 1, \ldots, n$ are independently and identically distributed (i.i.d.) draws from their joint distribution.

3. Large outliers are unlikely: $X_{1i}, \ldots, X_{ki}$ and Y_i have nonzero finite fourth moments.

4. There is no perfect multicollinearity.

THE DISTRIBUTION OF THE OLS ESTIMATORS IN MULTIPLE REGRESSION

Because the data differ from one sample to the next, different samples produce different values of the OLS estimators. This variation across possible samples gives rise to the uncertainty associated with the OLS estimators of the population regression coefficients, $\beta_0, \beta_1, \ldots, \beta_k$. Just as in the case of regression with a single regressor, this variation is summarized in the sampling distribution of the OLS estimators.

Recall from Chapter 5 that, under the least squares assumptions, the OLS estimators ($\hat{\beta}_0$ and $\hat{\beta}_1$) are unbiased and consistent estimators of the unknown coefficients (β_0 and β_1) in the linear regression model with a single regressor. In addition, in large samples, the sampling distribution of $\hat{\beta}_0$ and $\hat{\beta}_1$ is well approximated by a bivariate normal distribution.

These results carry over to multiple regression analysis. That is, under the least squares assumptions of Box 7-4, the OLS estimators $\hat{\beta}_0, \hat{\beta}_1, \ldots, \hat{\beta}_k$ are unbiased and consistent estimators of $\beta_0, \beta_1, \ldots, \beta_k$ in the linear multiple regression model. In large samples, the joint sampling distribution of $\hat{\beta}_0, \hat{\beta}_1, \ldots, \hat{\beta}_k$ is well approximated by a multivariate normal distribution, which is the extension of the bivariate normal distribution to the general case of two or more jointly normal random variables.

Although the algebra is more complicated when there are multiple regressors, the central limit theorem applies to the OLS estimators in the multiple regression model for the same reason that it applies to $\overline{Y}$ and to the OLS estimators when there is a single regressor: The OLS estimators $\hat{\beta}_0, \hat{\beta}_1, \ldots, \hat{\beta}_k$ are averages of the randomly sampled data, and if the sample size is sufficiently large the sampling distribution of those averages becomes normal. Because the multivariate normal distribution is best handled mathematically using matrix algebra, the expressions for the joint distribution of the OLS estimators are omitted.

Box 7-5 summarizes the result that, in large samples, the distribution of the OLS estimators in multiple regression is approximately jointly normal. In general, the OLS estimators are correlated; this correlation arises from the correlation between the regressors.

BOX 7-5 Large Sample Distribution of $\hat{\beta}_0, \hat{\beta}_1, \ldots, \hat{\beta}_k$

If the least squares assumptions (Box 7-4) hold, then in large samples the OLS estimators $\hat{\beta}_0, \hat{\beta}_1, \ldots, \hat{\beta}_k$ are jointly normally distributed and each $\hat{\beta}_j$ is distributed $N(\beta_j, \sigma^2_{\hat{\beta}_j}), j = 0, \ldots, k.$

MULTICOLLINEARITY

As discussed previously, perfect multicollinearity arises when one of the regressors is a perfect linear combination of the other regressors. This section provides some examples of perfect multicollinearity and discusses how perfect multicollinearity can arise, and can be avoided, in regressions with multiple binary regressors. Imperfect multicollinearity arises when one of the regressors is very highly correlated—but not perfectly correlated—with the other regressors. Unlike perfect multicollinearity, imperfect multicollinearity does not prevent estimation of the regression, nor does it imply a logical problem with the choice of regressors. However, it does mean that one or more regression coefficients could be estimated imprecisely.

Examples of Perfect Multicollinearity

We continue the discussion of perfect multicollinearity by examining three additional hypothetical regressions. In each, a third regressor is added to the regression of *TestScore$_i$* on *STR$_i$* and *PctEL$_i$* in Equation (7.12).

Example #1: Fraction of English Learners

Let *FracEL$_i$* be the fraction of English learners in the ith district, which varies between 0 and 1. If the variable *FracEL$_i$* were included as a third regressor in addition to *STR$_i$* and *PctEL$_i$*, the regressors would be perfectly multicollinear. The reason is that *PctEL* is the *percentage* of English learners, so that $PctEL_i = 100 \times FracEL_i$ for every district. Thus one of the regressors (*PctEL$_i$*) can be written as a perfect linear function of another regressor (*FracEL$_i$*).

Because of this perfect multicollinearity, it is impossible to compute the OLS estimates of the regression of *TestScore$_i$* on *STR$_i$*, *PctEL$_i$*, and *FracEL$_i$*. At an intuitive level, OLS fails because you are asking, What is the effect of a unit change in the *percentage* of English learners, holding constant the *fraction* of English learners? Because the percentage of English learners and the fraction of English learners move together in a perfect linear relationship, this question makes no sense and OLS cannot answer it.

Example #2: "Not Very Small" Classes

Let *NVS$_i$* be a binary variable that equals 1 if the student–teacher ratio in the ith district is "not very small," specifically, *NVS$_i$* equals 1 if $STR_i \geq 12$ and equals 0 otherwise. This regression also exhibits perfect multicollinearity, but for a more subtle reason than the regression in the previous example. There are in fact no districts in our data set with $STR_i < 12$; as you can see in the scatterplot in Figure 5-2, the smallest value of *STR* is 14. Thus, $NVS_i = 1$ for all observations. Now recall that the linear regression model with an intercept can equivalently be thought of as including a regressor, X_{0i}, that equals 1 for all i, as is shown in Equation (7.6). Thus we can write $NVS_i = 1 \times X_{0i}$ for all the observations in our data set; that is, *NVS$_i$* can be written as a perfect linear combination of the regressors; specifically, it equals X_{0i}.

This illustrates two important points about perfect multicollinearity. First, when the regression includes an intercept, then one of the regressors that can be implicated in perfect multicollinearity is the constant regressor X_{0i}. Second, perfect multicollinearity is a statement about the data set you have on hand. While it is possible to imagine a school district with fewer than 12 students per teacher, there are no such districts in our data set so we cannot analyze them in our regression.

Example #3: Percentage of English Speakers

Let *PctES$_i$* be the percentage of "English speakers" in the ith district, defined to be the percentage of students who are not English learners. Again the regressors will be perfectly multicollinear. Like the previous example, the perfect linear relationship among the regressors involves the constant regressor X_{0i}: For every district, $PctES_i = 100 \times X_{0i} - PctEL_i$.

This example illustrates another point: perfect multicollinearity is a feature of the entire set of regressors. If either the intercept (i.e., the regressor X_{0i}) or *PctEL$_i$* were excluded from this regression, the regressors would not be perfectly multicollinear.

The Dummy Variable Trap

Another possible source of perfect multicollinearity arises when multiple binary, or dummy, variables are used as regressors. For example, suppose you have partitioned the school districts into three categories: rural, suburban, and urban. Each district falls into one (and only one) category. Let these binary variables be $Rural_i$, which equals 1 for a rural district and equals 0 otherwise; $Suburban_i$, and $Urban_i$. If you include all three binary variables in the regression along with a constant, the regressors will be perfect multicollinearity: Because each district belongs to one and only one category, $Rural_i + Suburban_i + Urban_i = 1 = X_{0i}$, where X_{0i} denotes the constant regressor introduced in Equation (7.6). Thus, to estimate the regression, you must exclude one of these four variables, either one of the binary indicators or the constant term. By convention, the constant term is retained, in which case one of the binary indicators is excluded. For example, if $Rural_i$ were excluded, then the coefficient on $Suburban_i$ would be the average difference between test scores in suburban and rural districts, holding constant the other variables in the regression.

In general, if there are G binary variables, if each observation falls into one and only one category, if there is an intercept in the regression, and if all G binary variables are included as regressors, then the regression will fail because of perfect multicollinearity. This situation is called the **dummy variable trap**. The usual way to avoid the dummy variable trap is to exclude one of the binary variables from the multiple regression, so only $G - 1$ of the G binary variables are included as regressors. In this case, the coefficients on the included binary variables represent the incremental effect of being in that category, relative to the base case of the omitted category, holding constant the other regressors. Alternatively, all G binary regressors can be included if the intercept is omitted from the regression.

Solutions to Perfect Multicollinearity

Perfect multicollinearity typically arises when a mistake has been made in specifying the regression. Sometimes the mistake is easy to spot (as in the first example) but sometimes it is not (as in the second example). In one way or another your software will let you know if you make such a mistake because it cannot compute the OLS estimator if you have.

When your software lets you know that you have perfect multicollinearity, it is important that you modify your regression to eliminate it. Some software is unreliable when there is perfect multicollinearity, and at a minimum you will be ceding control over your choice of regressors to your computer if your regressors are perfectly multicollinear.

Imperfect Multicollinearity

Despite its similar name, imperfect multicollinearity is conceptually quite different than perfect multicollinearity. **Imperfect multicollinearity** means that two or more of the regressors are highly correlated, in the sense that there is a linear function of the regressors that is highly correlated with another regressor. Imperfect multicollinearity does not pose any problems for the theory of the OLS estimators; indeed, a purpose of OLS is to sort out the independent influences of the various regressors when these regressors are potentially correlated.

If the regressors are imperfectly multicollinear, then the coefficients on at least one individual regressor will be imprecisely estimated. For example, consider the regression of *TestScore* on *STR* and *PctEL*. Suppose we were to add a third regressor, the percentage the district's residents who are first-generation immigrants. First-generation immigrants often speak English as a second language, so the variables *PctEL* and percentage immigrants will be highly correlated: Districts with many recent immigrants will tend to have many students who are still learning English. Because these two variables are highly correlated, it would be difficult to use these data to estimate the partial effect on test scores of an increase in *PctEL,* holding constant the percentage immigrants. In other words, the data set provides little information about what happens to test scores when the percentage of English learners is low but the fraction of immigrants is high, or vice versa. If the least squares assumptions hold, then the OLS estimator of the coefficient on *PctEL* in this regression will be unbiased; however, it will have a larger variance than if the regressors *PctEL* and percentage immigrants were uncorrelated.

The effect of imperfect multicollinearity on the variance of the OLS estimators can be seen mathematically by inspecting the variance of $\hat{\beta}_1$ in a multiple regression with two regressors (X_1 and X_2) for the special case of a homoskedastic error.[1] In this case, the variance of $\hat{\beta}_1$ is inversely

---

[1] $\sigma_{\hat{\beta}_1}^2 = \dfrac{1}{n} \left[\dfrac{1}{1 - \rho_{X_1, X_2}^2} \right] \dfrac{\sigma_u^2}{\sigma_{X_1}^2}$

proportional to $1 - \rho^2_{X_1,X_2}$, where ρ_{X_1,X_2} is the correlation between X_1 and X_2. The larger is the correlation between the two regressors, the closer is this term to zero and the larger is the variance of $\hat{\beta}_1$. More generally, when multiple regressors are imperfectly multicollinear, then the coefficients on one or more of these regressors will be imprecisely estimated—that is, they will have a large sampling variance.

Perfect multicollinearity is a problem that often signals the presence of a logical error. In contrast, imperfect multicollinearity is not necessarily an error, but rather just a feature of OLS, your data, and the question you are trying to answer. If the variables in your regression are the ones you meant to include—the ones you chose to address the potential for omitted variable bias—then imperfect multicollinearity implies that it will be difficult to estimate precisely one or more of the partial effects using the data at hand.

CONCLUSION

Regression with a single regressor is vulnerable to omitted variable bias: If an omitted variable is a determinant of the dependent variable and is correlated with the regressor, then the OLS estimator of the slope coefficient will be biased and will reflect both the effect of the regressor and the effect of the omitted variable. Multiple regression makes it possible to mitigate omitted variable bias by including the omitted variable in the regression. The coefficient on a regressor, X_1, in multiple regression is the partial effect of a change in X_1, holding constant the other included regressors. In the test score example, including the percentage of English learners as a regressor made it possible to estimate the effect on test scores of a change in the student–teacher ratio, holding constant the percentage of English learners. Doing so reduced by half the estimated effect on test scores of a change in the student–teacher ratio.

The statistical theory of multiple regression builds on the statistical theory of regression with a single regressor. The least squares assumptions for multiple regression are extensions of the three least squares assumptions for regression with a single regressor, plus a fourth assumption ruling out perfect multicollinearity. Because the regression coefficients are estimated using a single sample, the OLS estimators have a joint sampling distribution and, therefore, have sampling uncertainty. This sampling

uncertainty must be quantified as part of an empirical study, and the ways to do so in the multiple regression model are the topic of the next chapter.

SUMMARY

1. Omitted variable bias occurs when an omitted variable (1) is correlated with an included regressor and (2) is a determinant of Y.

2. The multiple regression model is a linear regression model that includes multiple regressors, X_1, $X_2, \ldots, X_k$. Associated with each regressor is a regression coefficient, $\beta_1, \beta_2, \ldots, \beta_k$. The coefficient β_1 is the expected change in Y associated with a one-unit change in X_1, holding the other regressors constant. The other regression coefficients have an analogous interpretation.

3. The coefficients in multiple regression can be estimated by OLS. When the four least squares assumptions in Box 7-4 are satisfied, the OLS estimators are unbiased, consistent, and normally distributed in large samples.

4. Perfect multicollinearity, which occurs when one regressor is an exact linear function of the other regressors, usually arises from a mistake in choosing which regressors to include in a multiple regression. Solving perfect multicollinearity requires changing the set of regressors.

5. The standard error of the regression, the R^2, and the $\overline{R}^2$ are measures of fit for the multiple regression model.

Key Terms

omitted variable bias (96)
multiple regression model (100)
population regression line (100)
population regression function (100)
intercept (100)
slope coefficient of X_{1i} (100)
coefficient on X_{1i} (100)
slope coefficient of X_{2i} (100)
coefficient on X_{2i} (100)
control variable (100)
holding X_2 constant (100)
controlling for X_2 (100)
partial effect (100)

population multiple regression model (101)

constant regressor (101)

constant term (101)

homoskedastic (101)

heteroskedastic (101)

OLS estimators of $\beta_0, \beta_1, \ldots, \beta_k$ (102)

OLS regression line (102)

predicted value (102)

OLS residual (102)

R^2 and adjusted R^2 ($\overline{R}^2$) (104)

perfect multicollinearity or to exhibit perfect
multicollinearity (105)

dummy variable trap (108)

imperfect multicollinearity (108)

Hypothesis Tests and Confidence Intervals in Multiple Regression

■ Learning Objectives

Candidates, after completing this reading, should be able to:

- Construct, apply, and interpret hypothesis tests and confidence intervals for a single coefficient in a multiple regression.
- Construct, apply, and interpret hypothesis tests and confidence intervals for multiple coefficients in a multiple regression.
- Define and interpret the F-statistic.
- Describe and interpret tests of single restrictions involving multiple coefficients.

- Define and interpret confidence sets for multiple coefficients.
- Define and describe omitted variable bias in multiple regressions.
- Interpret the R^2 and adjusted-R^2 in a multiple regression.

Excerpt is Chapter 7 of Introduction to Econometrics, *Brief Edition, by James H. Stock and Mark W. Watson.*

As discussed in Chapter 7, multiple regression analysis provides a way to mitigate the problem of omitted variable bias by including additional regressors, thereby controlling for the effects of those additional regressors. The coefficients of the multiple regression model can be estimated by OLS. Like all estimators, the OLS estimator has sampling uncertainty because its value differs from one sample to the next.

This chapter presents methods for quantifying the sampling uncertainty of the OLS estimator through the use of standard errors, statistical hypothesis tests, and confidence intervals. One new possibility that arises in multiple regression is a hypothesis that simultaneously involves two or more regression coefficients. The general approach to testing such "joint" hypotheses involves a new test statistic, the F-statistic.

The first section extends the methods for statistical inference in regression with a single regressor to multiple regression. The next two sections show how to test hypotheses that involve two or more regression coefficients. Next the discussion extends the notion of confidence intervals for a single coefficient to confidence sets for multiple coefficients. Deciding which variables to include in a regression is an important practical issue, so the text includes ways to approach this problem. Finally, we apply multiple regression analysis to obtain improved estimates of the effect on test scores of a reduction in the student–teacher ratio using the California test score data set.

HYPOTHESIS TESTS AND CONFIDENCE INTERVALS FOR A SINGLE COEFFICIENT

This section describes how to compute the standard error, how to test hypotheses, and how to construct confidence intervals for a single coefficient in a multiple regression equation.

Standard Errors for the OLS Estimators

Recall that, in the case of a single regressor, it was possible to estimate the variance of the OLS estimator by substituting sample averages for expectations, which led to the estimator $\hat{\sigma}^2_{\hat{\beta}_1}$ given in Equation (6.4). Under the least squares assumptions, the law of large numbers implies that these sample averages converge to their population

counterparts, so for example $\hat{\sigma}^2_{\hat{\beta}_1}/\sigma^2_{\hat{\beta}_1} \xrightarrow{p} 1$. The square root of $\hat{\sigma}^2_{\hat{\beta}_1}$ is the standard error of $\hat{\beta}_1$, $SE(\hat{\beta}_1)$, an estimator of the standard deviation of the sampling distribution of $\hat{\beta}_1$.

All this extends directly to multiple regression. The OLS estimator $\hat{\beta}_j$ of the jth regression coefficient has a standard deviation, and this standard deviation is estimated by its standard error, $SE(\hat{\beta}_j)$. The formula for the standard error is most easily stated using matrices. The important point is that, as far as standard errors are concerned, there is nothing conceptually different between the single- or multiple-regressor cases. The key ideas—the large-sample normality of the estimators and the ability to estimate consistently the standard deviation of their sampling distribution—are the same whether one has one, two, or 12 regressors.

Hypothesis Tests for a Single Coefficient

Suppose that you want to test the hypothesis that a change in the student–teacher ratio has no effect on test scores, holding constant the percentage of English learners in the district. This corresponds to hypothesizing that the true coefficient β_1 on the student–teacher ratio is zero in the population regression of test scores on STR and PctEL. More generally, we might want to test the hypothesis that the true coefficient β_j on the jth regressor takes on some specific value, $\beta_{j,0}$. The null value $\beta_{j,0}$ comes either from economic theory or, as in the student–teacher ratio example, from the decision-making context of the application. If the alternative hypothesis is two-sided, then the two hypotheses can be written mathematically as

$$H_0: \beta_j = \beta_{j,0} \text{ vs. } H_1: \beta_j \neq \beta_{j,0} \quad \text{(two-sided alternative).} \quad \textbf{(8.1)}$$

For example, if the first regressor is STR, then the null hypothesis that changing the student–teacher ratio has no effect on class size corresponds to the null hypothesis that $\beta_1 = 0$ (so $\beta_{1,0} = 0$). Our task is to test the null hypothesis H_0 against the alternative H_1 using a sample of data.

Box 6-2 gives a procedure for testing this null hypothesis when there is a single regressor. The first step in this procedure is to calculate the standard error of the coefficient. The second step is to calculate the t-statistic using the general formula in Box 6-1. The third step is to compute the p-value of the test using the cumulative normal distribution in Appendix Table 1 on page 173 or, alternatively, to compare the t-statistic to the critical value corresponding

BOX 8-1 Testing the Hypothesis $\beta_j = \beta_{j,0}$ Against the Alternative $\beta_j \neq \beta_{j,0}$

1. Compute the standard error of $\hat{\beta}_j$, $SE(\hat{\beta}_j)$.
2. Compute the t-statistic,

$$t = \frac{\hat{\beta}_j - \beta_{j,0}}{SE(\hat{\beta}_j)} \qquad (8.2)$$

3. Compute the p-value,

$$p\text{-value} = 2\Phi(-|t^{act}|) \qquad (8.3)$$

where t^{act} is the value of the t-statistic actually computed. Reject the hypothesis at the 5% significance level if the p-value is less than 0.05 or, equivalently, if $|t^{act}| > 1.96$.

The standard error and (typically) the t-statistic and p-value testing $\beta_j = 0$ are computed automatically by regression software.

BOX 8-2 Confidence Intervals for a Single Coefficient in Multiple Regression

A 95% two-sided confidence interval for the coefficient β_j is an interval that contains the true value of β_j with a 95% probability; that is, it contains the true value of β_j in 95% of all possible randomly drawn samples. Equivalently, it is the set of values of β_j that cannot be rejected by a 5% two-sided hypothesis test. When the sample size is large, the 95% confidence interval is

$$95\% \text{ confidence interval for } \beta_j$$
$$= [\hat{\beta}_j - 1.96SE(\hat{\beta}_j), \hat{\beta}_j + 1.96SE(\hat{\beta}_j)]. \qquad (8.4)$$

A 90% confidence interval is obtained by replacing 1.96 in Equation (8.4) with 1.645.

---

to the desired significance level of the test. The theoretical underpinning of this procedure is that the OLS estimator has a large-sample normal distribution which, under the null hypothesis, has as its mean the hypothesized true value, and that the variance of this distribution can be estimated consistently.

This underpinning is present in multiple regression as well. As stated in Box 7-5, the sampling distribution of $\hat{\beta}_j$ is approximately normal. Under the null hypothesis the mean of this distribution is $\beta_{j,0}$. The variance of this distribution can be estimated consistently. Therefore we can simply follow the same procedure as in the single-regressor case to test the null hypothesis in Equation (8.1).

The procedure for testing a hypothesis on a single coefficient in multiple regression is summarized as Box 8-1. The t-statistic actually computed is denoted t^{act} in this Box. However, it is customary to denote this simply as t.

Confidence Intervals for a Single Coefficient

The method for constructing a confidence interval in the multiple regression model is also the same as in the single-regressor model. This method is summarized as Box 8-2.

The method for conducting a hypothesis test in Box 8-1 and the method for constructing a confidence interval in

Box 8-2 rely on the large-sample normal approximation to the distribution of the OLS estimator $\hat{\beta}_j$. Accordingly, it should be kept in mind that these methods for quantifying the sampling uncertainty are only guaranteed to work in large samples.

Application to Test Scores and the Student–Teacher Ratio

Can we reject the null hypothesis that a change in the student–teacher ratio has no effect on test scores, once we control for the percentage of English learners in the district? What is a 95% confidence interval for the effect on test scores of a change in the student–teacher ratio, controlling for the percentage of English learners? We are now able to find out. The regression of test scores against STR and PctEL, estimated by OLS, was given in Equation (7.12) and is restated here with standard errors in parentheses below the coefficients:

$$\widehat{TestScore} = 686.0 - 1.10 \times STR - 0.650 \times PctEL \qquad (8.5)$$
$$(8.7) \quad (0.43) \qquad (0.031)$$

To test the hypothesis that the true coefficient on STR is 0, we first need to compute the t-statistic in Equation (8.2). Because the null hypothesis says that the true value of this coefficient is zero, the t-statistic is $t = (-1.10 - 0)/0.43 = -2.54$. The associated p-value is $2\Phi(-2.54) = 1.1\%$; that is, the smallest significance level at which we can reject the null hypothesis is 1.1%. Because the p-value is less than 5%, the null hypothesis can be rejected at the 5% significance level (but not quite at the 1% significance level).

A 95% confidence interval for the population coefficient on STR is $-1.10 \pm 1.96 \times 0.43 = (-1.95, -0.26)$; that is, we can be 95% confident that the true value of the coefficient is between -1.95 and -0.26. Interpreted in the context of the superintendent's interest in decreasing the student–teacher ratio by 2, the 95% confidence interval for the effect on test scores of this reduction is $(-1.95 \times 2, -0.26 \times 2) = (-3.90, -0.52)$.

Adding Expenditures per Pupil to the Equation

Your analysis of the multiple regression in Equation (8.5) has persuaded the superintendent that, based on the evidence so far, reducing class size will help test scores in her district. Now, however, she moves on to a more nuanced question. If she is to hire more teachers, she can pay for those teachers either through cuts elsewhere in the budget (no new computers, reduced maintenance, and so on), or by asking for an increase in her budget, which taxpayers do not favor. What, she asks, is the effect on test scores of reducing the student–teacher ratio, holding expenditures per pupil (and the percentage of English learners) constant?

This question can be addressed by estimating a regression of test scores on the student–teacher ratio, total spending per pupil, and the percentage of English learners. The OLS regression line is

$$\widehat{TestScore} = 649.6 - 0.29 \times STR + 3.87 \qquad (8.6)$$
$$\qquad\quad (15.5) \quad (0.48) \qquad\quad (1.59)$$
$$\times Expn - 0.656 \times PctEL$$
$$(0.032)$$

where Expn is total annual expenditures per pupil in the district in thousands of dollars.

The result is striking. Holding expenditures per pupil and the percentage of English learners constant, changing the student–teacher ratio is estimated to have a very small effect on test scores: The estimated coefficient on STR is -1.10 in Equation (8.5) but, after adding Expn as a regressor in Equation (8.6), it is only -0.29. Moreover, the t-statistic for testing that the true value of the coefficient is zero is now $t = (-0.29 - 0)/0.48 = -0.60$, so the hypothesis that the population value of this coefficient is indeed zero cannot be rejected even at the 10% significance level ($|-0.60| < 1.645$). Thus Equation (8.6)

provides no evidence that hiring more teachers improves test scores if overall expenditures per pupil are held constant.

One interpretation of the regression in Equation (8.6) is that, in these California data, school administrators allocate their budgets efficiently. Suppose, counterfactually, that the coefficient on STR in Equation (8.6) were negative and large. If so, school districts could raise their test scores simply by decreasing funding for other purposes (textbooks, technology, sports, and so on) and transferring those funds to hire more teachers, thereby reducing class sizes while holding expenditures constant. However, the small and statistically insignificant coefficient on STR in Equation (8.6) indicates that this transfer would have little effect on test scores. Put differently, districts are already allocating their funds efficiently.

Note that the standard error on STR increased when Expn was added, from 0.43 in Equation (8.5) to 0.48 in Equation (8.6). This illustrates the general point, introduced in Chapter 7 in the context of imperfect multicollinearity, that correlation between regressors (the correlation between STR and Expn is -0.62) can make the OLS estimators less precise.

What about our angry taxpayer? He asserts that the population values of both the coefficient on the student–teacher ratio (β_1) and the coefficient on spending per pupil (β_2) are zero, that is, he hypothesizes that both $\beta_1 = 0$ and $\beta_2 = 0$. Although it might seem that we can reject this hypothesis because the t-statistic testing $\beta_2 = 0$ in Equation (8.6) is $t = 3.87/1.59 = 2.43$, this reasoning is flawed. The taxpayer's hypothesis is a joint hypothesis, and to test it we need a new tool, the F-statistic.

TESTS OF JOINT HYPOTHESES

This section describes how to formulate joint hypotheses on multiple regression coefficients and how to test them using an F-statistic.

Testing Hypotheses on Two or More Coefficients

Joint Null Hypotheses

Consider the regression in Equation (8.6) of the test score against the student–teacher ratio, expenditures per pupil, and the percentage of English learners. Our angry taxpayer hypothesizes that neither the student–teacher ratio nor expenditures per pupil have an effect on test scores, once we control for the percentage of English learners. Because *STR* is the first regressor in Equation (8.6) and *Expn* is the second, we can write this hypothesis mathematically as

$$H_0: \beta_1 = 0 \text{ and } \beta_2 = 0 \text{ vs. } H_1: \beta_1 \neq 0 \text{ and/or } \beta_2 \neq 0 \quad \textbf{(8.7)}$$

The hypothesis that *both* the coefficient on the student–teacher ratio (β_1) *and* the coefficient on expenditures per pupil (β_2) are zero is an example of a joint hypothesis on the coefficients in the multiple regression model. In this case, the null hypothesis restricts the value of two of the coefficients, so as a matter of terminology we can say that the null hypothesis in Equation (8.7) imposes two **restrictions** on the multiple regression model: $\beta_1 = 0$ *and* $\beta_2 = 0$.

In general, a **joint hypothesis** is a hypothesis that imposes two or more restrictions on the regression coefficients. We consider joint null and alternative hypotheses of the form

$$H_0: \beta_j = \beta_{j,0}, \beta_m = \beta_{m,0}, \ldots, \text{ for a total of } q \text{ restrictions, vs.}$$

$$H_1: \text{one or more of the } q \text{ restrictions under } H_0 \text{ does not hold,} \quad \textbf{(8.8)}$$

where $\beta_j, \beta_m, \ldots$, refer to different regression coefficients, and $\beta_{j,0}, \beta_{m,0}, \ldots$, refer to the values of these coefficients under the null hypothesis. The null hypothesis in Equation (8.7) is an example of Equation (8.8). Another example is that, in a regression with $k = 6$ regressors, the null hypothesis is that the coefficients on the 2nd, 4th, and 5th regressors are zero; that is, $\beta_2 = 0$, $\beta_4 = 0$, and $\beta_5 = 0$, so that there are $q = 3$ restrictions. In general, under the null hypothesis H_0 there are q such restrictions.

If any one (or more than one) of the equalities under the null hypothesis H_0 in Equation (8.8) is false, then the joint null hypothesis itself is false. Thus, the alternative hypothesis is that at least one of the equalities in the null hypothesis H_0 does not hold.

Why Can't I Just Test the Individual Coefficients One at a Time?

Although it seems it should be possible to test a joint hypothesis by using the usual *t*-statistics to test the restrictions one at a time, the following calculation shows that this approach is unreliable. Specifically, suppose that you are interested in testing the joint null hypothesis in Equation (8.6) that $\beta_1 = 0$ and $\beta_2 = 0$. Let t_1 be the

t-statistic for testing the null hypothesis that $\beta_1 = 0$, and let t_2 be the *t*-statistic for testing the null hypothesis that $\beta_2 = 0$. What happens when you use the "one at a time" testing procedure: Reject the joint null hypothesis if either t_1 or t_2 exceeds 1.96 in absolute value?

Because this question involves the two random variables t_1 and t_2, answering it requires characterizing the joint sampling distribution of t_1 and t_2. As mentioned previously, in large samples $\hat{\beta}_1$ and $\hat{\beta}_2$ have a joint normal distribution, so under the joint null hypothesis the *t*-statistics t_1 and t_2 have a bivariate normal distribution, where each *t*-statistic has mean equal to 0 and variance equal to 1.

First consider the special case in which the *t*-statistics are uncorrelated and thus are independent. What is the size of the "one at a time" testing procedure; that is, what is the probability that you will reject the null hypothesis when it is true? More than 5%! In this special case we can calculate the rejection probability of this method exactly. The null is *not* rejected only if both $|t_1| \leq 1.96$ and $|t_2| \leq 1.96$. Because the *t*-statistics are independent, $\Pr(|t_1| \leq 1.96 \text{ and } |t_2| \leq 1.96) = \Pr(|t_1| \leq 1.96) \times \Pr(|t_2| \leq 1.96) = 0.95^2 = 0.9025 = 90.25\%$. So the probability of rejecting the null hypothesis when it is true is $1 - 0.95^2 = 9.75\%$. This "one at a time" method rejects the null too often because it gives you too many chances: If you fail to reject using the first *t*-statistic, you get to try again using the second.

If the regressors are correlated, the situation is even more complicated. The size of the "one at a time" procedure depends on the value of the correlation between the regressors. Because the "one at a time" testing approach has the wrong size—that is, its rejection rate under the null hypothesis does not equal the desired significance level— a new approach is needed.

One approach is to modify the "one at a time" method so that it uses different critical values that ensure that its size equals its significance level. This method, called the Bonferroni method, is described in the Appendix. The advantage of the Bonferroni method is that it applies very generally. Its disadvantage is that it can have low power; it frequently fails to reject the null hypothesis when in fact the alternative hypothesis is true.

Fortunately, there is another approach to testing joint hypotheses that is more powerful, especially when the regressors are highly correlated. That approach is based on the *F*-statistic.

The *F*-Statistic

The **F-statistic** is used to test joint hypothesis about regression coefficients. The formulas for the *F*-statistic are integrated into modern regression software. We first discuss the case of two restrictions, then turn to the general case of *q* restrictions.

The F-*Statistic with* q *= 2 Restrictions*

When the joint null hypothesis has the two restrictions that $\beta_1 = 0$ and $\beta_2 = 0$, the *F*-statistic combines the two t-statistics t_1 and t_2 using the formula

$$F = \frac{1}{2}\left(\frac{t_1^2 + t_2^2 - 2\hat{\rho}_{t_1,t_2} t_1 t_2}{1 - \hat{\rho}_{t_1,t_2}^2}\right) \qquad \textbf{(8.9)}$$

where $\hat{\rho}_{t_1,t_2}$ is an estimator of the correlation between the two *t*-statistics.

To understand the *F*-statistic in Equation (8.9), first suppose that we know that the *t*-statistics are uncorrelated so we can drop the terms involving $\hat{\rho}_{t_1,t_2}$. If so, Equation (8.9) simplifies and $F = \frac{1}{2}(t_1^2 + t_2^2)$; that is, the *F*-statistic is the average of the squared *t*-statistics. Under the null hypothesis, t_1 and t_2 are independent standard normal random variables (because the *t*-statistics are uncorrelated by assumption), so under the null hypothesis F has an $F_{2,\infty}$ distribution. Under the alternative hypothesis that either β_1 is nonzero or β_2 is nonzero (or both), then either t_1^2 or t_2^2 (or both) will be large, leading the test to reject the null hypothesis.

In general the *t*-statistics are correlated, and the formula for the *F*-statistic in Equation (8.9) adjusts for this correlation. This adjustment is made so that, under the null hypothesis, the *F*-statistic has an $F_{2,\infty}$ distribution in large samples whether or not the *t*-statistics are correlated.

The F-*Statistic with* q *Restrictions*

The formula for the heteroskedasticity-robust *F*-statistic testing the *q* restrictions of the joint null hypothesis in Equation (8.8) is a matrix extension of the formula for the heteroskedasticity-robust *t*-statistic. This formula is incorporated into regression software, making the *F*-statistic easy to compute in practice.

Under the null hypothesis, the *F*-statistic has a sampling distribution that, in large samples, is given by the $F_{q,\infty}$ distribution. That is, in large samples, under the null hypothesis

the *F*-statistic is distributed $F_{q,\infty}$ **(8.10)**

Thus the critical values for the *F*-statistic can be obtained from the tables of the $F_{q,\infty}$ distribution for the appropriate value of *q* and the desired significance level.

Computing the Heteroskedasticity-Robust F-Statistic in Statistical Software

If the *F*-statistic is computed using the general heteroskedasticity-robust formula, its large-*n* distribution under the null hypothesis is $F_{q,\infty}$ regardless of whether the errors are homoskedastic or heteroskedastic. As discussed in Chapter 6, for historical reasons most statistical software computes homoskedasticity-only standard errors by default. Consequently, in some software packages you must select a "robust" option so that the *F*-statistic is computed using heteroskedasticity-robust standard errors (and, more generally, a heteroskedasticity-robust estimate of the "covariance matrix"). The homoskedasticity-only version of the *F*-statistic is discussed at the end of this section.

Computing the p-*Value Using the* F-*Statistic*

The *p*-value of the *F*-statistic can be computed using the large-sample $F_{q,\infty}$ approximation to its distribution. Let F^{act} denote the value of the *F*-statistic actually computed. Because the *F*-statistic has a large-sample $F_{q,\infty}$ distribution under the null hypothesis, the *p*-value is

$$p\text{-value} = Pr[F_{q,\infty} > F^{act}] \qquad \textbf{(8.11)}$$

The *p*-value in Equation (8.11) can be evaluated using a table of the $F_{q,\infty}$ distribution (or, alternatively, a table of the χ_q^2 distribution, because a χ_q^2-distributed random variable is *q* times an $F_{q,\infty}$-distributed random variable). Alternatively, the *p*-value can be evaluated using a computer, because formulas for the cumulative chi-squared and *F* distributions have been incorporated into most modern statistical software.

The "Overall" Regression F-*Statistic*

The "overall" regression *F*-statistic tests the joint hypothesis that *all* the slope coefficients are zero. That is, the null and alternative hypotheses are

$$H_0: \beta_1 = 0, \beta_2 = 0, \ldots, \beta_k = 0 \text{ vs.} \qquad \textbf{(8.12)}$$
$$H_1: \beta_j \neq 0, \text{ at least one } j, j = 1, \ldots, k$$

Under this null hypothesis, none of the regressors explains any of the variation in Y_j, although the intercept (which under the null hypothesis is the mean of Y_j) can be nonzero. The null hypothesis in Equation (8.12) is a special case of the general null hypothesis in Equation (8.8), and the overall regression F-statistic is the F-statistic computed for the null hypothesis in Equation (8.12). In large samples, the overall regression F-statistic has an $F_{k,\infty}$ distribution when the null hypothesis is true.

The F-*Statistic when* q = 1

When $q = 1$, the F-statistic tests a single restriction. Then the joint null hypothesis reduces to the null hypothesis on a single regression coefficient, and the F-statistic is the square of the t-statistic.

Application to Test Scores and the Student–Teacher Ratio

We are now able to test the null hypothesis that the coefficients on *both* the student–teacher ratio *and* expenditures per pupil are zero, against the alternative that at least one coefficient is nonzero, controlling for the percentage of English learners in the district.

To test this hypothesis, we need to compute the heteroskedasticity-robust F-statistic of the test that $\beta_1 = 0$ and $\beta_2 = 0$ using the regression of *TestScore* on *STR, Expn,* and *PctEL* reported in Equation (8.6). This F-statistic is 5.43. Under the null hypothesis, in large samples this statistic has an $F_{2,\infty}$ distribution. The 5% critical value of the $F_{2,\infty}$ distribution is 3.00, and the 1% critical value is 4.61. The value of the F-statistic computed from the data, 5.43, exceeds 4.61, so the null hypothesis is rejected at the 1% level. It is very unlikely that we would have drawn a sample that produced an F-statistic as large as 5.43 if the null hypothesis really were true (the p-value is 0.005). Based on the evidence in Equation (8.6) as summarized in this F-statistic, we can reject the taxpayer's hypothesis that *neither* the student–teacher ratio *nor* expenditures per pupil have an effect on test scores (holding constant the percentage of English learners).

The Homoskedasticity-Only F-Statistic

One way to restate the question addressed by the F-statistic is to ask whether relaxing the q restrictions that constitute the null hypothesis improves the fit of the regression by enough that this improvement is unlikely to be the result merely of random sampling variation if the null hypothesis is true. This restatement suggests that there is a link between the F-statistic and

the regression R^2: A large F-statistic should, it seems, be associated with a substantial increase in the R^2. In fact, if the error u_i is homoskedastic, this intuition has an exact mathematical expression. That is, if the error term is homoskedastic, the F-statistic can be written in terms of the improvement in the fit of the regression as measured either by the sum of squared residuals or by the regression R^2. The resulting F-statistic is referred to as the homoskedasticity-only F-statistic, because it is valid only if the error term is homoskedastic. In contrast, the heteroskedasticity-robust F-statistic is valid whether the error term is homoskedastic or heteroskedastic. Despite this significant limitation of the homoskedasticity-only F-statistic, its simple formula sheds light on what the F-statistic is doing. In addition, the simple formula can be computed using standard regression output, such as might be reported in a table that includes regression R^2's but not F-statistics.

The homoskedasticity-only F-statistic is computed using a simple formula based on the sum of squared residuals from two regressions. In the first regression, called the **restricted regression**, the null hypothesis is forced to be true. When the null hypothesis is of the type in Equation (8.8), where all the hypothesized values are zero, the restricted regression is the regression in which those coefficients are set to zero, that is, the relevant regressors are excluded from the regression. In the second regression, called the **unrestricted regression**, the alternative hypothesis is allowed to be true. If the sum of squared residuals is sufficiently smaller in the unrestricted than the restricted regression, then the test rejects the null hypothesis.

The **homoskedasticity-only F-statistic** is given by the formula

$$F = \frac{(SSR_{restricted} - SSR_{unrestricted})/q}{SSR_{unrestricted}/(n - k_{unrestricted} - 1)} \quad \textbf{(8.13)}$$

where $SSR_{restricted}$ is the sum of squared residuals from the restricted regression, $SSR_{unrestricted}$ is the sum of squared residuals from the unrestricted regression, q is the number of restrictions under the null hypothesis, and $k_{unrestricted}$ is the number of regressors in the unrestricted regression. An alternative equivalent formula for the homoskedasticity-only F-statistic is based on the R^2 of the two regressions:

$$F = \frac{(R^2_{unrestricted} - R^2_{restricted})/q}{(1 - R^2_{unrestricted})/(n - k_{unrestricted} - 1)} \quad \textbf{(8.14)}$$

If the errors are homoskedastic, then the difference between the homoskedasticity-only F-statistic computed using Equation (8.13) or (8.14) and the heteroskedasticity-robust F-statistic vanishes as the sample size n increases. Thus, if the errors are homoskedastic, the sampling distribution of the rule-of-thumb F-statistic under the null hypothesis is, in large samples, $F_{q,\infty}$.

The formulas in Equations (8.13) and (8.14) are easy to compute and have an intuitive interpretation in terms of how well the unrestricted and restricted regressions fit the data. Unfortunately, they are valid only if the errors are homoskedastic. Because homoskedasticity is a special case that cannot be counted on in applications with economic data, or more generally with data sets typically found in the social sciences, in practice the homoskedasticity-only F-statistic is not a satisfactory substitute for the heteroskedasticity-robust F-statistic.

Using the Homoskedasticity-Only F-Statistic when n Is Small

If the errors are homoskedastic and are i.i.d. normally distributed, then the homoskedasticity-only F-statistic defined in Equations (8.13) and (8.14) has an $F_{q,n-k_{unrestricted}-1}$ distribution under the null hypothesis. Critical values for this distribution depend on both q and $n - k_{unrestricted} - 1$. As discussed, the $F_{q,n-k_{unrestricted}-1}$ distribution converges to the $F_{q,\infty}$ distribution as n increases; for large sample sizes, the differences between the two distributions are negligible. For small samples, however, the two sets of critical values differ.

Application to Test Scores and the Student–Teacher Ratio

To test the null hypothesis that the population coefficients on *STR* and *Expn* are 0, controlling for *PctEL*, we need to compute the *SSR* (or R^2) for the restricted and unrestricted regression. The unrestricted regression has the regressors *STR*, *Expn*, and *PctEL*, and is given in Equation (8.6); its R^2 is 0.4366; that is, $R^2_{unrestricted} = 0.4366$. The restricted regression imposes the joint null hypothesis that the true coefficients on *STR* and *Expn* are zero; that is, under the null hypothesis *STR* and *Expn* do not enter the population regression, although *PctEL* does (the null hypothesis does not restrict the coefficient on *PctEL*). The restricted regression, estimated by OLS, is

$$\widehat{TestScore} = 664.7 - 0.671 \times PctEL, R^2 = 0.4149 \quad \textbf{(8.15)}$$
$$(1.0) \quad (0.032)$$

so $R^2_{restricted} = 0.4149$. The number of restrictions is $q = 2$, the number of observations is $n = 420$, and the number of regressors in the unrestricted regression is $k = 3$. The homoskedasticity-only F-statistic, computed using Equation (8.14), is

$$F = [(0.4366 - 0.4149)/2]/[(1 - 0.4366)/ (420 - 3 - 1)] = 8.01$$

Because 8.01 exceeds the 1% critical value of 4.61, the hypothesis is rejected at the 1% level using this rule-of-thumb approach.

This example illustrates the advantages and disadvantages of the homoskedasticity-only F-statistic. Its advantage is that it can be computed using a calculator. Its disadvantage is that the values of the homoskedasticity-only and heteroskedasticity-robust F-statistics can be very different: The heteroskedasticity-robust F-statistic testing this joint hypothesis is 5.43, quite different from the less reliable homoskedasticity-only rule-of-thumb value of 8.01.

TESTING SINGLE RESTRICTIONS INVOLVING MULTIPLE COEFFICIENTS

Sometimes economic theory suggests a single restriction that involves two or more regression coefficients. For example, theory might suggest a null hypothesis of the form $\beta_1 = \beta_2$; that is, the effects of the first and second regressor are the same. In this case, the task is to test this null hypothesis against the alternative that the two coefficients differ:

$$H_0: \beta_1 = \beta_2 \text{ vs. } H_1: \beta_1 \neq \beta_2 \quad \textbf{(8.16)}$$

This null hypothesis has a single restriction, so $q = 1$, but that restriction involves multiple coefficients (β_1 and β_2). We need to modify the methods presented so far to test this hypothesis. There are two approaches; which one will be easiest depends on your software.

Approach #1: Test the Restriction Directly

Some statistical packages have a specialized command designed to test restrictions like Equation (8.16) and the result is an F-statistic that, because $q = 1$, has an $F_{1,\infty}$ distribution under the null hypothesis. (Recall that the square of a standard normal random variable has an $F_{1,\infty}$ distribution, so the 95% percentile of the $F_{1,\infty}$ distribution is $1.96^2 = 3.84$.)

Approach #2: Transform the Regression

If your statistical package cannot test the restriction directly, the hypothesis in Equation (8.16) can be tested using a trick in which the original regression equation is rewritten to turn the restriction in Equation (8.16) into a restriction on a single regression coefficient. To be concrete, suppose there are only two regressors, X_{1i} and X_{2i}, in the regression, so the population regression has the form

$$Y_i = \beta_0 + \beta_1 X_{1i} + \beta_2 X_{2i} + u_i \qquad \textbf{(8.17)}$$

Here is the trick: By subtracting and adding $\beta_2 X_{1i}$, we have that $\beta_1 X_{1i} + \beta_2 X_{2i} = \beta_1 X_{1i} - \beta_2 X_{1i} + \beta_2 X_{1i} + \beta_2 X_{2i} = (\beta_1 - \beta_2) X_{1i} + \beta_2 (X_{1i} + X_{2i}) = \gamma_1 X_{1i} + \beta_2 W_i$, where $\gamma_1 = \beta_1 - \beta_2$ and $W_i = X_{1i} + X_{2i}$. Thus, the population regression in Equation (8.17) can be rewritten as

$$Y_i = \beta_0 + \gamma_1 X_{1i} + \beta_2 W_i + u_i \qquad \textbf{(8.18)}$$

Because the coefficient γ_1 in this equation is $\gamma_1 = \beta_1 - \beta_2$, under the null hypothesis in Equation (8.16), $\gamma_1 = 0$ while under the alternative, $\gamma_1 \neq 0$. Thus, by turning Equation (8.17) into Equation (8.18), we have turned a restriction on two regression coefficients into a restriction on a single regression coefficient.

Because the restriction now involves the single coefficient γ_1, the null hypothesis in Equation (8.16) can be tested using the t-statistic method explained earlier. In practice, this is done by first constructing the new regressor W_i as the sum of the two original regressors, then estimating the regression of Y_i on X_{1i} and W_i. A 95% confidence interval for the difference in the coefficients $\beta_1 - \beta_2$ can be calculated as $\hat{\gamma}_1 \pm 1.96 SE(\hat{\gamma}_1)$.

This method can be extended to other restrictions on regression equations using the same trick (see Exercise 9).

The two methods (Approaches #1 and #2) are equivalent, in the sense that the F-statistic from the first method equals the square of the t-statistic from the second method.

Extension to q > 1

In general it is possible to have q restrictions under the null hypothesis in which some or all of these restrictions involve multiple coefficients. The F-statistic from earlier extends to this type of joint hypothesis. The F-statistic can be computed by either of the two methods just discussed for $q = 1$. Precisely how best to do this in practice depends on the specific regression software being used.

CONFIDENCE SETS FOR MULTIPLE COEFFICIENTS

This section explains how to construct a confidence set for two or more regression coefficients. The method is conceptually similar to the method in the first section for constructing a confidence set for a single coefficient using the t-statistic, except that the confidence set for multiple coefficients is based on the F-statistic.

A **95% confidence set** for two or more coefficients is a set that contains the true population values of these coefficients in 95% of randomly drawn samples. Thus, a confidence set is the generalization to two or more coefficients of a confidence interval for a single coefficient.

Recall that a 95% confidence interval is computed by finding the set of values of the coefficients that are not rejected using a t-statistic at the 5% significance level. This approach can be extended to the case of multiple coefficients. To make this concrete, suppose you are interested in constructing a confidence set for two coefficients, β_1 and β_2. Previously we showed how to use the F-statistic to test a joint null hypothesis that $\beta_1 = \beta_{1,0}$ and $\beta_2 = \beta_{2,0}$. Suppose you were to test every possible value of $\beta_{1,0}$ and $\beta_{2,0}$ at the 5% level. For each pair of candidates $(\beta_{1,0}, \beta_{2,0})$, you construct the F-statistic and reject it if it exceeds the 5% critical value of 3.00. Because the test has a 5% significance level, the true population values of β_1 and β_2 will not be rejected in 95% of all samples. Thus, the set of values not rejected at the 5% level by this F-statistic constitutes a 95% confidence set for β_1 and β_2.

Although this method of trying all possible values of $\beta_{1,0}$ and $\beta_{2,0}$ works in theory, in practice it is much simpler to use an explicit formula for the confidence set. This formula for the confidence set for an arbitrary number of coefficients is based on the formula for the F-statistic. When there are two coefficients, the resulting confidence sets are ellipses.

As an illustration, Figure 8-1 shows a 95% confidence set (confidence ellipse) for the coefficients on the student–teacher ratio and expenditure per pupil, holding constant the percentage of English learners, based on the estimated regression in Equation (8.6). This ellipse does not include the point (0,0). This means that the null hypothesis that these two coefficients are both zero is rejected using the F-statistic at the 5% significance level, which we already knew from earlier. The confidence ellipse is a fat

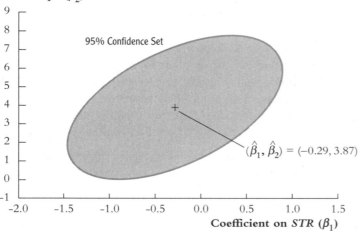

Coefficient on *Expn* (β_2)

$(\hat{\beta}_1, \hat{\beta}_2) = (-0.29, 3.87)$

95% Confidence Set

Coefficient on *STR* (β_1)

FIGURE 8-1 95% confidence set for coefficients on *STR* and *Expn* from Equation (8.6).

The 95% confidence set for the coefficients on *STR* (β_1) and *Expn* (β_2) is an ellipse. The ellipse contains the pairs of values of β_1 and β_2 that cannot be rejected using the *F*-statistic at the 5% significance level.

sausage with the long part of the sausage oriented in the lower-left/upper-right direction. The reason for this orientation is that the estimated correlation between $\hat{\beta}_1$ and $\hat{\beta}_2$ is positive, which in turn arises because the correlation between the regressors *STR* and *Expn* is negative (schools that spend more per pupil tend to have fewer students per teacher).

MODEL SPECIFICATION FOR MULTIPLE REGRESSION

The job of determining which variables to include in multiple regression—that is, the problem of choosing a regression specification—can be quite challenging, and no single rule applies in all situations. But do not despair, because some useful guidelines are available. The starting point for choosing a regression specification is thinking through the possible sources of omitted variable bias. It is important to rely on your expert knowledge of the empirical problem and to focus on obtaining an unbiased estimate of the causal effect of interest; do not rely solely on purely statistical measures of fit such as the R^2 or $\overline{R}^2$.

Omitted Variable Bias in Multiple Regression

The OLS estimators of the coefficients in multiple regression will have omitted variable bias if an omitted determinant of Y_i is correlated with at least one of the regressors. For example, students from affluent families often have more learning opportunities than do their less affluent peers, which could lead to better test scores. Moreover, if the district is a wealthy one, then the schools will tend to have larger budgets and lower student-teacher ratios. If so, the affluence of the students and the student–teacher ratio would be negatively correlated, and the OLS estimate of the coefficient on the student-teacher ratio would pick up the effect of average district income, even after controlling for the percentage of English learners. In short, omitting the students' economic background could lead to omitted variable bias in the regression of test scores on the student–teacher ratio and the percentage of English learners.

The general conditions for omitted variable bias in multiple regression are similar to those for a single regressor: If an omitted variable is a determinant of Y_i and if it is correlated with at least one of the regressors, then the OLS estimators will have omitted variable bias. As was discussed previously, the OLS estimators are correlated, so in general the OLS estimators of all the coefficients will be biased. The two conditions for omitted variable bias in multiple regression are summarized in Box 8-3.

At a mathematical level, if the two conditions for omitted variable bias are satisfied, then at least one of the

BOX 8-3 Omitted Variable Bias in Multiple Regression

Omitted variable bias is the bias in the OLS estimator that arises when one or more included regressors are correlated with an omitted variable. For omitted variable bias to arise, two things must be true:

1. At least one of the included regressors must be correlated with the omitted variable.
2. The omitted variable must be a determinant of the dependent variable, *Y*.

regressors is correlated with the error term. This means that the conditional expectation of u_i given $X_{1i}, \ldots, X_{ki}$ is nonzero, so that the first least squares assumption is violated. As a result, the omitted variable bias persists even if the sample size is large, that is, omitted variable bias implies that the OLS estimators are inconsistent.

Model Specification in Theory and in Practice

In theory, when data are available on the omitted variable, the solution to omitted variable bias is to include the omitted variable in the regression. In practice, however, deciding whether to include a particular variable can be difficult and requires judgment.

Our approach to the challenge of potential omitted variable bias is twofold. First, a core or base set of regressors should be chosen using a combination of expert judgment, economic theory, and knowledge of how the data were collected; the regression using this base set of regressors is sometimes referred to as a **base specification**. This base specification should contain the variables of primary interest and the control variables suggested by expert judgment and economic theory. Expert judgment and economic theory are rarely decisive, however, and often the variables suggested by economic theory are not the ones on which you have data. Therefore the next step is to develop a list of candidate **alternative specifications**, that is, alternative sets of regressors. If the estimates of the coefficients of interest are numerically similar across the alternative specifications, then this provides evidence that the estimates from your base specification are reliable. If, on the other hand, the estimates of the coefficients of interest change substantially across specifications, this often provides evidence that the original specification had omitted variable bias.

Interpreting the R^2 and the Adjusted R^2 in Practice

An R^2 or an $\overline{R}^2$ near 1 means that the regressors are good at predicting the values of the dependent variable in the sample, and an R^2 or an $\overline{R}^2$ near 0 means they are not. This makes these statistics useful summaries of the predictive ability of the regression. However, it is easy to read more into them than they deserve.

There are four potential pitfalls to guard against when using the R^2 or $\overline{R}^2$:

1. *An increase in the R^2 or $\overline{R}^2$ does not necessarily mean that an added variable is statistically significant.* The R^2 increases whenever you add a regressor, whether or not it is statistically significant. The $\overline{R}^2$ does not always increase, but if it does this does not necessarily mean that the coefficient on that added regressor is statistically significant. To ascertain whether an added variable is statistically significant, you need to perform a hypothesis test using the t-statistic.

2. *A high R^2 or $\overline{R}^2$ does not mean that the regressors are a true cause of the dependent variable.* Imagine regressing test scores against parking lot area per pupil. Parking lot area is correlated with the student–teacher ratio, with whether the school is in a suburb or a city, and possibly with district income—all things that are correlated with test scores. Thus the regression of test scores on parking lot area per pupil could have a high R^2 and $\overline{R}^2$, but the relationship is not causal (try telling the superintendent that the way to increase test scores is to increase parking space!).

3. *A high R^2 or $\overline{R}^2$ does not mean there is no omitted variable bias.* Recall the discussion which concerned omitted variable bias in the regression of test scores on the student–teacher ratio. The R^2 of the regression never came up because it played no logical role in this discussion. Omitted variable bias can occur in regressions with a low R^2, a moderate R^2, or a high R^2. Conversely, a low R^2 does not imply that there necessarily is omitted variable bias.

4. *A high R^2 or $\overline{R}^2$ does not necessarily mean you have the most appropriate set of regressors, nor does a low R^2 or $\overline{R}^2$ necessarily mean you have an inappropriate set of regressors.* The question of what constitutes the right set of regressors in multiple regression is difficult and we return to it throughout this textbook. Decisions about the regressors must weigh issues of omitted variable bias, data availability, data quality, and, most importantly, economic theory and the nature of the substantive questions being addressed. None of these questions can be answered simply by having a high (or low) regression R^2 or $\overline{R}^2$.

These points are summarized in Box 8-4.

ANALYSIS OF THE TEST SCORE DATA SET

This section presents an analysis of the effect on test scores of the student–teacher ratio using the California data set. Our primary purpose is to provide an example in which multiple regression analysis is used to mitigate omitted variable bias. Our secondary purpose is to demonstrate how to use a table to summarize regression results.

Discussion of the Base and Alternative Specifications

This analysis focuses on estimating the effect on test scores of a change in the student–teacher ratio, holding constant student characteristics that the superintendent cannot control. Many factors potentially affect the average test score in a district. Some of the factors that could affect test scores are correlated with the student–teacher ratio, so omitting them from the regression will result in omitted variable bias. If data are available on these omitted variables, the solution to this problem is to include them as additional regressors in the multiple regression. When we do this, the coefficient on the student–teacher ratio is the effect of a change in the student–teacher ratio, holding constant these other factors.

Here we consider three variables that control for background characteristics of the students that could affect test scores. One of these control variables is the one we have used previously, the fraction of students who are still learning English. The two other variables are new and control for the economic background of the students. There is no perfect measure of economic background in the data set, so instead we use two imperfect indicators of low income in the district. The first new variable is the percentage of students who are eligible for receiving a subsidized or free lunch at school. Students are eligible for this program if their family income is less than a certain threshold (approximately 150% of the poverty line). The second new variable is the percentage of students in the district whose families qualify for a California income assistance program. Families are eligible for this income assistance program depending in part on their family income, but the threshold is lower (stricter) than the threshold for the subsidized lunch program. These two variables thus measure the fraction of economically disadvantaged children in the district; although they are related, they are not perfectly correlated (their correlation coefficient is 0.74). Although theory suggests that economic background could be an important omitted factor, theory and expert judgment do not really help us decide which of these two variables (percentage eligible for a subsidized lunch or percentage eligible for income assistance) is a better measure of background. For our base specification, we choose the percentage eligible for a subsidized lunch as the economic background variable, but we consider an alternative specification that includes the other variable as well.

Scatterplots of tests scores and these variables are presented in Figure 8-2. Each of these variables exhibits a negative correlation with test scores. The correlation between test scores and the percentage of English learners is −0.64; between test scores and the percentage eligible for a subsidized lunch is −0.87; and between test scores and the percentage qualifying for income assistance is −0.63.

What Scale Should We Use for the Regressors?

A practical question that arises in regression analysis is what scale you should use for the regressors. In Figure 8-2, the units of the variables are percent, so the maximum possible range of the data is 0 to 100. Alternatively, we could have defined these variables to be a *decimal*

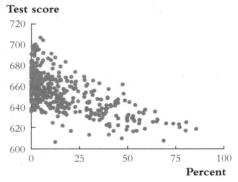

(a) Percentage of English language learners

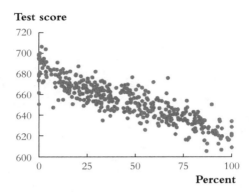

(b) Percentage qualifying for reduced price lunch

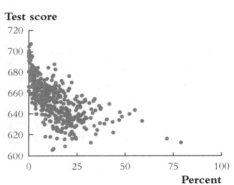

(c) Percentage qualifying for income assistance

FIGURE 8-2 Scatterplots of test scores vs. three student characteristics.

The scatterplots show a negative relationship between test scores and (a) the percentage of English learners (correlation = −0.64), (b) the percentage of students qualifying for a subsidized lunch (correlation = −0.87), and (c) the percentage qualifying for income assistance (correlation = −0.63).

R^2 and SER; however, the coefficient on $FracEL$ would have been −65.0. In the specification with $PctEL$, the coefficient is the predicted change in test scores for a one-percentage-point increase in English learners, holding STR constant; in the specification with $FracEL$, the coefficient is the predicted change in test scores for an increase by 1 in the fraction of English learners—that is, for a 100-percentage-point-increase—holding STR constant. Although these two specifications are mathematically equivalent, for the purposes of interpretation the one with $PctEL$ seems, to us, more natural.

Another consideration when deciding on a scale is to choose the units of the regressors so that the resulting regression coefficients are easy to read. For example, if a regressor is measured in dollars and has a coefficient of 0.00000356, it is easier to read if the regressor is converted to millions of dollars and the coefficient 3.56 is reported.

fraction rather than a percent; for example, *PctEL* could be replaced by the *fraction* of English learners, *FracEL* (= *PctEL*/100), which would range between 0 and 1 instead of between 0 and 100. More generally, in regression analysis some decision usually needs to be made about the scale of both the dependent and independent variables. How, then, should you choose the scale, or units, of the variables?

The general answer to the question of choosing the scale of the variables is to make the regression results easy to read and to interpret. In the test score application, the natural unit for the dependent variable is the score of the test itself. In the regression of *TestScore* on *STR* and *PctEL* reported in Equation (8.5), the coefficient on *PctEL* is −0.650. If instead the regressor had been *FracEL,* the regression would have had an identical

Tabular Presentation of Result

We are now faced with a communication problem. What is the best way to show the results from several multiple regressions that contain different subsets of the possible regressors? So far, we have presented regression results by writing out the estimated regression equations, as in Equation (8.6). This works well when there are only a few regressors and only a few equations, but with more regressors and equations this method of presentation can be confusing. A better way to communicate the results of several regressions is in a table.

Table 8-1 summarizes the results of regressions of the test score on various sets of regressors. Each column summarizes a separate regression. Each regression has the same dependent variable, test score. The entries in the first five

TABLE 8-1 Results of Regressions of Test Scores on the Student–Teacher Ratio and Student Characteristic Control Variables Using California Elementary School Districts

Dependent Variable: Average Test Score in the District

Regressor	(1)	(2)	(3)	(4)	(5)
Student–teacher ratio (X_1)	−2.28** (0.52)	−1.10* (0.43)	−1.00** (0.27)	−1.31** (0.34)	−1.01** (0.27)
Percent English learners (X_2)		−0.650** (0.031)	−0.122** (0.033)	−0.488** (0.030)	−0.130** (0.036)
Percent eligible for subsidized lunch (X_3)			−0.547** (0.024)		−0.529** (0.038)
Percent on public income assistance (X_4)				−0.790** (0.068)	0.048 (0.059)
Intercept	698.9** (10.4)	686.0** (8.7)	700.2** (5.6)	698.0** (6.9)	700.4** (5.5)
Summary Statistics					
SER	18.58	14.46	9.08	11.65	9.08
$\overline{R}^2$	0.049	0.424	0.773	0.626	0.773
n	420	420	420	420	420

These regressions were estimated using the data on K–8 school districts in California, described in Appendix A in Chapter 5. Standard errors are given in parentheses under coefficients. The individual coefficient is statistically significant at the *5% level or **1% significance level using a two-sided test.

rows are the estimated regression coefficients, with their standard errors below them in parentheses. The asterisks indicate whether the *t*-statistics, testing the hypothesis that the relevant coefficient is zero, is significant at the 5% level (one asterisk) or the 1% level (two asterisks). The final three rows contain summary statistics for the regression (the standard error of the regression, *SER*, and the adjusted R^2, $\overline{R}^2$) and the sample size (which is the same for all of the regressions, 420 observations).

All the information that we have presented so far in equation format appears as a column of this table. For example, consider the regression of the test score against the student–teacher ratio, with no control variables. In equation form, this regression is

$$\widehat{TestScore} = 698.9 - 2.28 \times STR, \ \overline{R}^2 = 0.049, \quad \textbf{(8.19)}$$
$$(10.4) \ (0.52)$$
$$SER = 18.58, n = 420$$

All this information appears in column (1) of Table 8-1. The estimated coefficient on the student–teacher ratio

(−2.28) appears in the first row of numerical entries, and its standard error (0.52) appears in parentheses just below the estimated coefficient. The intercept (698.9) and its standard error (10.4) are given in the row labeled "Intercept." (Sometimes you will see this row labeled "constant" because, as discussed earlier, the intercept can be viewed as the coefficient on a regressor that is always equal to 1.) Similarly, the $\overline{R}^2$ (0.049), the *SER* (18.58), and the sample size *n* (420) appear in the final rows. The blank entries in the rows of the other regressors indicate that those regressors are not included in this regression.

Although the table does not report *t*-statistics, these can be computed from the information provided; for example, the *t*-statistic testing the hypothesis that the coefficient on the student–teacher ratio in column (1) is zero is −2.28/0.52 = −4.38. This hypothesis is rejected at the 1% level, which is indicated by the double asterisk next to the estimated coefficient in the table.

Regressions that include the control variables measuring student characteristics are reported in columns (2)−(5).

Column (2), which reports the regression of test scores on the student–teacher ratio and on the percentage of English learners, was previously stated as Equation (8.5).

Column (3) presents the base specification, in which the regressors are the student–teacher ratio and two control variables, the percentage of English learners and the percentage of students eligible for a free lunch.

Columns (4) and (5) present alternative specifications that examine the effect of changes in the way the economic background of the students is measured. In column (4), the percentage of students on income assistance is included as a regressor, and in column (5) both of the economic background variables are included.

Discussion of Empirical Results

These results suggest three conclusions:

1. Controlling for these student characteristics cuts the effect of the student–teacher ratio on test scores approximately in half. This estimated effect is not very sensitive to which specific control variables are included in the regression. In all cases the coefficient on the student–teacher ratio remains statistically significant at the 5% level. In the four specifications with control variables, regressions (2)−(5), reducing the student–teacher ratio by one student per teacher is estimated to increase average test scores by approximately one point, holding constant student characteristics.

2. The student characteristic variables are very useful predictors of test scores. The student–teacher ratio alone explains only a small fraction of the variation in test scores: The $\overline{R}^2$ in column (1) is 0.049. The $\overline{R}^2$ jumps, however, when the student characteristic variables are added. For example, the $\overline{R}^2$ in the base specification, regression (3), is 0.773. The signs of the coefficients on the student demographic variables are consistent with the patterns seen in Figure 8-2: Districts with many English learners and districts with many poor children have lower test scores.

3. The control variables are not always individually statistically significant: In specification (5), the hypothesis that the coefficient on the percentage qualifying for income assistance is zero is not rejected at the 5% level (the t-statistic is −0.82). Because adding this control variable to the base specification (3) has a negligible effect on the estimated coefficient for the student–teacher

ratio and its standard error, and because the coefficient on this control variable is not significant in specification (5), this additional control variable is redundant, at least for the purposes of this analysis.

CONCLUSION

Chapter 7 began with a concern: In the regression of test scores against the student–teacher ratio, omitted student characteristics that influence test scores might be correlated with the student–teacher ratio in the district, and if so the student–teacher ratio in the district would pick up the effect on test scores of these omitted student characteristics. Thus, the OLS estimator would have omitted variable bias. To mitigate this potential omitted variable bias, we augmented the regression by including variables that control for various student characteristics (the percentage of English learners and two measures of student economic background). Doing so cuts the estimated effect of a unit change in the student–teacher ratio in half, although it remains possible to reject the null hypothesis that the population effect on test scores, holding these control variables constant, is zero at the 5% significance level. Because they eliminate omitted variable bias arising from these student characteristics, these multiple regression estimates, hypothesis tests, and confidence intervals are much more useful for advising the superintendent than the single-regressor estimates of Chapters 5 and 6.

The analysis in this and the preceding chapter has presumed that the population regression function is linear in the regressors—that is, that the conditional expectation of Y_i given the regressors is a straight line. There is, however, no particular reason to think this is so. In fact, the effect of reducing the student–teacher ratio might be quite different in districts with large classes than in districts that already have small classes. If so, the population regression line is not linear in the X's but rather is a nonlinear function of the X's.

SUMMARY

1. Hypothesis tests and confidence intervals for a single regression coefficient are carried out using essentially the same procedures that were used in the

one-variable linear regression model of Chapter 6. For example, a 95% confidence interval for β_1 is given by $\hat{\beta}_1 \pm 1.96SE(\hat{\beta}_1)$.

2. Hypotheses involving more than one restriction on the coefficients are called joint hypotheses. Joint hypotheses can be tested using an *F*-statistic.

3. Regression specification proceeds by first determining a base specification chosen to address concern about omitted variable bias. The base specification can be modified by including additional regressors that address other potential sources of omitted variable bias. Simply choosing the specification with the highest R^2 can lead to regression models that do not estimate the causal effect of interest.

Key Terms

restrictions (117)
joint hypothesis (117)
F-statistic (118)
restricted regression (119)
unrestricted regression (119)
homoskedasticity-only *F*-statistic (119)
95% confidence set (121)
base specification (123)
alternative specifications (123)
Bonferroni test (128)

APPENDIX

The Bonferroni Test of a Joint Hypothesis

The method described in the second section of this chapter is the preferred way to test joint hypotheses in multiple regression. However, if the author of a study presents regression results but did not test a joint restriction in which you are interested, and you do not have the original data, then you will not be able to compute the *F*-statistic as shown earlier. This appendix describes a way to test joint hypotheses that can be used when you only have a table of regression results. This method is an application of a very general testing approach based on Bonferroni's inequality.

The Bonferroni test is a test of a joint hypothesis based on the *t*-statistics for the individual hypotheses; that is, the

Bonferroni test is the one-at-a-time *t*-statistic test done properly. The **Bonferroni test** of the joint null hypothesis $\beta_1 = \beta_{1,0}$ and $\beta_2 = \beta_{2,0}$ based on the critical value $c > 0$ uses the following rule:

Accept if $|t_1| \leq c$ and if $|t_2| \leq c$; otherwise **(8.20)**

reject (Bonferroni one-at-a-time *t*-statistic test)

where t_1 and t_2 are the *t*-statistics that test the restrictions on β_1 and β_2, respectfully.

The trick is to choose the critical value *c* in such a way that the probability that the one-at-a-time test rejects when the null hypothesis is true is no more than the desired significance level, say 5%. This is done by using Bonferroni's inequality to choose the critical value *c* to allow both for the fact that two restrictions are being tested and for any possible correlation between t_1 and t_2.

Bonferroni's Inequality

Bonferroni's inequality is a basic result of probability theory. Let *A* and *B* be events. Let $A \cap B$ be the event "both *A* and *B*" (the intersection of *A* and *B*), and let $A \cup B$ be the event "*A* or *B* or both" (the union of *A* and *B*). Then $\Pr(A \cup B) = \Pr(A) + \Pr(B) - \Pr(A \cap B)$. Because $\Pr(A \cap B) \geq 0$, it follows that $\Pr(A \cup B) \leq \Pr(A) + \Pr(B)$. This inequality in turn implies that $1 - \Pr(A \cup B) \geq 1 - [\Pr(A) + \Pr(B)]$. Let A^c and B^c be the complements of *A* and *B*, that is, the events "not *A*" and "not *B*." Because the complement of $A \cup B$ is $A^c \cap B^c$, $1 - \Pr(A \cup B) = \Pr(A^c \cap B^c)$, which yields Bonferroni's inequality, $\Pr(A^c \cap B^c) \geq 1 - [\Pr(A) + \Pr(B)]$.

Now let *A* be the event that $|t_1| > c$ and *B* be the event that $|t_2| > c$. Then the inequality $\Pr(A \cup B) \leq \Pr(A) + \Pr(B)$ yields

$$\Pr(|t_1| > c \text{ or } |t_2| > c \text{ or both}) \quad \textbf{(8.21)}$$
$$\leq \Pr(|t_1| > c) + \Pr(|t_2| > c)$$

Bonferroni Tests

Because the event "$|t_1| > c$ or $|t_2| > c$ or both" is the rejection region of the one-at-a-time test, Equation (8.21) provides a way to choose the critical value *c* so that the "one at a time" *t*-statistic has the desired significance level in large samples. Under the null hypothesis in large samples, $\Pr(|t_1| > c) = \Pr(|t_2| > c) = \Pr(|Z| > c)$.

TABLE 8-2 Bonferroni Critical Values c for the One-at-a-Time t-Statistic Test of a Joint Hypothesis

Number of Restrictions (q)	Significance Level		
	10%	5%	1%
2	1.960	2.241	2.807
3	2.128	2.394	2.935
4	2.241	2.498	3.023

Thus Equation (8.21) implies that, in large samples, the probability that the one-at-a-time test rejects under the null is

$$\text{Pr}_{H_0}(\text{one-at-a-time test rejects}) \leq 2\text{Pr}(|Z| > c) \qquad \textbf{(8.22)}$$

The inequality in Equation (8.22) provides a way to choose critical value c so that the probability of the rejection under the null hypothesis equals the desired significance level. The Bonferroni approach can be extended to more than two coefficients; if there are q restrictions under the null, the factor of 2 on the right-hand side in Equation (8.22) is replaced by q.

Table 8-2 presents critical values c for the one-at-a-time Bonferroni test for various significance levels and $q = 2$, 3, and 4. For example, suppose the desired significance level is 5% and $q = 2$. According to Table 8-2, the critical value c is 2.241. This critical value is the 1.25% percentile of the standard normal distribution, so $\text{Pr}(|Z| > 2.241) = 2.5\%$. Thus Equation (8.22) tells us that, in large samples, the one-at-a-time test in Equation (8.20) will reject at most 5% of the time under the null hypothesis.

The critical values in Table 8-2 are larger than the critical values for testing a single restriction. For example, with $q = 2$, the one-at-a-time test rejects if at least one t-statistic exceeds 2.241 in absolute value. This critical value is greater than 1.96 because it properly corrects for the fact that, by looking at two t-statistics, you get a second chance to reject the joint null hypothesis.

If the individual t-statistics are based on heteroskedasticity-robust standard errors, then the Bonferroni test is valid whether or not there is heteroskedasticity, but if the t-statistics are based on homoskedasticity-only standard errors, the Bonferroni test is valid only under homoskedasticity.

Application to Test Scores

The t-statistics testing the joint null hypothesis that the true coefficients on test scores and expenditures per pupil in Equation (8.6) are, respectively, $t_1 = -0.60$ and $t_2 = 2.43$. Although $|t_1| < 2.241$, because $|t_2| > 2.241$, we can reject the joint null hypothesis at the 5% significance level using the Bonferroni test. However, both t_1 and t_2 are less than 2.807 in absolute value, so we cannot reject the joint null hypothesis at the 1% significance level using the Bonferroni test. In contrast, using the F-statistic, we were able to reject this hypothesis at the 1% significance level.

Simulation Modeling

■ Learning Objectives

Candidates, after completing this reading, should be able to:

- Describe different ways of choosing probability distributions in creating simulation models.
- Understand and interpret the results generated by Monte Carlo simulation.
- Describe the advantages of simulation modeling when multiple input variables and compounding distributions are involved.
- Describe how correlations can be incorporated into simulation modeling.
- Describe the relationship between the accuracy of a simulation model and the number of scenarios run in the simulation.
- Interpret discretization error bias and describe how to identify an efficient estimator.

- Describe the inverse transform method and its implementation in discrete and continuous distributions.
- Describe standards for an effective pseudorandom number generator and explain midsquare technique and congruential pseudorandom number generators.
- Describe quasi-random (low-discrepancy) sequences and explain how they work in simulations.
- Explain the mechanics and characteristics of the stratified sampling method and describe the Latin Hypercube Sampling method.

Excerpt is Chapter 4 of Simulation and Optimization in Finance, *by Dessislava A. Pachamanova and Frank Fabozzi.*

This chapter reviews the main idea behind Monte Carlo (MC) simulation, and discusses important issues in its application to business problems, such as number of scenarios to generate, interpretation of output, and efficient ways to simulate random numbers.

MONTE CARLO SIMULATION: A SIMPLE EXAMPLE

The analysis of risk is based on modeling uncertainty, and uncertainty can be represented mathematically by probability distributions. These probability distributions are the building blocks for simulation models. Namely, simulation models take probability distribution assumptions on the uncertainties as inputs, and generate scenarios (often referred to as *trials*) that happen with probabilities described by the probability distributions. They then record what happens to variables of interest (called *output variables*) over these scenarios, and let us analyze the characteristics of the output probability distributions (see Figure 9-1).

Let us start with a simple example. Suppose you want to invest $1,000 in the U.S. stock market for one year. To do so, you decide that you want to invest in a stock index that represents the performance of the stock market. Specifically, you invest in a mutual fund whose investment objective is to reproduce the return performance on the S&P 500. A mutual fund with such an objective is referred to as an *index fund.* We will denote the initial investment, or capital, invested in the index fund as C_0 (i.e., $C_0 =$ $1,000). How much money do you expect to have at the end of the year? Let us label the amount of capital at the end of the year by $\tilde{C}_1$.[1] Note that $\tilde{C}_1$ will be a random variable because it will depend on how the market (i.e., S&P 500) performs over the year. In fact, if we let $\tilde{r}_{0,1}$ denote the market return over the time period [0,1), then $\tilde{C}_1$ will equal

$$C_0 + \tilde{r}_{0,1} C_0$$

or, equivalently,

$$(1 + \tilde{r}_{0,1})C_0$$

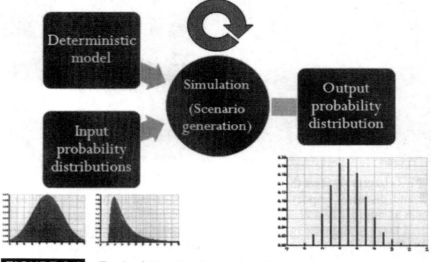

FIGURE 9-1 Typical Monte Carlo simulation system.

The return r_t, $t + 1$ over a time period $[t, t + 1)$ can be computed as

$$\frac{P_{t+1} - P_t + D_t}{P_t}$$

where P_t and P_{t+1} are the values of the S&P 500 at times t and $t + 1$, respectively, and D_t is the amount of dividends paid over that time period. In this case, we can think of P_t and P_{t+1} as the S&P 500 index levels at the beginning ($t = 0$) and at the end of the year ($t = 1$), respectively, and assume that D_t is 0.

To estimate the end of year capital you would have, you can guess the return on the market, and compute the resulting value for $\tilde{C}_1$. However, this would give you only a point estimate of the possible values for your investment. A more sophisticated approach is to generate scenarios for the market return over the year, and compute $\tilde{C}_1$ in each of these scenarios. In other words, you can represent future returns by a probability distribution,[2] generate scenarios that are representative of this probability distribution, and then analyze the resulting distribution of your end-of-year capital. The resulting probability

---

[1] Recall that we use tilde (~) to denote uncertain quantities and random variables.

[2] Note that there are an infinite number of values a return can take, since a return is expressed as a percentage. So, while you can certainly input a discrete set of possible scenarios for return, it is not unnatural to assume that the actual realization of the return is drawn from a *continuous* probability distribution.

distribution of $\tilde{C}_1$ will be a set of scenarios itself. You can create a histogram of the outcomes, that is, collect the outcomes of the scenarios into nonoverlapping bins and draw bars above all bins with heights corresponding to the percentage of times outcomes in each bin were obtained in the simulation. This will allow you to visualize the *approximate* probability distribution of $\tilde{C}_1$, and analyze it with the statistical measures (central tendency, skew, variability, etc.). The distribution for $\tilde{C}_1$ from the simulation will be only an approximation because it will depend both on the *number* of scenarios and on the *set* of scenarios you generated for $\tilde{r}_{0,1}$. Intuitively, if you generate 1,000 scenarios that cover the possible values for $\tilde{r}_{0,1}$ well, you would expect to obtain a better representation of the distribution of $\tilde{C}_1$ than if you generated only two scenarios.

Selecting Probability Distributions for the Inputs

The first question you need to ask yourself when creating the simulation model about the future values of your funds is what distribution is appropriate for modeling the future market returns. One possible starting point is to look at a historical distribution of past returns, and assume that the future will behave in the same way. When creating scenarios for future realizations, then, you can draw randomly from historical scenarios. This is a very simple approach, which is based on the *bootstrapping* technique.

Another possibility is to assume a particular probability distribution for future returns, and use historical data to estimate the *parameters* of this distribution, that is, the parameters that determine the specific shape of the distribution, such as the expected value (μ) and standard deviation (σ) for a normal distribution, λ for a Poisson distribution, or α and β for a beta distribution. For example, if you assume a normal distribution for returns, then you can use the historical variability of returns as a measure of the standard deviation σ of this normal distribution, and the historical average (mean) as the expected return μ of the normal distribution.

A third approach is not to start out with a particular distribution, but to use historical data to find a distribution for returns that provides the best *fit* to the data. The chi-square hypothesis test is one possible goodness-of-fit test. Other goodness-of-fit tests include the Kolmogorov-Smirnov (K-S) test, the Anderson-Darling (A-D) test, and

root-mean-squared-error (RMSE).[3] Most simulation software packages, have commands that can test the goodness of fit for different probability distributions.

Yet a fourth way is to ignore the past and look forward, constructing a probability distribution based on your subjective guess about how the uncertain variable in your model will behave. For example, using the beta distribution to model the future market return will express a more pessimistic view about the market than using the beta distribution or a normal distribution because most of the probability mass in the distribution is to the left, so low values for return will happen more often when scenarios are generated.

It is important to realize that none of these approaches will provide *the answer.* Simulation is a great tool for modeling uncertainty, but the outcome is only as good as the inputs we provide to our models. We discuss ways for defining input distributions in specific applications in the book. The art of simulation modeling is in providing good inputs and interpreting the results carefully.

Interpreting Monte Carlo Simulation Output

For purposes of our example, let us assume that the return on the market over the next year will follow a normal distribution. (This is a widely used assumption in practice, despite the fact that few empirical studies find evidence to support it.) Between 1977 and 2007,

---

[3] There is no rule for which goodness-of-fit test is "best." Each of them has advantages and disadvantages. The chi-square test is the most general one, and can be used for data that come from both continuous and discrete distributions; however, to calculate the chi-square test statistic, one needs to divide the data into "bins," and the results depend strongly on how the bins are determined. The K-S and the A-D tests apply only for continuous distributions. They do not depend on dividing the data into bins, so their results are less arbitrary. The K-S statistic is concerned primarily with whether the *centers* of the empirical and the expected distribution are "close," whereas A-D focuses on the discrepancy between the *tails* of the observed and the expected distribution. For all three tests, the smaller the value of the test statistic, the closer the fit is. (Most statistical software packages report a *p*-value, that is, a "probability," in addition to a test statistic. The larger the *p*-value, the closer the fit.) Finally, the RMSE measures the squared error of the differences between observed and the expected values. The smaller the number, the better, but the actual magnitude of the RMSE depends on the distribution and data at hand.

the S&P 500 returned 8.79% per annum on average, with a standard deviation of 14.65%. We will use these numbers as approximations for the average return and the standard deviation of the return on your investment in the stock market over the next year. Relying on historical data is flawed, but is a reasonable starting point.

Here, we discuss the output one would obtain after generating 100 scenarios for the market return over the next year. Note that to generate these scenarios, we simply need to draw 100 numbers from a normal distribution with mean 8.79% and standard deviation 14.65%. The input to the simulation would then be a sequence of 100 numbers such as

```
     0.0245
    -0.1561
     0.1063
     0.1300
    -0.0801
     0.2624
     0.2621
     0.0824
     0.1358
     0.1135
     0.0605
```

and so on.

The output graph would look like Figure 9-2. Summary statistics obtained based on the 100 values of the distribution are provided to the right of the graph.[4]

If historical trends hold, you would expect to have $1,087.90 on average at the end of the first year. The standard deviation of the end-year capital you would expect is $146.15, that is, on average, you would expect to be $146.15 off the mean value. With 5% probability, you will not be able to make more than $837.00 (the 5th percentile of the distribution), and with 95% probability you will make less than $1,324.00 (the 95th percentile of the distribution). The skewness is close to 0, and the kurtosis is

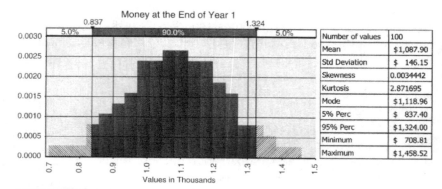

Number of values	100
Mean	$1,087.90
Std Deviation	$ 146.15
Skewness	0.0034442
Kurtosis	2.871695
Mode	$1,118.96
5% Perc	$ 837.40
95% Perc	$1,324.00
Minimum	$ 708.81
Maximum	$1,458.52

FIGURE 9-2 Histogram and summary statistics for the end-of-year distribution of 100 simulated values for $1,000 invested at the beginning of the year.

close to 3, which means that the simulated distribution is close to normal. (In fact, the output distribution is normal because the input distribution we provided for the simulation of this simple relationship was normal, but the estimate from the simulation will never be perfectly accurate.)

Be careful with the interpretation of minima and maxima in a simulation. Theoretically, the minimum and maximum we could have obtained in this simulation are negative and positive infinity because the probability distribution for the return (the normal distribution) has an infinite range. We did not obtain a particularly small minimum or a particularly large maximum because we only simulated 100 values. An event in the tail of the distribution with probability of occurring of less than 1/100 would be unlikely to appear in this set of simulated values. The minimum and the maximum are highly sensitive to the number of simulated values and whether the simulated values in the tails of the distribution provide good representation for the tails of the distribution. There are smart ways to simulate scenarios so that the tails are well represented (we will talk about such methods later in this chapter), but the minimum and the maximum values obtained in a simulation should nevertheless be interpreted with care.

The main idea of statistical concept of confidence interval (CI) estimates is the following: In statistics, when we want to estimate a specific parameter of a distribution, such as the mean, we take a sample and observe what the value of the parameter is in the sample (in technical terms, we record the value of the *sample statistic* for the mean). Instead of reporting a single value for our estimate for the mean, however, we could report an interval whose length is related to the

---

[4] Note that, depending on the specific set of 100 scenarios we have generated, the graph will look different. Therefore, the descriptive statistics and the look of the graph we present here will only be close to what you would obtain if you try to repeat this experiment.

probability that the true distribution parameter indeed lies in that interval.

Simulation is very similar to statistical sampling in that we try to represent the uncertainty by generating scenarios, that is, "sampling" values for the output parameter of interest from an underlying probability distribution. When we estimate the average (or any other parameter of interest) of the sample of scenarios, we run into the same issue statisticians do—we need to worry about the accuracy of our estimate. To compute a 95% CI estimate for the average end-of-year capital, we use the 95% CI formula and substitute the values obtained from the simulation statistics: $N = 100$, $\overline{X} = 1{,}087.90$, and $s = 146.15$. The value for $t_{(100-\alpha/2)\%,N-1}$ for 95% CI is the value of the 97.5th percentile of the standard t-distribution with 99 degrees of freedom, which is 1.98. The 95% CI is therefore

$$\left(1{,}087.90 - 1.98 \cdot \frac{146.15}{\sqrt{100}}, 1{,}087.90 + 1.98 \cdot \frac{146.15}{\sqrt{100}}\right)$$
$$= (\$1{,}058.90, \$1{,}116.90).$$

Therefore, if the 100 scenarios were *independent* when generated, we can be 95% confident that the true average end-of-year capital will be between $1,058.90 and $1,116.90. It just happens that because of the simplicity of the example, we know exactly what the true mean is. It is $(1 + 0.0879) \cdot 1{,}000 = \$1{,}087.90$ because 8.79% was assumed to be the true mean of the distribution of returns, and it is indeed contained inside the 95% CI. In 5% of all possible collections of 100 scenarios, however, we will be unlucky to draw a very extreme sample of scenarios, and the true mean will not be contained in the confidence interval we obtain. Note that if we had calculated a 99% confidence interval, then this would happen in only 1% of the cases. If we generated $4N$ (instead of N) scenarios, then the 95% confidence interval's length would be half of the current length. (This is because the square root of the number of scenarios is contained in the denominator of the expression that determines the length of the confidence interval.) We will revisit the issue of confidence interval estimation and the implications for accuracy again later in this chapter when we talk about the number of scenarios needed in a simulation.

Also later in this chapter, we will explain how random numbers are actually generated. We will see that drawing "independent" samples from distributions is not the most efficient way to simulate random numbers that provide good representation of the underlying probability distribution. Most simulation engines nowadays use sophisticated methodology that estimates parameters from the distribution of output variables of interest a lot more accurately. The previous CI formula we used is in fact a conservative bound, rather than an exact estimate, for the actual accuracy in estimating the mean. Still, it is a useful benchmark to have.

WHY USE SIMULATION?

The example in the previous section illustrated a very basic MC simulation system. We started out with a deterministic model that involved a relationship between an input variable (market return $\tilde{r}_{0,1}$) and an output variable of interest (capital at the end of one year $\tilde{C}_1$). We modeled the input variable as a realization of a probability distribution (we assumed a normal distribution), generated scenarios for that input variable, and tracked what the value of the output variable was in every scenario by computing it through the formula that defines the relationship between $\tilde{C}_1$ and $\tilde{r}_{0,1}$. This is the general form of simulation models illustrated in Figure 9-1.

Despite its simplicity, this example allows us to point out one of the advantages of simulation modeling over pure mathematical modeling. Simulation enables us to evaluate (approximately) a *function* of a random variable. In this case, the function is very simple—the end-of-year capital, $\tilde{C}_1$, is dependent on the realization of the returns through the equation $(1 + \tilde{r}_{0,1})C_0$. If we are given a probability distribution for $\tilde{r}_{0,1}$, in some cases we can compute the probability distribution for $\tilde{C}_1$ in closed form. For example, if $\tilde{r}_{0,1}$ followed a normal distribution with mean $\mu_{0,1} = E[\tilde{r}_{0,1}]$ and standard deviation $\sigma_{0,1}$, then $\tilde{C}_1$ would follow a normal distribution too, with mean $(1 + \mu_{0,1})C_0$ and standard deviation $\sigma_{0,1}C_0$.

However, if $\tilde{r}_{0,1}$ did not follow a normal distribution, or if the output variable $\tilde{C}_1$ were a more complex function of the input variable $\tilde{r}_{0,1}$, it would be difficult and practically impossible to derive the probability distribution of $\tilde{C}_1$ from the probability distribution of $\tilde{r}_{0,1}$. Using simulation simplifies matters substantially.

There are three other important advantages of simulation that can only be appreciated in more complex situations. The first one is that simulation enables us to visualize the probability distribution resulting from compounding probability distributions for multiple input variables. The second is that it allows us to incorporate correlations between input variables. The third is that simulation is a low-cost tool for checking the effect of changing a strategy on an output variable of interest. Next, we extend the investment example to provide illustrations of such situations.

Multiple Input Variables and Compounding Distributions

Suppose now that you are planning for retirement and decide to invest in the market for the next 30 years (instead of only the next year). Suppose that your initial capital is still $1,000. You are interested in the return (and, ultimately, in the end-of-year capital, $\tilde{C}_{30}$) you will have after 30 years.

Let us assume that every year, your investment returns from investing in the S&P 500 will follow a normal distribution with the mean and standard deviation from the example mentioned earlier. The final capital you have will depend on the realizations of 30 random variables—one for each year you are invested in the market.[5] We found through simulation earlier that the probability distribution of the capital at the end of the first year will be normal. What do you think the probability distributions for the total return and the capital at the end of the 30th year will look like? Will they be normal?

An investment of $1 at time 0 will grow to $(1 + \tilde{r}_{0,1})$ $(1 + \tilde{r}_{1,2}) \ldots (1 + \tilde{r}_{t-1,t})$ dollars at the end of year t, and the total return $\tilde{r}_{0,t}$ from time 0 to time t equals

$$\tilde{r}_{0,t} = (1 + \tilde{r}_{0,1})(1 + \tilde{r}_{1,2}) \ldots (1 + \tilde{r}_{t-1,t}) - 1.$$

Interestingly, the probability distribution of $\tilde{r}_{0,t}$ is not normal, and neither is the distribution of the capital at the end of 30 years. (The latter is basically a scaled version of the distribution of total return, since it can be obtained as $\tilde{C}_{0,t} = (1 + \tilde{r}_{0,t}) \cdot C_0$, and the initial capital C_0 is a constant [nonrandom] number). In general, here are some useful facts to keep in mind when dealing with multiple input probability distributions:

- When a constant is added to a random variable, as in 1 added to the random variable $\tilde{r}_{0,1}$, the distribution of $(1 + \tilde{r}_{0,1})$ has the same shape as the distribution of $\tilde{r}_{0,1}$; however, it is shifted to the right by 1.

- When a random variable is added to another random variable (e.g., $\tilde{r}_{0,1} + \tilde{r}_{1,2}$), we cannot simply "add" the two probability distributions. In fact, even in cases when the two distributions have the same shape, the probability distribution of the sum of the random variables does not necessarily have the same shape. There are some exceptions—for instance, if we add two independent normal random variables, the probability distribution of the sum is normal. However, holding aside this case, this is not true in general.

- In our example, we are *multiplying* two random variables, $(1 + \tilde{r}_{0,1})$ and $(1 + \tilde{r}_{1,2})$ in order to obtain the total return. Products of random variables are even more difficult to visualize than sums of random variables. Again, it virtually never happens that a product of several random variables, even if the random variables all follow the same probability distributions, results in a random variable with that same probability distribution. The lognormal distribution is a rare exception, and this is one of the reasons that the lognormal distribution is used so often in financial modeling.

Fortunately, simulation makes visualizing the probability distribution of the product easy. Figure 9-3 presents the output distributions for total return and capital at the end of 30 years. We can observe (both from the graph and from the statistics for skewness and kurtosis) that the distribution is very skewed, even though the distributions for individual returns in each of the 30 years were symmetric.

Incorporating Correlations

Let us now complicate the situation more. Suppose that you have the opportunity to invest in stocks and Treasury bonds over the next 30 years. Suppose that today you allocate 50% of your capital to the stock market by investing in the index fund, and 50% in bonds. Furthermore, suppose over the 30 years you never rebalance your portfolio (i.e., you do not change the allocation between stocks and bonds). What will be the portfolio return after 30 years?

Historically, stock market and Treasury bond market returns have exhibited extremely low, but often statistically significant, negative correlation. This is because these two asset classes tend to move in opposite directions. When the stock market is performing poorly, investors tend to move their money to what they perceive to be safer investments such as bonds; conversely, when the stock market is performing

---

[5] We do not discuss the possibility that returns in different years may be correlated here.

well, investors tend to reallocate their portfolio increasing their allocation to the stock market and reducing their allocation to bonds.

Visualizing the impact of multiple input variables at the same time and incorporating correlations between these variables is very difficult to do in an analytical way. Simulation eliminates the need for complex mathematics, but preserves the benefits of creating richer and more accurate models. Correlations can be incorporated implicitly (by generating joint scenarios for realizations of input variables, e.g., by sampling from observed past data) or explicitly, by specifying a correlations matrix as an input to the simulation. Here, we give an example in which the correlations are specified as an input.

Let us assume that the correlation between the stock market and the Treasury bond market returns will be about −0.2. Let us also assume for the purposes of this exercise that the annualized return on the Treasury bonds in your portfolio will be normally distributed with mean 4% and standard deviation 7%. Therefore, the returns on the stock market and the bond market follow a multivariate normal distribution with correlation coefficient −0.2.

Figure 9-4 shows the output distribution after generating 5,000 scenarios for stock market (as measured by the S&P 500) returns and Treasury bond returns over 30 years. The shape of the distribution of the capital available after 30 years is similar to the shape of the distribution from Figure 9-3, but the variability is smaller. This issue is discussed further in the next section.

Evaluating Decisions

In the end, the goal of using simulation is to help us make decisions. Is a 50–50 portfolio allocation in stocks and bonds "better" than a 30–70 allocation? We will refer to the former allocation as Strategy A, and to the latter as Strategy B. Let us evaluate the distribution of the capital at the end of 30 years for each allocation strategy, and use that knowledge to decide on the "better" allocation. Notice that it is unclear what "better" means in the context of uncertainty. We need

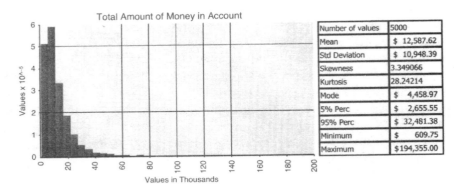

FIGURE 9-3 Output distribution for amount of capital after 30 years.

Number of values	5000
Mean	$ 12,587.62
Std Deviation	$ 10,948.39
Skewness	3.349066
Kurtosis	28.24214
Mode	$ 4,458.97
5% Perc	$ 2,655.55
95% Perc	$ 32,481.38
Minimum	$ 609.75
Maximum	$194,355.00

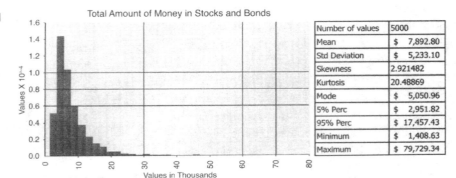

FIGURE 9-4 Histogram and summary statistics of the capital after 30 years from investing in the S&P 500 and Treasury bonds, taking into account the correlation between the returns on stocks and bonds.

Number of values	5000
Mean	$ 7,892.80
Std Deviation	$ 5,233.10
Skewness	2.921482
Kurtosis	20.48869
Mode	$ 5,050.96
5% Perc	$ 2,951.82
95% Perc	$ 17,457.43
Minimum	$ 1,408.63
Maximum	$ 79,729.34

to think about whether "better" for us means higher return on average, lower risk, acceptable trade-off between the two, and so on. Figure 9-5 contains the summary statistics of the simulated capital at the end of 30 years with each allocation over 5,000 scenarios.

We can observe that although Strategy A performs better than Strategy B as evaluated based on the mean capital at the end of 30 years, Strategy A's standard deviation is higher. In terms of risk–return tradeoff, as measured by the coefficient of variation, Strategy A's CV is 67.57% (=$5,341.57/$7,905.30), whereas Strategy B's CV is 53.29% (=$3,219.06/$6,040.17), which makes Strategy A appear riskier than Strategy B. This is apparent also from the overlay chart shown in Figure 9-5—much of the mass of the histogram for Strategy B is contained within the histogram for Strategy A, which means that Strategy B has less variability and results in less extreme outcomes than Strategy A. One lesson here, however, is that the standard deviation may not be a good measure of risk when the underlying distributions are asymmetric. Strategy A's 5th percentile, for example, is higher than Strategy B's 5th percentile, meaning that if you are concerned with events that happen with 5% probability, Strategy A would be less risky. Strategy A also has a higher upside—its 95th percentile is higher than Strategy B's 95th percentile.[6] The fact that Strategy A has a high upside "penalizes" its standard deviation relative to the standard deviation of Strategy B because it results in more outcomes that are far away from the mean. A high standard deviation is not necessarily a bad thing if the largest deviations from the mean happen on the upside.

It should be clear from the discussion so far that the summary statistics do not tell the whole story. It is important to look at the entire distribution of outcomes. Suppose now that we would like to compare Strategy A to Strategy B on a scenario-by-scenario basis. In what percentage of scenarios does Strategy B perform better than Strategy A? One efficient way to answer this question is to create an additional variable, Difference (A-B), that keeps track of the difference between the capital at the end of 30 years from Strategy A and from Strategy B during the simulation. Figure 9-6 shows a histogram of Difference (A-B) and presents its summary statistics.

It is interesting to observe that even though Strategy A appeared riskier than Strategy B based on the summary statistics in Figure 9-5 (Strategy A's standard deviation was almost twice the standard deviation of Strategy B), Strategy A results in lower realized outcomes than Strategy B in only 10.2% of the 5,000 generated scenarios. (As the graph in Figure 9-6 illustrates, 10.2% of the 5,000 scenarios for Difference (A-B) have values less than 0.) This perspective on the risk of one strategy versus the risk of

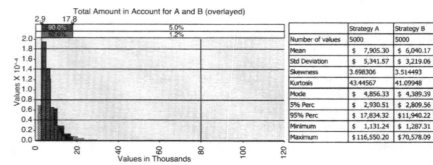

	Strategy A	Strategy B
Number of values	5000	5000
Mean	$ 7,905.30	$ 6,040.17
Std Deviation	$ 5,341.57	$ 3,219.06
Skewness	3.698306	3.514493
Kurtosis	43.44567	41.09948
Mode	$ 4,856.33	$ 4,389.39
5% Perc	$ 2,930.51	$ 2,809.56
95% Perc	$ 17,834.32	$11,940.22
Minimum	$ 1,131.24	$ 1,287.31
Maximum	$116,550.20	$70,578.09

FIGURE 9-5 Comparison of Strategy A (equal allocation to stocks and bonds) and Strategy B (allocation of 30% to stocks and 70% to bonds).

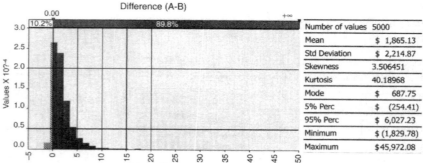

Number of values	5000
Mean	$ 1,865.13
Std Deviation	$ 2,214.87
Skewness	3.506451
Kurtosis	40.18968
Mode	$ 687.75
5% Perc	$ (254.41)
95% Perc	$ 6,027.23
Minimum	$ (1,829.78)
Maximum	$45,972.08

FIGURE 9-6 Histogram and summary statistics for the difference between the capital at the end of 30 years with Strategy A and with Strategy B.

another is valuable because it can substantially impact the final decision on which strategy to choose. For example, the problematic scenarios can be specifically identified, and in some situations, such as capital budgeting, managerial action can be taken to avoid them. A strategy that appears more risky may therefore be selected if it is desirable for other qualitative reasons.

When comparing two alternative decisions under uncertainty, it is technically correct (and fair) to evaluate them under the same set of scenarios. For example, when obtaining the summary statistics for Strategy A and Strategy B earlier, we should have used the same set of 5,000 scenarios for both. This would eliminate circumstances in which we happened to generate more favorable scenarios when evaluating one of the strategies than the other, which would have led us to conclude erroneously that the strategy evaluated over the more favorable set of scenarios is better.

In principle, if we generate a huge number of scenarios for the two strategies, even if the scenarios are not the same,

[6] We could be looking at the minimum and maximum realized outcomes as measures of the "riskiness" of Strategy A and Strategy B as well, but recall that those are very sensitive to the number of trials in the simulation, and should be interpreted with care.

the estimates will be quite accurate. However, generating a large number of scenarios is time consuming. Moreover, even a difference of a few digits after the decimal point may be significant in some financial applications.

IMPORTANT QUESTIONS IN SIMULATION MODELING

How Many Scenarios?

A simulation may not be able to capture all possible realizations of uncertainties in the model. For instance, think about the distribution of the end-of-year capital in an earlier section. As we explained, the possible number of values for the simulation output variable—the end-of-year capital—is technically infinite. Thus, we could never obtain the exact distribution of $\tilde{C}_1$ or the exact expected value $\tilde{C}_1$ by simulation. We can, however, get close. The accuracy of the estimation will depend on the number of generated scenarios. As discussed earlier, if the scenario generation is truly random, then the variability (the standard error) of the estimate of the true expected value will be $s/\sqrt{N}$, where s is the standard deviation of the simulated values for the output variable, and n is the number of scenarios.

Hence, to double the accuracy of estimating the mean of the output distribution, we would need to quadruple (roughly) the number of scenarios. For instance, in the example earlier, we generated 100 scenarios, and calculated that the average capital after one year is $1,087.90, and that the 95% CI for the estimate of the average capital is ($1,058.90, $1,116.90). We concluded that we can be 95% confident that the true expected capital will be between $1,058.90 and $1,116.90, that is, that the true mean will not be further than $29 from the mean estimated from the simulation ($1,087.90). Now suppose that we had obtained the same numbers for sample mean ($1,087.90) and sample standard deviation ($146.15), but we had generated four times as many (400) scenarios. The 95% CI would have been

$$\left(1,087.90 - 1.97 \cdot \frac{146.15}{\sqrt{400}}, 1,087.90 + 1.97 \cdot \frac{146.15}{\sqrt{400}}\right)$$
$$= (\$1,073.53, \$1,102.27)^7$$

---

[7] Note that the value for $t_{(100-\alpha/2)\%,n-1}$ has decreased slightly as well—this is because we now have more observations, that is, more degrees of freedom, so the t-distribution is less spread out and is closer to the normal distribution.

This means that we could be 95% confident that the true mean would not be more than $14.37 from the simulated mean of $1,087.90, which is about half of the amount by which we could be off ($29) when we generate 100 scenarios. Therefore, our accuracy has increased about twofold after quadrupling the number of generated scenarios.

Increasing the number of scenarios to improve accuracy can get expensive computationally, especially in more complicated multiperiod situations such as the simulation of a 30-year investment earlier. Fortunately, there are modern methods for generation of random numbers and scenarios that can help reduce the computational burden.

While the average output from a simulation is important, it is often not the only quantity of interest, something that practitioners tend to forget when using simulation to value complex financial instruments. As we will see from the applications in this book, for example, in assessing the risk of a portfolio, a portfolio manager may be interested in the percentiles of the distribution of outputs, or the worst-case and best-case scenarios. Unfortunately, it is not as straightforward to determine the accuracy of estimates of percentiles and other sample statistics from a simulation. There are some useful results from probability theory that apply (see, for example, Chapter 9 in Glasserman 2004), and we can use bootstrapping. However, in general, the question of how many scenarios we should generate to get a good representation of the output distribution does not have an easy answer. This issue is complicated further by the fact that results from probability theory do not necessarily apply to many of the scenario generating methods used in practice, which do not simulate "pure" random samples of observations, but instead use smarter simulation methods that reduce the number of scenarios needed to achieve good estimate accuracy. Some of these methods are discussed later in this chapter.

Estimator Bias

The statistical concept of *estimator bias* is important in simulation applications because it shows whether an estimator (a sample statistic) estimates the "right thing" on average (i.e., whether it approaches the true parameter one needs to estimate given a sufficient number of replications). For example, the average obtained from a sample of scenarios is an unbiased estimator of the true mean of a distribution because if we generate many samples and compute the sample averages, the average of these averages will approach the true mean. Depending on the way scenarios are generated, however, one may introduce a bias in the estimate of the parameter of interest. (This parameter does not need to be the mean of the distribution.) The magnitude of the bias is determined by the difference between the average value of the estimator that would be obtained if we generated many, many samples, and the true value of the parameter we are trying to estimate.

Let us go back to the multiperiod retirement planning example in an earlier section. We compounded the returns of the original capital of $1,000 every year to obtain the return distribution of over 30 years. Intuitively, though, returns should be compounded a lot more frequently to obtain a fair representation of a continuously compounded total return. The fact that we "discretized" the sample space by considering specific points of evaluation of the returns introduced an error, a bias, in our estimate of the total return. This issue is important in the evaluation of financial derivatives. Prices of financial instruments are typically assumed to follow continuous random processes, but time is often discretized when constructing simulation models. The average of the outcomes (the expected present value) is considered the fair price of the financial instrument; however, simulating asset prices in this manner generates a bias in the estimate of the expected present value because the simulated changes in the asset price along the way are not continuous or instantaneous, but happen over a fixed-length time interval. This kind of bias is referred to as *discretization error bias.* In some cases, such as the case of geometric Brownian motion with fixed drift and volatility, we can obtain an unbiased estimator of the average financial derivative payoff by simulating future asset prices with a continuous-time formula. However, in many instances it is not possible to find such a closed-form expression for the future asset price. For example, such a formula does not exist when the volatilities for asset prices are time-dependent, or when one uses a mean-reversion process to describe the evolution of the underlying price. In such cases, we can reduce the time interval length to reduce the bias, but it is important to keep in mind that reducing the time interval length increases the number of steps necessary to generate a random "path" for the future asset price, and becomes computationally expensive.

Estimator Efficiency

If there are two ways to obtain an estimate of a quantity of interest and the estimators are otherwise equivalent in terms of bias, which estimator should be preferred; that is, which estimator is more "efficient"? For example, consider two unbiased estimators of the mean, both of which are obtained as averages from a sample of independent replications. Their standard errors will be given by

$$\frac{s_1}{\sqrt{N_1}} \text{ and } \frac{s_2}{\sqrt{N_2}}$$

where s_1 and s_2 are the standard deviations from the samples of scenarios, and N_1 and N_2 are the number of scenarios for each of the estimators. Statistical theory states that one should prefer the estimator with the smaller standard deviation because it is more accurate.

In the case of simulation, however, such statistical concepts need to be extended to include numerical and computational considerations. For example, suppose that it takes longer to generate the scenarios for the estimator with the smaller standard deviation. Is that estimator still preferable, given that one can use the extra time to generate additional scenarios for the other estimator, thus reducing the latter estimator's standard error? It is natural (and theoretically justified) to modify the statistical measure of variability and efficiency so that it includes a concept of time. If τ_1 and τ_2 are the times it takes to generate one scenario for each of the two estimators, then one should select the estimator with the smaller of the time-adjusted standard errors $s_1\sqrt{\tau_1}, s_2\sqrt{\tau_2}$.

RANDOM NUMBER GENERATION

At the core of Monte Carlo simulation is the generation of random numbers. In fact, however, generating random numbers from a wide variety of distributions reduces to generating random numbers from the continuous uniform distribution on the unit interval [0,1], that is, to generating random numbers on the interval [0,1] in such a way that each value between 0 and 1 is equally likely to occur.[8] Many computer languages and software packages have a command for generating a random number between 0 and 1: =RAND () in Excel, rand (1) in MATLAB and FORTRAN, and ''rand ()'' in C++.

---

[8] Recall that the continuous uniform distribution looks like a simple rectangle, and it is very easy to compute probabilities and cumulative probabilities for the values for the continuous uniform random variable. Because the length of the interval is 1 and the total area under the PDF must be 1, the height of the curve should be 1 as well. Therefore, the probability that the continuous uniform random variable takes a value between two numbers a and b (the area under the PDF between a and b) is simply $(b - a) \cdot 1$, that is, $b - a$.

Inverse Transform Method

A common method for converting a random number between 0 and 1 to a number from an arbitrary probability distribution is to evaluate the so-called "inverse" of the cumulative probability distribution function at the random number u generated from a continuous uniform distribution (denoted by $F^{-1}(u)$). The idea works because the total mass for a probability distribution is always 1, and the cumulative probability for any value of the distribution (defined as the probability that this particular value or any value below it will occur) is always between 0 and 1. In effect, you can imagine that by generating a random number between 0 and 1, you are picking a number on the horizontal axis of the cumulative distribution function (CDF) plot for the random variable. The shape of the CDF depends on the specific probability distribution. To generate a random number from a probability distribution with a specific CDF, we can track the x-coordinate for the point on the CDF that has the random number between 0 and 1 as a y-coordinate. Note that if a particular value from the distribution of the random variable happens with high probability, the CDF evaluated at that point on the horizontal axis will contain a long vertical segment. A uniform random number generated on [0,1] will have a larger chance of falling in a segment that is long, and so the value from the distribution we would like to simulate will indeed happen with higher probability.

The Inverse Transform for Discrete Distributions

To give a concrete example, let us see how "inverting" the cumulative probability distribution works for discrete distributions. Suppose that given a random number generator for numbers between 0 and 1, we would like to simulate values for a random variable that takes the value 5 with probability 50%, the value 15 with probability 30%, and the value 35 with probability 20%. Figure 9-7 illustrates the CDF of this probability distribution. Let us split the unit interval [0,1] on the vertical axis into three intervals based on the cumulative probabilities 50%, 80%, and 100% for obtaining the values 5, 15, and 35: [0,0.5], (0.5,0.8], and (0.8,1]. If the random number that is drawn from the uniform distribution falls in the interval [0,0.5] (which happens 50% of the time if the number generator is truly random), then we trace the value on the horizontal axis that corresponds to the point on the CDF with y-coordinate equal to the generated random number, and record that value (which is 5) for that trial. If the random

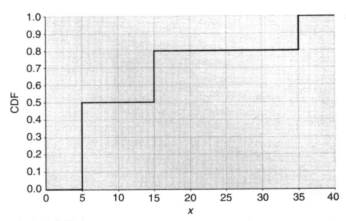

FIGURE 9-7 Graph of the CDF of a discrete distribution.

number is in the interval (0.05, 0.8] (which happens with probability 30%), then we record a value of 15 for that trial. Finally, if the random number is in the third interval (which happens with probability 20%), we record a value of 35. Thus, if many trials are run, the values 5, 15, and 35 are generated with the desired probabilities.[9]

The Inverse Transform for Continuous Distributions

Some probability distributions have closed-form expressions for their inverse cumulative distributions. The exponential distribution is one such example. Previously, we introduced the PDF of the exponential distribution:

$$f(x) = \lambda e^{-\lambda x}, x \geq 0$$

The CDF of the exponential distribution can be computed as[10]

$$F(x) = P(X \leq x) = \int_0^x \lambda e^{-\lambda t} dt$$

$$= \left(-\frac{1}{\lambda} \lambda e^{-\lambda t} \right)\Big|_{t=x} - \left(-\frac{1}{\lambda} \lambda e^{-\lambda t} \right)\Big|_{t=0}$$

$$= -e^{-\lambda x} - (-e^{-\lambda 0})$$

$$= 1 - e^{-\lambda x}.$$

---

[9] To understand better how this works, you can practice generating values from a general discrete probability distribution in Excel. For example, we can simulate these values with the corresponding probabilities by creating a table with the interval ranges in the first two columns, and the corresponding values (5, 15, and 35) in the third column, and using the Excel function

`VLOOKUP (lookup_value, table_array, col_index_num)`

to look up the range in which a number generated with RAND () falls.

[10] We present the calculation here because the exponential distribution is widely used in modeling the arrival time of credit risky events when pricing credit derivatives and managing bond portfolio risk.

To compute the inverse function, we express x in terms of the CDF $F(x)$. We have

$$e^{-\lambda x} = 1 - F(x),$$

therefore,

$$x = -\frac{1}{\lambda} \ln(1 - F(x)).$$

If we generate a random number between 0 and 1 for $F(x)$, we can use this expression to find the corresponding random number x that comes from an exponential distribution.

The inverse transform method can be viewed as a method of picking *random percentiles* from a particular distribution. To build further intuition, let us generate a random number from a normal distribution with mean μ and standard deviation σ. Suppose we request a random number between 0 and 1, and the random number generator returns 0.975. To find the uniquely corresponding random number from a normal distribution with mean μ and standard deviation σ, we find the value on the horizontal axis for a normal distribution with mean μ and standard deviation σ so that 97.5% of the probability mass (the area under the PDF) is to the left of that value.[11] In contrast to the exponential distribution, however, the percentiles of the normal distribution cannot be calculated in closed form. A random number generator would *approximate* the inverse of the cumulative normal distribution function at a particular point.

While the inverse transform method is widely used, alternative methods exist for generating random numbers from distributions for which the inverse of the CDF is not easy to compute. Such methods include:

- The acceptance-rejection method.
- The composition method.
- The ratio of uniforms method.

Most of these methods, however, still rely on generating random numbers from the uniform distribution on [0,1]. For more details, see Fishman (2006) and Glasserman (2004).

Because the normal distribution is so widely used in practice, a number of methods have been developed specifically for efficient simulation of univariate and multivariate normal random variables. Such methods include the Box-Muller algorithm (Box and Muller 1958), and the Beasley-Springer-Moro methodology for approximating the inverse normal distribution (Beasley and Springer 1977; Moro 1995).

What Defines a "Good" Random Number Generator?

Given the discussion in the previous section, generating "good" uniform random numbers on [0,1] is critical for the performance of simulation algorithms. Interestingly, defining "good" random number generation is not as straightforward as it appears. Early random number generators tried to use "truly random" events for random number generation, such as the amount of background cosmic radiation. In practice, however, this kind of random number generation is time consuming and difficult. Moreover, it was realized that the ability to reproduce the random number sequence and to analyze the random number characteristics is actually a desirable property for random number generators. In particular, the ability to reproduce a sequence of random numbers allows for reducing the variance of estimates and for debugging computer code by rerunning experiments in the same conditions in which they were run in previous iterations of code development.

Most simulation software employs random number generation algorithms that produce streams of numbers that appear to be random, but in fact are a result of a clearly defined series of calculation steps in which the next "random number" x_n in the sequence is a function of the previous "random number" x_{n-1}, that is, $x_n = g(x_{n-1})$. The sequence starts with a number called the *seed*, and if the same seed is used in several simulations, each simulation sequence will contain exactly the same numbers, which is helpful for running fair comparisons between different strategies evaluated under uncertainty. It is quite an amazing statistical fact that some of these recursion formulas (named *pseudorandom number generators*) define sequences of numbers that imitate random behavior well and appear to obey (roughly) some major laws of probability, such as the the central limit theorem and the Glivenko-Cantelli Theorem.[12]

---

[11] In Excel, the function =NORMINV (RAND (), mean, standard deviation) can be used to find that random number on the x-axis (the x-percentile) of a normal distribution with the specified mean and standard deviation. Specialized simulation software packages use such algorithms to generate a random variable from any distribution.

[12] The Glivenko-Cantelli Theorem is a statement about the behavior of an empirical CDF as the number of independent and identically distribution (IID) observations recorded from the underlying distribution grows. Glivenko and Cantelli showed that as the number of observations grows, the empirical CDF approaches the true CDF uniformly.

In general, a pseudorandom number generator is considered "good" if it satisfies the following conditions:

- The numbers in the generated sequence are uniformly distributed between 0 and 1. This can be tested by running a chi-square or a Kolmogorov-Smirnov test.

- The sequence has a long cycle (i.e., it takes many iterations before the sequence begins repeating itself).[13]

- The numbers in the sequence are not autocorrelated. This can be verified by running a Durbin-Watson test on the sequence of numbers. The Durbin-Watson test is widely used in statistics for identifying autocorrelation in time series of observations.

Next, some important types of pseudorandom number generators are surveyed. The goal is not to provide comprehensive coverage of random number generators, but rather to give you a flavor of the main ideas behind the method of producing apparently random numbers with deterministic algorithms.

Pseudorandom Number Generators

One of the earliest pseudorandom number generators is called the *midsquare technique*. It takes a number (the seed), squares it, and uses the set of middle digits as the next random number. For example, suppose that the seed is 5381. (It can be any number.) The members of the sequence of random numbers between 0 and 1 are then generated as

$5381^2 = 28955161$; middle four digits = 9551; random number
= **0.9551,**

$9551^2 = 91221601$; middle four digits = 2216; random number
= **0.2216,**

and so forth.

It is easy to predict when such an approach may run into difficulties. As soon as the "middle digits" become a small number such as 1 or 0, the sequence ends with the same numbers generated over and over again, that is, the sequence converges to a constant value such as 0 or to a very short cycle of values.

A better, commonly used type of pseudorandom number generator is *congruential* pseudorandom number generators. They generate a sequence of numbers of the form

$$x_n = g(x_{n-1}) \bmod m,$$

where mod m stands for "*modulus m.*" $g(x_{n-1}) \bmod m$ is the remainder after dividing $g(x_{n-1})$ by m. For example, 5 mod 3 = 2, 15 mod 5 = 0, and so on. The remainder is then scaled by another number, for example, divided by m, and the resulting number is used as the uniform random number on the interval [0,1]. Note that $g(x_{n-1}) \bmod m$ will always be an integer between 0 and $m-1$. Thus, to create a good representation of randomness, one would want to make the range for the modulus as large as possible. For a 32-bit computer, for example, the maximum integer that can be stored is $2^{31} - 1$, which is large enough for practical purposes.

As an example, consider a simple *linear congruential pseudorandom generator* of the form

$$x_n = Ax_{n-1} \bmod m.$$

(It is called linear because Ax_{n-1} is a linear function of x_{n-1}.) The first number in the sequence, x_0, is the seed. Algebraically, the expression for generating x_n above can be written as[14]

$$x_n = Ax_{n-1} - m\left[\frac{Ax_{n-1}}{m}\right].$$

(The lower brackets notation is standard for "largest integer less than or equal to Ax_{n-1}/m.") Then, the sequence of fractions x_n/m is used as a sequence of pseudorandom numbers on the interval [0,1].

Suppose $A = 3$, $m = 10$, and the seed $x_0 = 1052$. We have the following sequence of random numbers:

$$x_1 = 3 \cdot 1052 - 10 \cdot \left[\frac{3 \cdot 1052}{10}\right] = 3 \cdot 1052 - 10 \cdot [315.6]$$
$$= 3 \cdot 1052 - 10 \cdot 315 = 6.$$

Therefore, the random number is 6/10, or 0.6.

$$x_2 = 3 \cdot 6 - 10 \cdot \left[\frac{3 \cdot 6}{10}\right] = 3 \cdot 6 - 10 \cdot [1.8] = 3 \cdot 6 - 10 \cdot 1 = 8$$

Therefore, the next random number is 8/10, or 0.8, and so on.

---

[13] A long cycle is desirable because if the random number generator converges to only a small set of values for the random number, we cannot obtain a good representation of the probability distribution we are trying to sample.

---

[14] The intuition is that the remainder after division with m is the difference between the number Ax_{n-1} and the largest number that is divisible by m but is still less than Ax_{n-1}.

More generally, advanced random number generators include:

- Linear congruential generators (LCGs).
- Multiplicative recursive generators (MRGs).
- Feedback shift registers (FSRs).
- Generalized feedback shift registers (GFSRs).
- Combined multiplicative recursive generators (CMRGs).
- Twisted generalized feedback shift registers (TGFSRs).
- Add-with-carry (AWC) and subtract-with-borrow (SWB) generators.
- Inversive generators (IG).

FSRs, GFSRs, and TGFSRs generate new numbers by operating recursively on *bits* of previously generated random numbers. LCGs, MRGs, CMRGs, AWC/SWB and IGs operate recursively on previously generated random numbers. For more details, see, for example, McLeish (2005) and Fishman (2006). Most pseudorandom number generators used in popular software products nowadays have been thoroughly tested and are quite good, but it is important to keep in mind that pseudorandom number generators in software packages that are not explicitly built for simulation purposes (such as Excel) are usually not as good as random number generators in specialized simulation/mathematical software.

Quasirandom (Low-Discrepancy) Sequences

A truly random number generator may produce clustered observations (see Figure 9-8(A)), which necessitates generating many scenarios in order to obtain a good representation of the output distribution of interest. Quasirandom sequences instead ensure a smooth representation of the range by continuously "filling in" gaps on the unit interval [0,1] left by previously generated random numbers (see an example of 1,000 generated values of a quasirandom sequence in Figure 9-8(B)). The term "quasirandom" is actually a misnomer because, unlike pseudorandom number sequences, quasirandom number sequences do not pretend to be random. They are deterministic on purpose, and their roots can be found in real analysis and abstract algebra rather than in simulation or probability theory. The term *low discrepancy sequences* is often used interchangeably with the term *quasirandom sequences*, and is more accurate.

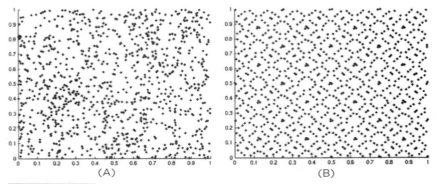

(A)   (B)

FIGURE 9-8 One thousand simulated number values for two uniform random variables on the interval [0,1]: (A) Pseudorandom number generator; (B) Sobol quasirandom sequence.

Famous quasirandom sequences include Sobol (1967), Faure (1982), Halton (1960), and Hammersley (1960). These sequences build on a family of so-called Van der Corput sequences. For example, the Van der Corput sequence of base 2 is

$$\frac{1}{2}, \frac{1}{4}, \frac{3}{4}, \frac{1}{8}, \frac{5}{8}, \frac{3}{8}, \frac{7}{8}, \cdots$$

The actual generation of Van der Corput sequences is somewhat technical, but the outcome is intuitive. Note that as new points are added to the sequence, they appear on alternate sides of $\frac{1}{2}$ in a balanced way. The main idea is that as the number of generated values increases, the sequence covers uniformly the unit interval.

The values generated with quasirandom sequences are treated as "random" numbers for the purposes of simulation modeling. In particular, instead of generating random numbers between 0 and 1 and "inverting" them to obtain an arbitrary probability distribution, we would "invert" the numbers in the quasirandom sequence. Different sequences have different advantages for specific financial applications, but the Faure and Sobol sequences in particular have been proven to generate very accurate estimates for derivative pricing in tests.[15]

Stratified Sampling

A variety of so-called *variance reduction techniques* are used to speed up execution and improve accuracy in simulations. Here, we will introduce one kind of random number generation—stratified sampling—that is now the default method of sampling in some simulation software

_____

[15] See the survey in Boyle, Broadie, and Glasserman (1997).

packages such as @RISK. The term *stratified sampling* is used because of the analogy with the statistical methodology of collecting a representative sample by dividing the population into groups, or *strata*, of similar characteristics, and collecting information about each strata. This technique ensures that all important groups are represented in the final sample.

Similar to quasirandom number generation, stratified sampling tries to address the problem of "clustering observations" we mentioned earlier. In contrast to quasirandom number generator techniques, however, which are deliberately nonrandom, stratified sampling preserves some degree of randomness. It just tries to "distribute" the randomness along the entire range of the probability distribution by dividing the ranges of possible values for every input random variable into a fixed number of strata, and simulating values over these ranges.

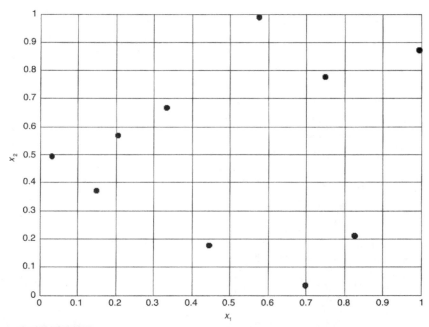

FIGURE 9-9 A Latin hypercube sample for two random variables ($p = 2$) and 10 strata along each dimension ($k = 10$).

Stratified sampling is valuable not only because it improves accuracy, but also because it helps include extreme observations into the simulation. Observations in the tails of input distributions that are typically less likely to be generated may never occur in a simulation because the probability of their occurrence is small. Such observations, however, contain important information about extreme events that are of particular interest in financial applications. In order to ensure that they appear in the simulation, one would have to generate a huge number of scenarios.

A simple example of stratifying the numbers in the [0,1] interval is to divide the [0,1] interval into k smaller intervals of equal length:

$$\left[0, \frac{1}{k}\right], \left(\frac{1}{k}, \frac{2}{k}\right], \ldots, \left(\frac{k-1}{k}, 1\right].$$

Random numbers can then be drawn sequentially from each small interval. Therefore, values from the tails of the distribution of interest (which will be generated when uniform random numbers from the intervals $[0, \frac{1}{k}]$ and $(\frac{k-1}{k}, 1]$ are drawn) obtain better representation.

In multiple dimensions (i.e., when simulating several random variables), this method extends to dividing a hypercube (as opposed to an interval) into smaller hypercubes, and drawing an observation along each dimension of the smaller hypercubes. The sample size required to cover all strata, however, may become prohibitive. Suppose, for example, that you have k intervals (strata) for each of p dimensions (each of p random variables). This means that there are k^p hypercubes, that is, we need to simulate at least k^p random numbers in order to have a number in each stratum. Generating random numbers, however, is computationally expensive. An enhanced extension to the basic stratified sampling method is *Latin Hypercube Sampling*, which permutes the coordinates of an initially generated random vector of observations—one observation within each small hypercube—to reduce the number of times an actual random number is generated while ensuring that all strata are sufficiently well-represented (see Figure 9-9).

The method works as follows. First, we generate a random number within each small interval along each dimension. In the example in Figure 9-9, where we have two random variables (i.e., two dimensions), we would generate random numbers

$$x_1^{(1)}, \ldots, x_1^{(k)}$$

along the first dimension, and numbers

$$x_2^{(1)}, \ldots, x_2^{(k)}$$

along the second dimension. If we consider points with coordinates

$$(x_1^{(1)}, x_2^{(1)}), \ldots, (x_1^{(k)}, x_2^{(k)})$$

we would have random points in all of the little squares along the diagonal of the large [0,1] square. The first point is a point in the little square $[0, \frac{1}{k}]^2$, the second point is a point in the little square $(\frac{1}{k}, \frac{2}{k}]^2$, and so on. (In multiple dimensions, combining the random numbers for the corresponding small intervals to create random points with p coordinates would create random points in the little *hypercubes* along the main diagonal of the [0,1] hypercube.)

Now permute the coordinates of the points along each dimension.[16] For example, consider the points

$$(x_1^{(10)}, x_2^{(3)}), (x_1^{(2)}, x_2^{(1)}), \ldots, (x_1^{(k-3)}, x_2^{(2)}).$$

In other words, the first coordinates are still the random numbers we generated along the first dimension, and the second coordinates are still the random numbers we generated along the second dimension, but the order of the random numbers within each dimension has changed. The new points are not all in the hypercubes around the diagonal, and, as Figure 9-9 illustrates, exactly one random point falls in each of the k small intervals into which each axis is partitioned. If we consider all possible permutations of these coordinates, we will fill all small hypercubes. Thus, we would perform stratified sampling by generating only $k \cdot p$ random numbers (and permuting them), rather than generating k^p random numbers.[17]

SUMMARY

- Monte Carlo (MC) simulation is a valuable tool for evaluating functional relationships between variables, visualizing the effect of multiple-correlated variables, and testing strategies.

- MC simulation involves creating scenarios for output variables of interest by generating scenarios for input variables for which we have more information. The art

---

[16] To permute, you can first draw one of the coordinates at random, then draw one coordinate from the remaining ones, and so on until only one is left.

[17] The Latin Hypercube method works well for generating independent random variables, but complications occur when we need to generate correlated random variables. See Chapter 4 in Glasserman (2004) for further discussion and examples.

of MC simulation modeling is in selecting input probability distributions wisely and interpreting output distributions carefully.

- The distributions of output variables can be analyzed by statistical techniques. Statistics of interest include measures of central tendency (average, mode), measures of volatility (standard deviation, percentiles), skewness, and kurtosis. Minima and maxima from simulations should be interpreted with care because they often depend on the input assumptions and are very sensitive to the number of trials in the simulation.

- The accuracy of estimation through simulation is related to the number of generated scenarios. Unfortunately, the relationship is nonlinear—in order to double the accuracy, we need to more than quadruple the number of scenarios.

- Generating a random number from an arbitrary probability distribution in many cases reduces to generating a random number from the uniform distribution on the interval [0,1].

- Random number generation is not trivial, and simulation software packages do not produce truly "random" numbers. There is value, however, in generating random number sequences that are replicable, and thus not completely random.

- Pseudorandom number generators attempt to imitate random behavior by creating sequences of random numbers that obey statistical laws.

- Quasirandom number generators do not pretend to generate random numbers—they try to address the "clustering" problem observed in truly random number generation, and ensure a smooth representation of the range of the distribution by continuously "filling in" gaps on the unit interval [0,1] left by previously generated random numbers. Quasirandom sequences that have been particularly successful in financial applications include the Faure and Sobol sequences.

- Stratified sampling, of which Latin Hypercube Sampling is an advanced example, aims to provide good representation of a probability distribution by dividing the range of the random variable into smaller ranges or "strata," and generating random numbers within each stratum. This method "disperses" simulated values more evenly over the range of the distribution, addresses the clustering problem of random number generation, and provides better representation for the tails of the distribution.

Estimating Volatilities and Correlations

10

Learning Objectives

Candidates, after completing this reading, should be able to:

- Explain how historical data and various weighting schemes can be used in estimating volatility.
- Describe the exponentially weighted moving average (EWMA) model for estimating volatility and its properties, and estimate volatility using the EWMA model.
- Describe the generalized auto regressive conditional heteroskedasticity (GARCH(p, q)) model for estimating volatility and its properties:
  - Calculate volatility using the GARCH(1, 1) model
  - Explain mean reversion and how it is captured in the GARCH(1, 1) model

- Explain how the parameters of the GARCH(1,1) and the EWMA models are estimated using maximum likelihood methods.
- Explain how GARCH models perform in volatility forecasting.
- Describe the volatility term structure and the impact of volatility changes.
- Describe how correlations and covariances are calculated, and explain the consistency condition for covariances.

Excerpt is Chapter 22 of Options, Futures, and Other Derivatives, *Eighth Edition, by John Hull.*

In this chapter we explain how historical data can be used to produce estimates of the current and future levels of volatilities and correlations. The chapter is relevant both to the calculation of value-at-risk using the model-building approach and to the valuation of derivatives. When calculating value-at-risk, we are most interested in the current levels of volatilities and correlations because we are assessing possible changes in the value of a portfolio over a very short period of time. When valuing derivatives, forecasts of volatilities and correlations over the whole life of the derivative are usually required.

The chapter considers models with imposing names such as exponentially weighted moving average (EWMA), autoregressive conditional heteroscedasticity (ARCH), and generalized autoregressive conditional heteroscedasticity (GARCH). The distinctive feature of the models is that they recognize that volatilities and correlations are not constant. During some periods, a particular volatility or correlation may be relatively low, whereas during other periods it may be relatively high. The models attempt to keep track of the variations in the volatility or correlation through time.

ESTIMATING VOLATILITY

Define σ_n as the volatility of a market variable on day n, as estimated at the end of day $n - 1$. The square of the volatility, σ_n^2, on day n is the *variance rate*. We described the standard approach to estimating σ_n from historical data. Suppose that the value of the market variable at the end of day i is S_i. The variable u_i is defined as the continuously compounded return during day i (between the end of day $i - 1$ and the end of day i):

$$u_i = \ln \frac{S_i}{S_{i-1}}$$

An unbiased estimate of the variance rate per day, σ_n^2, using the most recent m observations on the u_i s

$$\sigma_n^2 = \frac{1}{m-1}\sum_{i=1}^{m}\left(u_{n-i} - \bar{u}\right)^2 \qquad (10.1)$$

where $\bar{u}$ is the mean of the u_i is:

$$\bar{u} = \frac{1}{m}\sum_{i=1}^{m}u_{n-i}$$

For the purposes of monitoring daily volatility, the formula in Equation (10.1) is usually changed in a number of ways:

1. u_i is defined as the percentage change in the market variable between the end of day $i - 1$ and the end of day i, so that:[1]

$$u_i = \frac{S_i - S_{i-1}}{S_{i-1}} \qquad (10.2)$$

2. $\bar{u}$ is assumed to be zero.[2]
3. $m - 1$ is replaced by m.[3]

These three changes make very little difference to the estimates that are calculated, but they allow us to simplify the formula for the variance rate to

$$\sigma_n^2 = \frac{1}{m}\sum_{i=1}^{m}u_{n-i}^2 \qquad (10.3)$$

where u_i is given by Equation (10.2).[4]

Weighting Schemes

Equation (10.3) gives equal weight to u_{n-1}^2, u_{n-2}^2, . . . , u_{n-m}^2. Our objective is to estimate the current level of volatility, σ_n. It therefore makes sense to give more weight to recent data. A model that does this is

$$\sigma_n^2 = \sum_{i=1}^{m}\alpha_i u_{n-i}^2 \qquad (10.4)$$

The variable α_i is the amount of weight given to the observation i days ago. The α's are positive. If we choose

----

[1] This is consistent with the point made earlier about the way that volatility is defined for the purposes of VaR calculations.

[2] This assumption usually has very little effect on estimates of the variance because the expected change in a variable in one day is very small when compared with the standard deviation of changes.

[3] Replacing $m - 1$ by m moves us from an unbiased estimate of the variance to a maximum likelihood estimate. Maximum likelihood estimates are discussed later in the chapter.

[4] Note that the u's in this chapter play the same role as the Δx's. Both are daily percentage changes in market variables. In the case of the u's, the subscripts count observations made on different days on the same market variable. In the case of the Δx's, they count observations made on the same day on different market variables. The use of subscripts for σ is similarly different. In this chapter, the subscripts refer to days.

them so that $\alpha_i < \alpha_j$ when $i > j$, less weight is given to older observations. The weights must sum to unity, so that

$$\sum_{i=1}^{m} \alpha_i = 1$$

An extension of the idea in Equation (10.4) is to assume that there is a long-run average variance rate and that this should be given some weight. This leads to the model that takes the form

$$\sigma_n^2 = \gamma V_L + \sum_{i=1}^{m} \alpha_i u_{n-i}^2 \qquad (10.5)$$

where V_L is the long-run variance rate and γ is the weight assigned to V_L. Since the weights must sum to unity, it follows that

$$\gamma + \sum_{i=1}^{m} \alpha_i = 1$$

This is known as an ARCH(m) model. It was first suggested by Engle.[5] The estimate of the variance is based on a long-run average variance and m observations. The older an observation, the less weight it is given. Defining $\omega = \gamma V_L$, the model in Equation (10.5) can be written

$$\sigma_n^2 = \omega + \sum_{i=1}^{m} \alpha_i u_{n-i}^2 \qquad (10.6)$$

In the next two sections we discuss two important approaches to monitoring volatility using the ideas in Equations (10.4) and (10.5).

THE EXPONENTIALLY WEIGHTED MOVING AVERAGE MODEL

The exponentially weighted moving average (EWMA) model is a particular case of the model in Equation (10.4) where the weights α_i decrease exponentially as we move back through time. Specifically, $\alpha_{i+1} = \lambda \alpha_i$, where λ is a constant between 0 and 1.

It turns out that this weighting scheme leads to a particularly simple formula for updating volatility estimates. The formula is

$$\sigma_n^2 = \lambda \sigma_{n-1}^2 + (1 - \lambda) u_{n-1}^2 \qquad (10.7)$$

[5] See R. Engle "Autoregressive Conditional Heteroscedasticity with Estimates of the Variance of UK Inflation," *Econometrica*, 50 (1982): 987–1008.

The estimate, σ_n, of the volatility of a variable for day n (made at the end of day $n - 1$) is calculated from σ_{n-1} (the estimate that was made at the end of day $n - 2$ of the volatility for day $n - 1$) and u_{n-1} (the most recent daily percentage change in the variable).

To understand why Equation (10.7) corresponds to weights that decrease exponentially, we substitute for σ_{n-1}^2 to get

$$\sigma_n^2 = \lambda \left[\lambda \sigma_{n-2}^2 + (1 - \lambda) u_{n-2}^2 \right] + (1 - \lambda) u_{n-1}^2$$

or

$$\sigma_n^2 = (1 - \lambda)\left(u_{n-1}^2 + \lambda u_{n-2}^2 \right) + \lambda^2 \sigma_{n-2}^2$$

Substituting in a similar way for σ_{n-2}^2 gives

$$\sigma_n^2 = (1 - \lambda)\left(u_{n-1}^2 + \lambda u_{n-2}^2 + \lambda^2 u_{n-3}^2 \right) + \lambda^3 \sigma_{n-3}^2$$

Continuing in this way gives

$$\sigma_n^2 = (1 - \lambda) \sum_{i=1}^{m} \lambda^{i-1} u_{n-i}^2 + \lambda^m \sigma_{n-m}^2$$

For large m, the term $\lambda^m \sigma_{n-m}^2$ is sufficiently small to be ignored, so that Equation (10.7) is the same as Equation (10.4) with $\alpha_i = (1 - \lambda)\lambda^{i-1}$. The weights for the u_i decline at rate λ as we move back through time. Each weight is λ times the previous weight.

Example 10.1

Suppose that λ is 0.90, the volatility estimated for a market variable for day $n - 1$ is 1% per day, and during day $n - 1$ the market variable increased by 2%. This means that $\sigma_{n-1}^2 = 0.01^2 = 0.0001$ and $u_{n-1}^2 = 0.02^2 = 0.0004$. Equation (10.7) gives

$$\sigma_n^2 = 0.9 \times 0.0001 + 0.1 \times 0.0004 = 0.00013$$

The estimate of the volatility, σ_n, for day n is therefore $\sqrt{0.00013}$, or 1.14%, per day. Note that the expected value of u_{n-1}^2 is σ_{n-1}^2, or 0.0001. In this example, the realized value of u_{n-1}^2 is greater than the expected value, and as a result our volatility estimate increases. If the realized value of u_{n-1}^2 had been less than its expected value, our estimate of the volatility would have decreased.

The EWMA approach has the attractive feature that relatively little data need to be stored. At any given time, only the current estimate of the variance rate and the most recent observation on the value of the market variable need be remembered. When a new observation on the market variable is obtained, a new daily percentage change is calculated and Equation (10.7) is used to update the estimate of the variance rate. The old estimate of the variance rate and the old value of the market variable can then be discarded.

The EWMA approach is designed to track changes in the volatility. Suppose there is a big move in the market variable on day $n - 1$, so that u_{n-1}^2 is large. From Equation (10.7) this causes the estimate of the current volatility to move upward. The value of λ governs how responsive the estimate of the daily volatility is to the most recent daily percentage change. A low value of λ leads to a great deal of weight being given to the u_{n-1}^2 when σ_n calculated. In this case, the estimates produced for the volatility on successive days are themselves highly volatile. A high value of λ (i.e., a value close to 1.0) produces estimates of the daily volatility that respond relatively slowly to new information provided by the daily percentage change.

The RiskMetrics database, which was originally created by J. P. Morgan and made publicly available in 1994, uses the EWMA model with $\lambda = 0.94$ for updating daily volatility estimates in its RiskMetrics database. The company found that, across a range of different market variables, this value of λ gives forecasts of the variance rate that come closest to the realized variance rate.[6] The realized variance rate on a particular day was calculated as an equally weighted average of the u_i^2 on the subsequent 25 days (see Problem 10.19).

THE GARCH(1, 1) MODEL

We now move on to discuss what is known as the GARCH(1, 1) model, proposed by Bollerslev in 1986.[7] The difference between the GARCH(1, 1) model and the EWMA model is analogous to the difference between Equation (10.4) and Equation (10.5). In GARCH(1, 1), σ_n^2 is

calculated from a long-run average variance rate, V_L, as well as from σ_{n-1} and u_{n-1}. The equation for GARCH(1, 1) is

$$\sigma_n^2 = \gamma V_L + \alpha u_{n-1}^2 + \beta \sigma_{n-1}^2 \qquad \textbf{(10.8)}$$

where γ is the weight assigned to V_L, α is the weight assigned to u_{n-1}^2, and β is the weight assigned to σ_{n-1}^2. Since the weights must sum to unity, it follows that

$$\gamma + \alpha + \beta = 1$$

The EWMA model is a particular case of GARCH(1, 1) where $\gamma = 0$, $\alpha = 1 - \lambda$, and $\beta = \lambda$.

The "(1, 1)" in GARCH(1, 1) indicates that σ_n^2 is based on the most recent observation of u^2 and the most recent estimate of the variance rate. The more general GARCH(p,q) model calculates σ_n^2 from the most recent p observations on u^2 and the most recent q estimates of the variance rate.[8] GARCH(1, 1) is by far the most popular of the GARCH models.

Setting $\omega = \gamma V_L$, the GARCH(1, 1) model can also be written

$$\sigma_n^2 = \omega + \alpha u_{n-1}^2 + \beta \sigma_{n-1}^2 \qquad \textbf{(10.9)}$$

This is the form of the model that is usually used for the purposes of estimating the parameters. Once ω, α, and β have been estimated, we can calculate γ as $1 - \alpha - \beta$. The long-term variance V_L can then be calculated as ω/γ. For a stable GARCH(1, 1) process we require $\alpha + \beta < 1$. Otherwise the weight applied to the long-term variance is negative.

Example 10.2

Suppose that a GARCH(1, 1) model is estimated from daily data as

$$\sigma_n^2 = 0.000002 + 0.13u_{n-1}^2 + 0.86\sigma_{n-1}^2$$

This corresponds to $\alpha = 0.13$, $\beta = 0.86$, and $\omega = 0.000002$. Because $\gamma = 1 - \alpha - \beta$, it follows that $\gamma = 0.01$. Because

---

[6] See J. P. Morgan, *RiskMetrics Monitor*, Fourth Quarter, 1995. We will explain an alternative (maximum likelihood) approach to estimating parameters later in the chapter.

[7] See T. Bollerslev, "Generalized Autoregressive Conditional Heteroscedasticity," *Journal of Econometrics*, 31 (1986): 307–27.

[8] Other GARCH models have been proposed that incorporate asymmetric news. These models are designed so that σ_n depends on the sign of u_{n-1}. Arguably, the models are more appropriate for equities than GARCH(1, 1). The volatility of an equity's price tends to be inversely related to the price so that a negative u_{n-1} should have a bigger effect on σ_n than the same positive u_{n-1}. For a discussion of models for handling asymmetric news, see D. Nelson, "Conditional Heteroscedasticity and Asset Returns: A New Approach," *Econometrica*, 59 (1990): 347–70; R. F. Engle and V. Ng, "Measuring and Testing the Impact of News on Volatility," *Journal of Finance*, 48 (1993): 1749–78.

$\omega = \gamma V_L$, it follows that $V_L = 0.0002$. In other words, the long-run average variance per day implied by the model is 0.0002. This corresponds to a volatility of $\sqrt{0.0002} = 0.014$, or 1.4%, per day.

Suppose that the estimate of the volatility on day $n - 1$ is 1.6% per day, so that $\sigma_{n-1}^2 = 0.016^2 = 0.000256$, and that on day $n - 1$ the market variable decreased by 1%, so that $u_{n-1}^2 = 0.01^2 = 0.0001$. Then

$$\sigma_n^2 = 0.000002 + 0.13 \times 0.0001 + 0.86 \times 0.000256 = 0.00023516$$

The new estimate of the volatility is therefore $\sqrt{0.00023516} = 0.0153$, or 1.53%, per day.

The Weights

Substituting for σ_{n-1}^2 in Equation (10.9) gives

$$\sigma_n^2 = \omega + \alpha u_{n-1}^2 + \beta\left(\omega + \alpha u_{n-2}^2 + \beta\sigma_{n-2}^2\right)$$

or

$$\sigma_n^2 = \omega + \beta\omega + \alpha u_{n-1}^2 + \alpha\beta u_{n-2}^2 + \beta^2\sigma_{n-2}^2$$

Substituting for σ_{n-2}^2 gives

$$\sigma_n^2 = \omega + \beta\omega + \beta^2\omega + \alpha u_{n-1}^2 + \alpha\beta u_{n-2}^2 + \alpha\beta^2 u_{n-3}^2 + \beta^3\sigma_{n-3}^2$$

Continuing in this way, we see that the weight applied to u_{n-1}^2 is $\alpha\beta^{j-1}$. The weights decline exponentially at rate β. The parameter β can be interpreted as a "decay rate". It is similar to λ in the EWMA model. It defines the relative importance of the observations on the u's in determining the current variance rate. For example, if $\beta = 0.9$, then u_{n-2}^2 is only 90% as important as u_{n-1}^2; u_{n-3}^2 is 81% as important as u_{n-1}; and so on. The GARCH(1, 1) model is similar to the EWMA model except that, in addition to assigning weights that decline exponentially to past u^2, it also assigns some weight to the long-run average volatility.

Mean Reversion

The GARCH(1, 1) model recognizes that over time the variance tends to get pulled back to a long-run average level of V_L. The amount of weight assigned to V_L is $\gamma = 1 - \alpha - \beta$. The GARCH(1, 1) is equivalent to a model where the variance V follows the stochastic process

$$dV = a\left(V_L - V\right)dt + \xi V\, dz$$

where time is measured in days, $a = 1 - \alpha - \beta$, and $\xi = \alpha\sqrt{2}$ (see Exercise 14). This is a mean-reverting model. The variance has a drift that pulls it back to V_L at rate a.

When $V > V_L$, the variance has a negative drift; when $V < V_L$, it has a positive drift. Superimposed on the drift is a volatility ξ.

CHOOSING BETWEEN THE MODELS

In practice, variance rates do tend to be mean reverting. The GARCH(1, 1) model incorporates mean reversion, whereas the EWMA model does not. GARCH(1, 1) is therefore theoretically more appealing than the EWMA model.

In the next section, we will discuss how best-fit parameters ω, α, and β in GARCH(1, 1) can be estimated. When the parameter ω is zero, the GARCH(1, 1) reduces to EWMA. In circumstances where the best-fit value of ω turns out to be negative, the GARCH(1, 1) model is not stable and it makes sense to switch to the EWMA model.

MAXIMUM LIKELIHOOD METHODS

It is now appropriate to discuss how the parameters in the models we have been considering are estimated from historical data. The approach used is known as the *maximum likelihood method*. It involves choosing values for the parameters that maximize the chance (or likelihood) of the data occurring.

To illustrate the method, we start with a very simple example. Suppose that we sample 10 stocks at random on a certain day and find that the price of one of them declined on that day and the prices of the other nine either remained the same or increased. What is the best estimate of the probability of a price decline? The natural answer is 0.1. Let us see if this is what the maximum likelihood method gives.

Suppose that the probability of a price decline is p. The probability that one particular stock declines in price and the other nine do not is $p(1 - p)^9$. Using the maximum likelihood approach, the best estimate of p is the one that maximizes $p(1 - p)^9$. Differentiating this expression with respect to p and setting the result equal to zero, we find that $p = 0.1$ maximizes the expression. This shows that the maximum likelihood estimate of p is 0.1, as expected.

Estimating a Constant Variance

Our next example of maximum likelihood methods considers the problem of estimating the variance of a variable X from m observations on X when the underlying distribution is normal with zero mean. Assume that the observations are $u_1, u_2, \ldots, u_m$. Denote the variance by v. The likelihood of u_i being observed is defined as the probability density function for X when $X = u_i$. This is

$$\frac{1}{\sqrt{2\pi v}} \exp\left(\frac{-u_i^2}{2v}\right)$$

The likelihood of m observations occurring in the order in which they are observed is

$$\prod_{i=1}^{m} \left[\frac{1}{\sqrt{2\pi v}} \exp\left(\frac{-u_i^2}{2v}\right) \right] \qquad \textbf{(10.10)}$$

Using the maximum likelihood method, the best estimate of v is the value that maximizes this expression.

Maximizing an expression is equivalent to maximizing the logarithm of the expression. Taking logarithms of the expression in Equation (10.10) and ignoring constant multiplicative factors, it can be seen that we wish to maximize

$$\sum_{i=1}^{m} \left[-\ln(v) - \frac{u_i^2}{v} \right] \qquad \textbf{(10.11)}$$

or

$$-m \ln(v) - \sum_{i=1}^{m} \frac{u_i^2}{v}$$

Differentiating this expression with respect to v and setting the resulting equation to zero, we see that the maximum likelihood estimator of v is[9]

$$\frac{1}{m} \sum_{i=1}^{m} u_i^2$$

Estimating GARCH(1, 1) Parameters

We now consider how the maximum likelihood method can be used to estimate the parameters when GARCH(1, 1) or some other volatility updating scheme is used. Define $v_i = \sigma_i^2$ as the variance estimated for day i. Assume that the probability distribution of u_i conditional on the variance is normal. A similar analysis to the

one just given shows the best parameters are the ones that maximize

$$\prod_{i=1}^{m} \left[\frac{1}{\sqrt{2\pi v_i}} \exp\left(\frac{-u_i^2}{2v_i}\right) \right]$$

Taking logarithms, we see that this is equivalent to maximizing

$$\sum_{i=1}^{m} \left[-\ln(v_i) - \frac{u_i^2}{v_i} \right] \qquad \textbf{(10.12)}$$

This is the same as the expression in Equation (10.11), except that v is replaced by v_i. It is necessary to search iteratively to find the parameters in the model that maximize the expression in Equation (10.12).

The spreadsheet in Table 10-1 indicates how the calculations could be organized for the GARCH(1, 1) model. The table analyzes data on the S&P 500 between July 18, 2005, and August 13, 2010.[10] The numbers in the table are based on trial estimates of the three GARCH(1, 1) parameters: ω, α, and β. The first column in the table records the date. The second column counts the days. The third column shows the S&P 500, S_i, at the end of day i. The fourth column shows the proportional change in the S&P 500 between the end of day $i - 1$ and the end of day i. This is $u_i = (S_i - S_{i-1})/S_{i-1}$. The fifth column shows the estimate of the variance rate, $v_i = \sigma_i^2$ for day i made at the end of day $i - 1$. On day 3, we start things off by setting the variance equal to u_2^2. On subsequent days, Equation (10.9) is used. The sixth column tabulates the likelihood measure, $-\ln(v_i) - u_i^2/v_i$. The values in the fifth and sixth columns are based on the current trial estimates of ω, α, and β. We are interested in choosing ω, α, and β to maximize the sum of the numbers in the sixth column. This involves an iterative search procedure.[11]

In our example, the optimal values of the parameters turn out to be

$$\omega = 0.000001347, \quad \alpha = 0.083394, \quad \beta = 0.910116$$

---

[9] This confirms the point made in footnote 3.

[10] The data and calculations can be found at www.rotman.utoronto.ca/-hull/OFOD/GarchExample.

[11] As discussed later, a general purpose algorithm such as Solver in Microsoft's Excel can be used. Alternatively, a special purpose algorithm, such as Levenberg–Marquardt, can be used. See, e.g., W. H. Press, B. P. Flannery, S. A. Teukolsky, and W. T. Vetterling. *Numerical Recipes in C: The Art of Scientific Computing*, Cambridge University Press, 1988.

TABLE 10-1 Estimation of Parameters in GARCH(1, 1) Model for S&P 500 between July 18, 2005, and August 13, 2010

Date	Day i	S_i	u_i	$v_i = \sigma_i^2$	$-\ln(v_i) - u_i^2/v_i$
18-Jul-2005	1	1221.13			
19-Jul-2005	2	1229.35	0.006731		
20-Jul-2005	3	1235.20	0.004759	0.00004531	9.5022
21-Jul-2005	4	1227.04	−0.006606	0.00004447	9.0393
22-Jul-2005	5	1233.68	0.005411	0.00004546	9.3545
25-Jul-2005	6	1229.03	−0.003769	0.00004517	9.6906
⋮	⋮	⋮	⋮	⋮	⋮
11-Aug-2010	1277	1089.47	−0.028179	0.00011834	2.3322
12-Aug-2010	1278	1083.61	−0.005379	0.00017527	8.4841
13-Aug-2010	1279	1079.25	−0.004024	0.00016327	8.6209
					10,228.2349

Trial estimates of GARCH parameters
$\omega = 0.000001347$ $\alpha = 0.08339$ $\beta = 0.9101$

and the maximum value of the function in Equation (10.12) is 10,228.2349. The numbers shown in Table 10-1 were calculated on the final iteration of the search for the optimal ω, α, and β.

The long-term variance rate, V_L, in our example is

$$\frac{\omega}{1 - \alpha - \beta} = \frac{0.000001347}{0.006490} = 0.0002075$$

The long-term volatility is $\sqrt{0.0002075}$, or 1.4404%, per day.

Figures 10-1 and 10-2 show the S&P 500 index and its GARCH(1, 1) volatility during the 5-year period covered by the data. Most of the time, the volatility was less than 2% per day, but volatilities as high as 5% were experienced during the credit crisis.

An alternative approach to estimating parameters in GARCH(1, 1), which is sometimes more robust, is known as *variance targeting*.[12] This involves setting the long-run

average variance rate, V_L, equal to the sample variance calculated from the data (or to some other value that is believed to be reasonable). The value of ω then equals $V_L(1 - \alpha - \beta)$ and only two parameters have to be estimated. For the data in Table 10-1, the sample variance is 0.0002412, which gives a daily volatility of 1.5531%. Setting V_L equal to the sample variance, the values of α and β that maximize the objective function in Equation (10.12) are 0.08445 and 0.9101, respectively. The value of the objective function is 10,228.1941, only marginally below the value of 10,228.2349 obtained using the earlier procedure.

When the EWMA model is used, the estimation procedure is relatively simple. We set $\omega = 0$, $\alpha = 1 - \lambda$, and $\beta = \lambda$, and only one parameter has to be estimated. In the data in Table 10-1, the value of λ that maximizes the objective function in Equation (10.12) is 0.9374 and the value of the objective function is 10,192.5104.

Both GARCH(1, 1) and the EWMA method can be implemented by using the Solver routine in Excel to search for the values of the parameters that maximize the likelihood function. The routine works well provided that the spreadsheet is structured so that the parameters being

---

[12] See R. Engle and J. Mezrich, "GARCH for Groups," *Risk*, August 1996: 36–40.

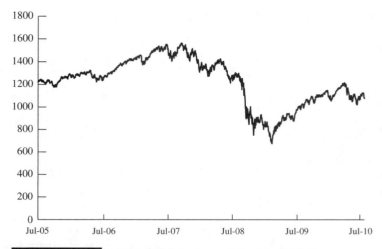

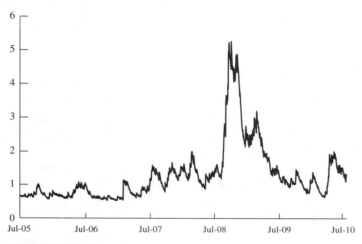

FIGURE 10-1 S&P 500 index: July 18, 2005, to August 13, 2010.

FIGURE 10-2 Daily volatility of S&P 500 index: July 18, 2005, to August 13, 2010.

How Good Is the Model?

The assumption underlying a GARCH model is that volatility changes with the passage of time. During some periods volatility is relatively high; during other periods it is relatively low. To put this another way, when u_i^2 is high, there is a tendency for u_{i+1}^2, u_{i+2}^2, . . . to be high; when u_i^2 is low, there is a tendency for u_{i+1}^2, u_{i+2}^2, . . . to be low. We can test how true this is by examining the autocorrelation structure of the u_i^2.

Let us assume the u_i^2 do exhibit autocorrelation. If a GARCH model is working well, it should remove the autocorrelation. We can test whether it has done so by considering the autocorrelation structure for the variables u_i^2/σ_i^2. If these show very little autocorrelation, our model for σ_i has succeeded in explaining autocorrelations in the u_i^2.

Table 10-2 shows results for the S&P 500 data used above. The first column shows the lags considered when the autocorrelation is calculated. The second shows autocorrelations for u_i^2; the third shows autocorrelations for u_i^2/σ_i^2.[13] The table shows that the autocorrelations are positive for u_i^2 for all lags between 1 and 15. In the case of u_i^2/σ_i^2, some of the autocorrelations are positive and some are negative. They are all much smaller in magnitude than the autocorrelations for u_i^2.

The GARCH model appears to have done a good job in explaining the data. For a more scientific test, we can use what is known as the Ljung–Box statistic.[14] If a certain series has m observations the Ljung–Box statistic is

$$m\sum_{k=1}^{K} \omega_k \eta_k^2$$

where η_k is the autocorrelation for a lag of k, K is the number of lags considered, and

$$\omega_k = \frac{m+2}{m-k}$$

searched for have roughly equal values. For example, in GARCH(1, 1) we could let cells A1, A2, and A3 contain $\omega \times 10^5$, 10α, and β. We could then set B1 = A1/100,000, B2 = A2/10, and B3 = A3. We would use B1, B2, and B3 to calculate the likelihood function. We would ask Solver to calculate the values of A1, A2, and A3 that maximize the likelihood function. Occasionally Solver gives a local maximum, so testing a number of different starting values for parameters is a good idea.

---

[13] For a series x_i, the autocorrelation with a lag of k is the coefficient of correlation between x_i and x_{i+k}.

[14] See G. M. Ljung and G. E. P. Box, "On a Measure of Lack of Fit in Time Series Models," *Biometrica*, 65 (1978): 297–303.

TABLE 10-2 Autocorrelations Before and After the Use of a GARCH Model for S&P 500 Data

Time Lag	Autocorrelation for u_i^2	Autocorrelation for u_i^2/σ_i^2
1	0.183	-0.063
2	0.385	-0.004
3	0.160	-0.007
4	0.301	0.022
5	0.339	0.014
6	0.308	-0.011
7	0.329	0.026
8	0.207	0.038
9	0.324	0.041
10	0.269	0.083
11	0.431	-0.007
12	0.286	0.006
13	0.224	0.001
14	0.121	0.017
15	0.222	-0.031

For $K = 15$, zero autocorrelation can be rejected with 95% confidence when the Ljung–Box statistic is greater than 25.

From Table 10-2, the Ljung–Box Statistic for the u_i^2 series is about 1,566. This is strong evidence of autocorrelation. For the u_i^2/σ_i^2 series, the Ljung–Box statistic is 21.7, suggesting that the autocorrelation has been largely removed by the GARCH model.

USING GARCH(1, 1) TO FORECAST FUTURE VOLATILITY

The variance rate estimated at the end of day $n - 1$ for day n, when GARCH(1, 1) is used, is

$$\sigma_n^2 = (1 - \alpha - \beta)V_L + \alpha u_{n-1}^2 + \beta\sigma_{n-1}^2$$

so that

$$\sigma_n^2 - V_L = \alpha\left(u_{n-1}^2 - V_L\right) + \beta\left(\sigma_{n-1}^2 - V_L\right)$$

On day $n + t$ in the future,

$$\sigma_{n+t}^2 - V_L = \alpha\left(u_{n+t-1}^2 - V_L\right) + \beta\left(\sigma_{n+t-1}^2 - V_L\right)$$

The expected value of u_{n+t-1}^2 is σ_{n+t-1}^2. Hence,

$$E\left[\sigma_{n+t}^2 - V_L\right] = (\alpha + \beta)E\left[\sigma_{n+t-1}^2 - V_L\right]$$

where E denotes expected value. Using this equation repeatedly yields

$$E\left[\sigma_{n+t}^2 - V_L\right] = \left(\alpha + \beta\right)^t\left(\sigma_n^2 - V_L\right)$$

or

$$E\left[\sigma_{n+t}^2\right] = V_L + \left(\alpha + \beta\right)^t\left(\sigma_n^2 - V_L\right) \qquad \textbf{(10.13)}$$

This equation forecasts the volatility on day $n + t$ using the information available at the end of day $n - 1$. In the EWMA model, $\alpha + \beta = 1$ and Equation (10.13) shows that the expected future variance rate equals the current variance rate. When $\alpha + \beta < 1$, the final term in the equation becomes progressively smaller as t increases. Figure 10-3 shows the expected path followed by the variance rate for situations where the current variance rate is different from V_L. As mentioned earlier, the variance rate exhibits mean reversion with a reversion level of V_L and a reversion rate of $1 - \alpha - \beta$. Our forecast of the future variance rate tends towards V_L as we look further and further ahead. This analysis emphasizes the point that we must have $\alpha + \beta < 1$ for a stable GARCH(1, 1) process. When $\alpha + \beta > 1$, the weight given to the long-term average variance is negative and the process is "mean fleeing" rather than "mean reverting."

For the S&P 500 data considered earlier, $\alpha + \beta = 0.9935$ and $V_L = 0.0002075$. Suppose that the estimate of the current variance rate per day is 0.0003. (This corresponds to a volatility of 1.732% per day.) In 10 days the expected variance rate is

$$0.0002075 + 0.9935^{10}\,(0.0003 - 0.0002075)$$
$$= 0.0002942$$

The expected volatility per day is 1.72%, still well above the long-term volatility of 1.44% per day. However, the expected variance rate in 500 days is

$$0.0002075 + 0.9935^{500}\,(0.0003 - 0.0002075)$$
$$= 0.0002110$$

and the expected volatility per day is 1.45%, very close to the long-term volatility.

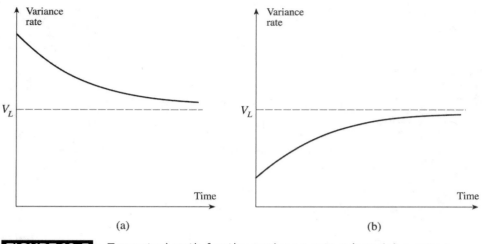

Variance rate

V_L

Time

(a)

Variance rate

V_L

Time

(b)

FIGURE 10-3 Expected path for the variance rate when (a) current variance rate is above long-term variance rate and (b) current variance rate is below long-term variance rate.

Volatility Term Structures

Suppose it is day n. Define:

$$V(t) = E\left(\sigma_{n+t}^2\right)$$

and

$$\alpha = \ln\frac{1}{\alpha + \beta}$$

so that Equation (10.13) becomes

$$V(t) = V_L + e^{-\alpha t}\left[V(0) - V_L\right]$$

Here, $V(t)$ is an estimate of the instantaneous variance rate in t days. The average variance rate per day between today and time T is given by

$$\frac{1}{T}\int_0^T V(t)dt = V_L + \frac{1 - e^{-aT}}{aT}\left[V(0) - V_L\right]$$

The larger T is, the closer this is to V_L. Define $\sigma(T)$ as the volatility per annum that should be used to price a T-day option under GARCH(1, 1). Assuming 252 days per year, $\sigma(T)^2$ is 252 times the average variance rate per day, so that

$$\sigma(T)^2 = 252\left(V_L + \frac{1 - e^{-aT}}{aT}\left[V(0) - V_L\right]\right) \quad \textbf{(10.14)}$$

The market prices of different options on the same asset are often used to calculate a *volatility term structure*. This is the relationship between the implied volatilities of the options and their maturities. Equation (10.14) can be used to estimate a volatility term structure based on the GARCH(1, 1) model. The estimated volatility term structure is not usually the same as the actual volatility term structure. However, as we will show, it is often used to predict the way that the actual volatility term structure will respond to volatility changes.

When the current volatility is above the long-term volatility, the GARCH(1, 1) model estimates a downward-sloping volatility term structure. When the current volatility is below the long-term volatility, it estimates an upward-sloping volatility term structure. In the case of the S&P 500 data, $a = \ln(1/0.99351) = 0.006511$ and $V_L = 0.0002075$. Suppose that the current variance rate per day, $V(0)$, is estimated as 0.0003 per day. It follows from Equation (10.14) that

$$\sigma(T)^2 = 252\left(0.0002075 + \frac{1 - e^{-0.006511T}}{0.065117T}(0.0003 - 0.0002075)\right)$$

where T is measured in days. Table 10-3 shows the volatility per year for different values of T.

Impact of Volatility Changes

Equation (10.14) can be written

$$\sigma(T)^2 = 252\left[V_L + \frac{1 - e^{-aT}}{aT}\left(\frac{\sigma(0)^2}{252} - V_L\right)\right]$$

When $\sigma(0)$ changes by $\Delta\sigma(0)$, $\sigma(T)$ changes by approximately

$$\frac{1 - e^{-aT}}{aT}\frac{\sigma(0)}{\sigma(T)}\Delta\sigma(0) \quad \textbf{(10.15)}$$

Table 10-4 shows the effect of a volatility change on options of varying maturities for the S&P 500 data considered above. We assume as before that $V(0) = 0.0003$, so that $\sigma(0) = \sqrt{252} \times \sqrt{0.0003} = 27.50\%$. The table considers a 100-basis-point change in the instantaneous volatility from 27.50% per year to 28.50% per year. This means that $\Delta\sigma(0) = 0.01$, or 1%.

Many financial institutions use analyses such as this when determining the exposure of their books to volatility changes. Rather than consider an across-the-board

TABLE 10-3 S&P 500 Volatility Term Structure Predicted from GARCH(1,1)

Option Life (days)	10	30	50	100	500
Option volatility (% per annum)	27.36	27.10	26.87	26.35	24.32

TABLE 10-4 Impact of 1% Change in the Instantaneous Volatility Predicted from GARCH(1,1)

Option Life (days)	10	30	50	100	500
Increase in volatility (%)	0.97	0.92	0.87	0.77	0.33

increase of 1% in implied volatilities when calculating vega, they relate the size of the volatility increase that is considered to the maturity of the option. Based on Table 10-4, a 0.97% volatility increase would be considered for a 10-day option, a 0.92% increase for a 30-day option, a 0.87% increase for a 50-day option, and so on.

CORRELATIONS

The discussion so far has centered on the estimation and forecasting of volatility. Correlations also play a key role in the calculation of VaR. In this section, we show how correlation estimates can be updated in a similar way to volatility estimates.

The correlation between two variables X and Y can be defined as

$$\frac{cov(X,Y)}{\sigma_X \sigma_Y}$$

where σ_X and σ_Y are the standard deviations of X and Y and $cov(X, Y)$ is the covariance between X and Y. The covariance between X and Y is defined as

$$E\left[\left(X - \mu_x\right)\left(Y - \mu_Y\right)\right]$$

where μ_x and μ_Y are the means of X and Y, and E denotes the expected value. Although it is easier to develop

intuition about the meaning of a correlation than it is for a covariance, it is covariances that are the fundamental variables of our analysis.[15]

Define x_i and y_i as the percentage changes in X and Y between the end of day $i - 1$ and the end of day i:

$$x_i = \frac{X_i - X_{i-1}}{X_{i-1}}, \quad y_i = \frac{Y_i - Y_{i-1}}{Y_{i-1}}$$

where X_i and Y_i are the values of X and Y at the end of day i. We also define the following:

$\sigma_{x,n}$: Daily volatility of variable X, estimated for day n

$\sigma_{y,n}$: Daily volatility of variable Y, estimated for day n

cov_n: Estimate of covariance between daily changes in X and Y, calculated on day n.

The estimate of the correlation between X and Y on day n is

$$\frac{cov_n}{\sigma_{x,n}\sigma_{y,n}}$$

Using equal weighting and assuming that the means of x_i and y_i are zero, Equation (10.3) shows that the variance rates of X and Y can be estimated from the most recent m observations as

$$\sigma_{x,n}^2 = \frac{1}{m}\sum_{i=1}^{m} x_{n-i}^2, \quad \sigma_{y,n}^2 = \frac{1}{m}\sum_{i=1}^{m} y_{n-i}^2$$

A similar estimate for the covariance between X and Y is

$$cov_n = \frac{1}{m}\sum_{i=1}^{m} x_{n-1}y_{n-1} \qquad \textbf{(10.16)}$$

One alternative for updating covariances is an EWMA model similar to Equation (10.7). The formula for updating the covariance estimate is then

$$cov_n = \lambda\, cov_{n-1} + (1 - \lambda)x_{n-i}y_{n-i}$$

A similar analysis to that presented for the EWMA volatility model shows that the weights given to observations on the $x_i y_i$ decline as we move back through time. The lower the value of λ, the greater the weight that is given to recent observations.

---

[15] An analogy here is that variance rates were the fundamental variables for the EWMA and GARCH procedures in the first part of this chapter, even though volatilities are easier to understand.

Example 10.3

Suppose that $\lambda = 0.95$ and that the estimate of the correlation between two variables X and Y on day $n - 1$ is 0.6. Suppose further that the estimate of the volatilities for the X and Y on day $n - 1$ are 1% and 2%, respectively. From the relationship between correlation and covariance, the estimate of the covariance between the X and Y on day $n - 1$ is

$$0.6 \times 0.01 \times 0.02 = 0.00012$$

Suppose that the percentage changes in X and Y on day $n - 1$ are 0.5% and 2.5%, respectively. The variance and covariance for day n would be updated as follows:

$$\sigma_{x,n}^2 = 0.95 \times 0.01^2 + 0.05 \times 0.005^2 = 0.00009625$$
$$\sigma_{y,n}^2 = 0.95 \times 0.02^2 + 0.05 \times 0.025^2 = 0.00041125$$
$$\text{cov}_n = 0.95 \times 0.00012 + 0.05 \times 0.005 \times 0.025 = 0.00012025$$

The new volatility of X is $\sqrt{0.00009625} = 0.981\%$ and the new volatility of Y is $\sqrt{0.00041125} = 2.028\%$. The new coefficient of correlation between X and Y is

$$\frac{0.00012025}{0.00981 \times 0.02028} = 0.6044$$

GARCH models can also be used for updating covariance estimates and forecasting the future level of covariances. For example, the GARCH(1, 1) model for updating a covariance is

$$\text{cov}_n = \omega + \alpha x_{n-1} y_{n-1} + \beta \text{cov}_{n-1}$$

and the long-term average covariance is $\omega/(1 - \alpha - \beta)$. Formulas similar to those in Equations (10.13) and (10.14) can be developed for forecasting future covariances and calculating the average covariance during the life of an option.[16]

Consistency Condition for Covariances

Once all the variances and covariances have been calculated, a variance–covariance matrix can be constructed. When $i \neq j$, the (i, j)th element of this matrix shows the covariance between variable i and variable j. When $i = j$, it shows the variance of variable i.

Not all variance–covariance matrices are internally consistent. The condition for an $N \times N$ variance–covariance matrix Ω to be internally consistent is

$$\omega^T \Omega \omega > 0 \qquad \text{(10.17)}$$

for all $N \times 1$ vectors ω, where ω^T is the transpose of ω. A matrix that satisfies this property is known as *positive-semidefinite*.

To understand why the condition in Equation (10.17) must hold, suppose that ω^T is $[\omega_1, \omega_2, \ldots, \omega_n]$ The expression $\omega^T \Omega \omega$ is the variance of $\omega_1 x_1 + \omega_2 x_2 + \ldots, + \omega_n x_n$, where x_i is the value of variable i. As such, it cannot be negative.

To ensure that a positive-semidefinite matrix is produced, variances and covariances should be calculated consistently. For example, if variances are calculated by giving equal weight to the last m data items, the same should be done for covariances. If variances are updated using an EWMA model with $\lambda = 0.94$, the same should be done for covariances.

An example of a variance–covariance matrix that is not internally consistent is

$$\begin{bmatrix} 1 & 0 & 0.9 \\ 0 & 1 & 0.9 \\ 0.9 & 0.9 & 1 \end{bmatrix}$$

The variance of each variable is 1.0, and so the covariances are also coefficients of correlation. The first variable is highly correlated with the third variable and the second variable is highly correlated with the third variable. However, there is no correlation at all between the first and second variables. This seems strange. When ω is set equal to $(1, 1, -1)$, the condition in Equation (10.17) is not satisfied, proving that the matrix is not positive-semidefinite.[17]

---

[16] The ideas in this chapter can be extended to multivariate GARCH models, where an entire variance–covariance matrix is updated in a consistent way. For a discussion of alternative approaches, see R. Engle and J. Mezrich, "GARCH for Groups," *Risk*, August 1996: 36–40.

[17] It can be shown that the condition for a 3 x 3 matrix of correlations to be internally consistent is

$$\rho_{12}^2 + \rho_{13}^2 + \rho_{23}^2 - 2\rho_{12}\rho_{13}\rho_{23} < 1$$

where ρ_{ij} is the coefficient of correlation between variables i and j.

APPLICATION OF EWMA TO FOUR-INDEX EXAMPLE

This example is a portfolio on September 25, 2008, consisting of a $4 million investment in the Dow Jones Industrial Average, a $3 million investment in the FTSE 100, a $1 million investment in the CAC 40, and a $2 million investment in the Nikkei 225. Daily returns were collected over 500 days ending on September 25, 2008. Data and all calculations presented here can be found at: www.rotman .utoronto.ca/hull/OFOD/VaRExample.

The correlation matrix that would be calculated on September 25, 2008, by giving equal weight to the last 500 returns is shown in Table 10-5. The FTSE 100 and CAC 40 are very highly correlated. The Dow Jones Industrial Average is moderately highly correlated with both the FTSE 100 and the CAC 40. The correlation of the Nikkei 225 with other indices is less high.

The covariance matrix for the equal-weight case is shown in Table 10-6. This matrix gives the variance of the portfolio losses ($000s) as 8,761.833. The standard deviation is the square root of this, or 93.60. The one-day 99% VaR in $000s is therefore 2.33 × 93.60 = 217.757. This is $217,757, which compares with $253,385, calculated using the historical simulation approach.

Instead of calculating variances and covariances by giving equal weight to all observed returns, we now use the exponentially weighted moving average method with λ = 0.94. This gives the variance-covariance matrix in

TABLE 10-5 Correlation Matrix on September 25, 2008, Calculated by Giving Equal Weight to the Last 500 Daily Returns: variable 1 is DJIA; variable 2 is FTSE 100; variable 3 is CAC 40; variable 4 is Nikkei 225

$$
\begin{bmatrix}
1 & 0.489 & 0.496 & -0.062 \\
0.489 & 1 & 0.918 & 0.201 \\
0.496 & 0.918 & 1 & 0.211 \\
-0.062 & 0.201 & 0.211 & 1
\end{bmatrix}
$$

TABLE 10-6 Covariance Matrix on September 25, 2008, Calculated by Giving Equal Weight to the Last 500 Daily Returns: variable 1 is DJIA; variable 2 is FTSE 100; variable 3 is CAC 40; variable 4 is Nikkei 225

$$
\begin{bmatrix}
0.0001227 & 0.0000768 & 0.0000767 & -0.0000095 \\
0.0000768 & 0.0002010 & 0.0001817 & 0.0000394 \\
0.0000767 & 0.0001817 & 0.0001950 & 0.0000407 \\
-0.0000095 & 0.0000394 & 0.0000407 & 0.0001909
\end{bmatrix}
$$

TABLE 10-7 Covariance Matrix on September 25, 2008, Calculated Using the EWMA Method with λ = 0.94: variable 1 is DJIA; variable 2 is FTSE 100; variable 3 is CAC 40; variable 4 is Nikkei 225

$$
\begin{bmatrix}
0.0004801 & 0.0004303 & 0.0004257 & -0.0000396 \\
0.0004303 & 0.0010314 & 0.0009630 & 0.0002095 \\
0.0004257 & 0.0009630 & 0.0009535 & 0.0001681 \\
-0.0000396 & 0.0002095 & 0.0001681 & 0.0002541
\end{bmatrix}
$$

Table 10-7.[18] The variance of portfolio losses ($000s) is 40,995.765. The standard deviation is the square root of this, or 202.474. The one-day 99% VaR is therefore

$$2.33 \times 202.474 = 471.025$$

This is $471,025, over twice as high as the value given when returns are equally weighted. Tables 10-8 and 10-9 show the reasons. The standard deviation of a portfolio consisting of long positions in securities increases with the standard deviations of security returns and also with the correlations between security returns. Table 10-8 shows that the estimated daily standard deviations are much higher when EWMA is used than when data are equally weighted. This is because volatilities were much higher

---

[18] In the EWMA calculations, the variance is initially set equal to the population variance. But all reasonable starting variances give essentially the same result because in this case all we are interested in is the final variance.

during the period immediately preceding September 25, 2008, than during the rest of the 500 days covered by the data. Comparing Table 10-9 with Table 10-5, we see that correlations had also increased.[19]

TABLE 10-8 Volatilities (% per day) Using Equal Weighting and EWMA

	DJIA	FTSE 100	CAC 40	Nikkei 225
Equal weighting:	1.11	1.42	1.40	1.38
EWMA:	2.19	3.21	3.09	1.59

TABLE 10-9 Correlation Matrix on September 25, 2008, Calculated Using the EWMA Method: variable 1 is DJIA; variable 2 is FTSE 100; variable 3 is CAC 40; variable 4 is Nikkei 225

$$\begin{bmatrix} 1 & 0.611 & 0.629 & -0.113 \\ 0.611 & 1 & 0.971 & 0.409 \\ 0.629 & 0.971 & 1 & 0.342 \\ -0.113 & 0.409 & 0.342 & 1 \end{bmatrix}$$

SUMMARY

Most popular option pricing models, such as Black–Scholes, assume that the volatility of the underlying asset is constant. This assumption is far from perfect. In practice, the volatility of an asset, like the asset's price, is a stochastic variable. Unlike the asset price, it is not directly observable. This chapter has discussed procedures for attempting to keep track of the current level of volatility.

We define u_i as the percentage change in a market variable between the end of day $i - 1$ and the end of day i. The variance rate of the market variable (that is, the square of its volatility) is calculated as a weighted average of the u_i^2. The key feature of the procedures that have been discussed here is that they do not give equal weight to the observations on the u_i^2. The more recent an observation, the greater the weight assigned to it. In the EWMA and the GARCH(1, 1) models, the weights assigned to observations

decrease exponentially as the observations become older. The GARCH(1, 1) model differs from the EWMA model in that some weight is also assigned to the long-run average variance rate. It has a structure that enables forecasts of the future level of variance rate to be produced relatively easily.

Maximum likelihood methods are usually used to estimate parameters from historical data in the EWMA, GARCH(1, 1), and similar models. These methods involve using an iterative procedure to determine the parameter values that maximize the chance or likelihood that the historical data will occur. Once its parameters have been determined, a GARCH(1, 1) model can be judged by how well it removes autocorrelation from the u_i^2.

For every model that is developed to track variances, there is a corresponding model that can be developed to track covariances. The procedures described here can therefore be used to update the complete variance-covariance matrix used in value-at-risk calculations.

Further Reading

Bollerslev, T. "Generalized Autoregressive Conditional Heteroscedasticity," *Journal of Econometrics,* 31 (1986): 307–27.

Cumby, R., S. Figlewski, and J. Hasbrook. "Forecasting Volatilities and Correlations with EGARCH Models," *Journal of Derivatives*, 1, 2 (Winter 1993): 51–63.

Engle, R. F. "Autoregressive Conditional Heteroscedasticity with Estimates of the Variance of UK Inflation," *Econometrica* 50 (1982): 987–1008.

Engle R. F., and J. Mezrich. "Grappling with GARCH," *Risk*, September 1995: 112–117.

Engle, R. F., and J. Mezrich, "GARCH for Groups," *Risk*, August 1996: 36–40.

Engle, R. F., and V. Ng, "Measuring and Testing the Impact of News on Volatility," *Journal of Finance*, 48 (1993): 1749–78.

Nelson, D. "Conditional Heteroscedasticity and Asset Returns: A New Approach," *Econometrica,* 59 (1990): 347–70.

Noh, J., R. F. Engle, and A. Kane. "Forecasting Volatility and Option Prices of the S&P 500 Index," *Journal of Derivatives*, 2 (1994): 17–30.

---

[19] This is an example of the phenomenon that correlations tend to increase in adverse market conditions.

SAMPLE EXAM QUESTIONS—QUANTITATIVE ANALYSIS

1. For a sample of the past 30 monthly stock returns for McCreary, Inc., the mean return is 4% and the sample standard deviation is 20%. Since the population variance is unknown, the standard error of the sample is estimated to be:

$$S_x = \frac{20\%}{\sqrt{30}} = 3.65\%$$

The related t-table values are ($t_{i,j}$ denotes the $(100-j)^{th}$ percentile of t-distribution value with i degrees of freedom):

$t_{29,2.5}$	2.045
$t_{29,5.0}$	1.699
$t_{30,2.5}$	2.042
$t_{29,5.0}$	1.697

What is the 95% confidence interval for the mean monthly return?

   A. [−3.453%, 11.453%]
   B. [−2.201%, 10.201%]
   C. [−2.194%, 10.194%]
   D. [−3.464%, 11.464%]

2. Suppose that a quiz consists of 20 true-false questions. A student has not studied for the exam and just randomly guesses the answers. How would you find the probability that the student will get 8 or fewer answers correct?

   A. Find the probability that $X = 8$ in a binomial distribution with $n = 20$ and $p = 0.5$.
   B. Find the area between 0 and 8 in a uniform distribution that goes from 0 to 20.
   C. Find the probability that $X = 8$ for a normal distribution with mean of 10 and standard deviation of 5.
   D. Find the cumulative probability for 8 in a binomial distribution with $n = 20$ and $p = 0.5$.

3. Assume that a random variable follows a normal distribution with a mean of 80 and a standard deviation of 24. What percentage of this distribution is not between 32 and 116?

   A. 4.56%
   B. 8.96%
   C. 13.36%
   D. 18.15%

4. An insurance company estimates that 40% of policyholders who have only an auto policy will renew next year, and 60% of policyholders who have only a homeowner policy will renew next year. The company estimates that 80% of policyholders who have both an auto and a homeowner policy will renew at least one of those policies next year. Company records show that 65% of policyholders have an auto policy, 50% of policyholders have a homeowner policy, and 15% of policyholders have both an auto and a homeowner policy. Using the company's estimates, what is the percentage of policyholders that will renew at least one policy next year?

   A. 20%

   B. 29%

   C. 41%

   D. 53%

5. The following graphs show the cumulative distribution function (CDF) of four different random variables. The dotted vertical line indicates the mean of the distribution. Assuming each random variable can only be values between −10 and 10, which distribution has the highest variance?

A.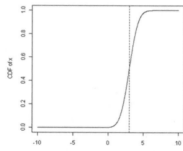

B.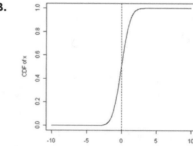

C.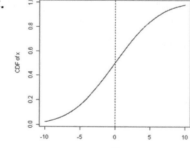

D.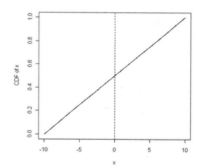

6. You simulate the price path of stock HHF using a geometric Brownian motion model with the following parameters:

Drift: $\mu = 0$

Volatility: $\sigma = 0.2$

Time step: $\Delta t = 0.01$.

Assuming that S_t is the price of the stock at time t, if $S_0 = 50$ and the simulated standard normal random variables in the first two steps are $\varepsilon_1 = -0.521$ and $\varepsilon_2 = 1.225$, respectively, by what percent will the stock price change in the second step of the simulation?

   A. −1.04%

   B. 0.43%

   C. 1.12%

   D. 2.45%

7. Which of the following statements about Monte Carlo simulation is incorrect?

   A. Correlations among variables can be incorporated into a Monte Carlo simulation.

   B. Monte Carlo simulations can handle time-varying volatility.

   C. Monte Carlo methods can be used to estimate value-at-risk (VaR) but cannot be used to price options.

   D. For estimating VaR, Monte Carlo methods generally require more computing power than historical simulations.

8. The recent performance of Prudent Fund, with USD 50 million in assets, has been weak and the institutional sales group is recommending that it be merged with Aggressive Fund, a USD 200 million fund. The returns on Prudent Fund are normally distributed with a mean of 3% and a standard deviation of 7% and the returns on Aggressive Fund are normally distributed with a mean of 7% and a standard deviation of 15%. Senior management has asked you to estimate the likelihood that returns on the combined portfolio will exceed 26%. Assuming the returns on the two funds are independent, your estimate for the probability that the returns on the combined fund will exceed 26% is closest to:

   A. 1.0%

   B. 2.5%

   C. 5.0%

   D. 10.0%

9. Which of the following four statements on models for estimating volatility is INCORRECT?

   A. In the exponentially weighted moving average (EWMA) model, some positive weight is assigned to the long-run average variance.

   B. In the EWMA model, the weights assigned to observations decrease exponentially as the observations become older.

   C. In the GARCH (1, 1) model, a positive weight is estimated for the long-run average variance.

   D. In the GARCH (1, 1) model, the weights estimated for observations decrease exponentially as the observations become older.

10. Based on 21 daily returns of an asset, a risk manager estimates the standard deviation of the asset's daily returns to be 2%. Assuming that returns are normally distributed and that there are 260 trading days in a year, what is the appropriate Chi-square test statistic if the risk manager wants to test the null hypothesis that the true annual volatility is 25% at a 5% significance level?

   A. 25.80

   B. 33.28

   C. 34.94

   D. 54.74

SAMPLE EXAM ANSWERS AND EXPLANATIONS— QUANTITATIVE ANALYSIS

1. Answer: D

Explanation: Here the t-reliability factor is used since the population variance is unknown. Since there are 30 observations, the degrees of freedom are $30 - 1 = 29$. The t-test is a two-tailed test. So the correct critical t-value is $t_{29,2.5} = 2.045$, thus the 95% confidence interval for the mean return is:

$$[4\% - 2.045\left(\frac{20\%}{\sqrt{30}}\right), 4\% + 2.045\left(\frac{20\%}{\sqrt{30}}\right)] = [-3.464\%, 11.464\%]$$

2. Answer: D

Explanation: A binomial distribution is a probability distribution, and it refers to the various probabilities associated with the number of correct answers out of the total sample.

The correct approach is to find the cumulative probability for 8 in a binomial distribution with $N = 20$ and $p = 0.5$. The cumulative probability is to be calculated on the basis of a binomial distribution with number of questions (n) equaling 20 and probability of a single event occurring being 50% ($p = 0.5$).

3. Answer: B

Explanation:

Prob(mean $- 2^*\sigma < X <$ mean $+ 1.5^*\sigma$) = $(0.5 - 0.0228) + (0.5 - 0.0668) = 0.9104$

Prob(mean $- 2^*\sigma > X$ or $X >$ mean $+ 1.5^*\sigma$) = $1 -$ Prob(mean $- 2^*\sigma < X <$ mean $+ 1.5^*\sigma$) = 0.0896

4. Answer: D

Explanation: Let:

A = event that a policyholder has an auto policy

H = event that a policyholder has a homeowners policy

Then, based on the information given:

$$P(A \cap H) = 0.15$$

$$P(A \cap H^c) = P(A) - P(A \cap H) = 0.65 - 0.15 = 0.5$$

$$P(A^c \cap H) = P(H) - P(A \cap H) = 0.5 - 0.15 = 0.35$$

Therefore, the proportion of policyholders that will renew at least one policy is shown below:

$$0.4 \cdot P(A \cap H^c) + 0.6 \cdot P(A^c \cap H) + 0.8 \cdot P(A \cap H)$$

$$= 0.4 \times 0.5 + 0.6 \times 0.35 + 0.8 \times 0.15 = 0.53$$

5. **Answer: D**

   Explanation: Variance is a measure of the mean deviation. In the above four graphs, it can be seen that (D) has the highest proportion of the distribution that deviates from the mean, and it also has a relatively higher density in both tails. Hence, "D" has the highest variance.

6. **Answer: D**

   Explanation: In the simulation S_t is assumed to move as follows over an interval of time of length Δt:

   $$\frac{\Delta S_t}{S_{t-1}} = \left(\mu \, \Delta t + \sigma \, \varepsilon_t (\Delta t)^{\frac{1}{2}} \right)$$

   where ε_t is a standard normal random variable simulated in each time step.
   Therefore, the second step price percentage change is $(S_2 - S_1) / S_1 = 0.2 * 1.225 * \sqrt{0.01} = 0.0245$.

7. **Answer: C**

   Explanation: Monte Carlo simulations *cannot* price options with early exercise accurately. All of the other statements are correct.

8. **Answer: C**

   Explanation: Since these are independent normally distributed random variables, the combined expected mean return is:

   $$\mu = 0.2 * 3\% + 0.8 * 7\% = 6.2\%$$

   Combined volatility is:

   $$\sigma = \sqrt{0.2^2 0.07^2 + 0.8^2 0.15^2} = 0.121 = 12.1\%$$

   The appropriate Z-statistic is $Z = \dfrac{26\% - 6.2\%}{12.1\%} = 1.64$
   and therefore $P(Z>1.64) = 1 - .095 = .05 = 5\%$

9. **Answer: A**

   Explanation: The EWMA model does not involve the long-run average variance in updating volatility, in other words, the weight assigned to the long-run average variance is zero. Only the current estimate of the variance is used. The other statements are all correct.

10. **Answer: B**

    Explanation: The formula for Chi-squared test statistic is $(n - 1)*$ sample variance/ hypothesis variance annualized. So,

    Vol = sqrt (260) 2% = 32.25%. The test stat = $(21 - 1)* 0.3225^2/0.25^2 = 33.28$

APPENDIX TABLE 1

Reference Table: Let Z be a standard normal random variable.

z	P(Z < z)	z	P(Z < z)	z	P(Z < z)	z	P(Z < z)	z	P(Z < z)	z	P(Z < z)
-3.00	0.0013	-2.50	0.0062	-2.00	0.0228	-1.50	0.0668	-1.00	0.1587	-0.50	0.3085
-2.99	0.0014	-2.49	0.0064	-1.99	0.0233	-1.49	0.0681	-0.99	0.1611	-0.49	0.3121
-2.98	0.0014	-2.48	0.0066	-1.98	0.0239	-1.48	0.0694	-0.98	0.1635	-0.48	0.3156
-2.97	0.0015	-2.47	0.0068	-1.97	0.0244	-1.47	0.0708	-0.97	0.1660	-0.47	0.3192
-2.96	0.0015	-2.46	0.0069	-1.96	0.0250	-1.46	0.0721	-0.96	0.1685	-0.46	0.3228
-2.95	0.0016	-2.45	0.0071	-1.95	0.0256	-1.45	0.0735	-0.95	0.1711	-0.45	0.3264
-2.94	0.0016	-2.44	0.0073	-1.94	0.0262	-1.44	0.0749	-0.94	0.1736	-0.44	0.3300
-2.93	0.0017	-2.43	0.0075	-1.93	0.0268	-1.43	0.0764	-0.93	0.1762	-0.43	0.3336
-2.92	0.0018	-2.42	0.0078	-1.92	0.0274	-1.42	0.0778	-0.92	0.1788	-0.42	0.3372
-2.91	0.0018	-2.41	0.0080	-1.91	0.0281	-1.41	0.0793	-0.91	0.1814	-0.41	0.3409
-2.90	0.0019	-2.40	0.0082	-1.90	0.0287	-1.40	0.0808	-0.90	0.1841	-0.40	0.3446
-2.89	0.0019	-2.39	0.0084	-1.89	0.0294	-1.39	0.0823	-0.89	0.1867	-0.39	0.3483
-2.88	0.0020	-2.38	0.0087	-1.88	0.0301	-1.38	0.0838	-0.88	0.1894	-0.38	0.3520
-2.87	0.0021	-2.37	0.0089	-1.87	0.0307	-1.37	0.0853	-0.87	0.1922	-0.37	0.3557
-2.86	0.0021	-2.36	0.0091	-1.86	0.0314	-1.36	0.0869	-0.86	0.1949	-0.36	0.3594
-2.85	0.0022	-2.35	0.0094	-1.85	0.0322	-1.35	0.0885	-0.85	0.1977	-0.35	0.3632
-2.84	0.0023	-2.34	0.0096	-1.84	0.0329	-1.34	0.0901	-0.84	0.2005	-0.34	0.3669
-2.83	0.0023	-2.33	0.0099	-1.83	0.0336	-1.33	0.0918	-0.83	0.2033	-0.33	0.3707
-2.82	0.0024	-2.32	0.0102	-1.82	0.0344	-1.32	0.0934	-0.82	0.2061	-0.32	0.3745
-2.81	0.0025	-2.31	0.0104	-1.81	0.0351	-1.31	0.0951	-0.81	0.2090	-0.31	0.3783
-2.80	0.0026	-2.30	0.0107	-1.80	0.0359	-1.30	0.0968	-0.80	0.2119	-0.30	0.3821
-2.79	0.0026	-2.29	0.0110	-1.79	0.0367	-1.29	0.0985	-0.79	0.2148	-0.29	0.3859
-2.78	0.0027	-2.28	0.0113	-1.78	0.0375	-1.28	0.1003	-0.78	0.2177	-0.28	0.3897
-2.77	0.0028	-2.27	0.0116	-1.77	0.0384	-1.27	0.1020	-0.77	0.2206	-0.27	0.3936
-2.76	0.0029	-2.26	0.0119	-1.76	0.0392	-1.26	0.1038	-0.76	0.2236	-0.26	0.3974
-2.75	0.0030	-2.25	0.0122	-1.75	0.0401	-1.25	0.1056	-0.75	0.2266	-0.25	0.4013
-2.74	0.0031	-2.24	0.0125	-1.74	0.0409	-1.24	0.1075	-0.74	0.2296	-0.24	0.4052
-2.73	0.0032	-2.23	0.0129	-1.73	0.0418	-1.23	0.1093	-0.73	0.2327	-0.23	0.4090
-2.72	0.0033	-2.22	0.0132	-1.72	0.0427	-1.22	0.1112	-0.72	0.2358	-0.22	0.4129
-2.71	0.0034	-2.21	0.0136	-1.71	0.0436	-1.21	0.1131	-0.71	0.2389	-0.21	0.4168
-2.70	0.0035	-2.20	0.0139	-1.70	0.0446	-1.20	0.1151	-0.70	0.2420	-0.20	0.4207
-2.69	0.0036	-2.19	0.0143	-1.69	0.0455	-1.19	0.1170	-0.69	0.2451	-0.19	0.4247
-2.68	0.0037	-2.18	0.0146	-1.68	0.0465	-1.18	0.1190	-0.68	0.2483	-0.18	0.4286
-2.67	0.0038	-2.17	0.0150	-1.67	0.0475	-1.17	0.1210	-0.67	0.2514	-0.17	0.4325
-2.66	0.0039	-2.16	0.0154	-1.66	0.0485	-1.16	0.1230	-0.66	0.2546	-0.16	0.4364
-2.65	0.0040	-2.15	0.0158	-1.65	0.0495	-1.15	0.1251	-0.65	0.2578	-0.15	0.4404
-2.64	0.0041	-2.14	0.0162	-1.64	0.0505	-1.14	0.1271	-0.64	0.2611	-0.14	0.4443
-2.63	0.0043	-2.13	0.0166	-1.63	0.0516	-1.13	0.1292	-0.63	0.2643	-0.13	0.4483
-2.62	0.0044	-2.12	0.0170	-1.62	0.0526	-1.12	0.1314	-0.62	0.2676	-0.12	0.4522
-2.61	0.0045	-2.11	0.0174	-1.61	0.0537	-1.11	0.1335	-0.61	0.2709	-0.11	0.4562
-2.60	0.0047	-2.10	0.0179	-1.60	0.0548	-1.10	0.1357	-0.60	0.2743	-0.10	0.4602
-2.59	0.0048	-2.09	0.0183	-1.59	0.0559	-1.09	0.1379	-0.59	0.2776	-0.09	0.4641
-2.58	0.0049	-2.08	0.0188	-1.58	0.0571	-1.08	0.1401	-0.58	0.2810	-0.08	0.4681
-2.57	0.0051	-2.07	0.0192	-1.57	0.0582	-1.07	0.1423	-0.57	0.2843	-0.07	0.4721
-2.56	0.0052	-2.06	0.0197	-1.56	0.0594	-1.06	0.1446	-0.56	0.2877	-0.06	0.4761
-2.55	0.0054	-2.05	0.0202	-1.55	0.0606	-1.05	0.1469	-0.55	0.2912	-0.05	0.4801
-2.54	0.0055	-2.04	0.0207	-1.54	0.0618	-1.04	0.1492	-0.54	0.2946	-0.04	0.4840
-2.53	0.0057	-2.03	0.0212	-1.53	0.0630	-1.03	0.1515	-0.53	0.2981	-0.03	0.4880
-2.52	0.0059	-2.02	0.0217	-1.52	0.0643	-1.02	0.1539	-0.52	0.3015	-0.02	0.4920
-2.51	0.0060	-2.01	0.0222	-1.51	0.0655	-1.01	0.1562	-0.51	0.3050	-0.01	0.4960

Index